ALGEBRAIC NUMBERS

BY

L. E. DICKSON, ET AL.

CHELSEA PUBLISHING COMPANY
BRONX, N.Y.

TWO VOLUMES IN ONE

Originally published as Report of the Committee on Algebraic Numbers of the National Research Council --
Report Number 28, February, 1923
Report Number 62, February, 1928

The authors are: L. E. Dickson, H. H. Mitchell, H. S. Vandiver, and G. E. Wahlin

Library of Congress Cat. Card 67-16998

Printed in the United States of America

CONTENTS

PREFACE

One of the two objects of this report is to bring up to date the extensive report on the theory of algebraic number fields by D. Hilbert, *Jahresbericht der Deutschen Mathematiker-Vereinigung*, vol. 4, 1894–5, pp. 175–546; French translation in *Annales de la Faculté des Sciences de Toulouse*, series 3, vol. I, 1909, 257–328; II, 1910, 226–456; III, 1911, 1–62 (notes by Humbert and Got, and errata). The present supplementary report deals with the papers subsequent to Hilbert's report and those earlier papers which were not cited by him. A brief report to 1915 is given in the *Enyclopédie des Sciences Mathématiques*, tome I, vol. 3, fac. 5, pp. 390–473.

The second object of this report is to deal with the literature, not cited in Hilbert's report, on fields of functions and related topics, such as Hensel's p-adic numbers and modular systems. A report to 1911 on these topics is given in the *French Encyclopedia*, tome I, vol. 2, fac. 2, pp. 233–385. Aside from two special cases mentioned explicitly, the new report is independent of the *Encyclopedia*. Hence the present report and that by Hilbert together exhaust the literature.

Much time was spent in an effort to make the list of references complete. The *Fortschritte der Mathematik* was examined not merely under Zahlentheorie, but also under the various parts of both Algebra and Function theorie. Use was also made of the *Revue semestrielle*. Moreover, this search, mainly by Dickson, was independent of his earlier exhaustive examination of the literature on all parts of the theory of numbers made while writing his History of the Theory of Numbers (Carnegie Institution, Washington, D. C.). For the recent literature not yet indexed in the two year books cited, a direct examination was made of the various journals and academy publications.

The authorship of the various sections is as follows: Sections 1, 3, 4, 5, Mitchell; 2, 6–9, part of 11, 18–20, Vandiver; 10–17, 39–45, Dickson; 21–38, Wahlin.

To be enabled to accomplish his share in this work, Vandiver was for a time relieved from the duties of teaching through a grant from the Heckscher Foundation for the Advancement of Research, established by August Heckscher at Cornell University.

Chapter I

ALGEBRAIC NUMBERS

1. Quadratic Fields

The subject of quadratic fields, being closely connected with binary quadratic forms,[1] the development of which dates back to Lagrange and Gauss, has been considered much less in the last twenty-five years by writers of prominence than have some of the newer topics. On the other hand it is usually the subject in the domain of algebraic numbers which first attracts the beginner, so that we find a considerable number of papers of lesser importance dealing with it.

The closely allied subject of the complex multiplication of elliptic functions will not be discussed here, but the papers dealing with it are listed under the more general topic of class fields (§8).

A development of a new concept of ideal numbers, which, though capable of extension to fields of any degree, has been considered mainly in the quadratic case, is due to F. Klein.[2] An exposition of the subject has been given by P. Bachmann[3] and an extension to the case of cubic fields by P. Furtwängler.[4]

The central idea in Klein's concept of ideals is the notion of "lattices" ("Gitter"), which are infinite systems of algebraic integers, which do not in general belong to the quadratic realm under consideration. As in his Evanston lectures their relation to the corresponding quadratic forms are shown, it seems appropriate here to define them in terms of the ideals as conceived by Dedekind.

Let A be any ideal of a given field, and let the lowest power of A that is a principal ideal be $A^\kappa = (\alpha)$, where α is an integer of the field. The lattice corresponding to the ideal A is then the infinite system of integers that is obtained by dividing each of the integers of the ideal A by a primitive κth root of α, or of $\epsilon\alpha$, where ϵ is any unit of the field.

The lattice corresponding to any ideal B belonging to the same class as A is the same as that corresponding to A. For in this case there will exist two integers γ, δ such that $A\delta = B\gamma$, and hence an integer β, such that $\alpha\delta^\kappa = \beta\gamma^\kappa$, $B^\kappa = (\beta)$. Hence, if the two primitive κth roots be properly selected, $A/\sqrt[\kappa]{\alpha} = B/\sqrt[\kappa]{\beta}$, i. e., the two ideals may be made to correspond to the same lattice.

---

[1] Cf. L. E. Dickson, History of the Theory of Numbers, Carnegie Institution, Washington, D. C., 1922, vol. 3, chapters 1–8.

[2] Ausgewählte Kapitel der Zahlentheorie, Göttingen, II, 1897, 94–221; Evanston Colloquium Lectures, Amer. Math. Soc., New York, 1893, 58–66.

[3] Grundlehren der Neueren Zahlentheorie, Leipzig, 1907, 240–270. 2nd ed., 1921.

[4] Zur Theorie der in Linearfaktoren zerlegbaren, ganzzahligen ternären cubischen Formen, Diss., Göttingen, 1896.

Since the ideal A is reduced to the same lattice if it is divided by $\epsilon\sqrt[\kappa]{\alpha}$, where ϵ is any unit of the field, it follows that for any ideal there are a set of associated integers (not in general belonging to the given field) that have this property. Relations between ideals may be translated into relations between such sets of associated integers. If associated integers be regarded as the same, any such integer may be expressed in one and only one way as the product of prime integers.

The h lattices corresponding to the h classes of ideals may be so selected that they combine under multiplication in the same way as the classes themselves. The lattice corresponding to the principal class ("Hauptgitter") is the set of all the integers of the given field. The choice of the other lattices ("Nebengitter") is not unique.

In the case of an imaginary quadratic field the h lattices may be represented geometrically in the ordinary complex plane. By the introduction of hyperbolic geometry a geometrical representation is also found possible in the case of a real quadratic field.

While Klein has elaborated the idea to a much greater extent, it should be stated that Dedekind[5] has also shown that ideals may be replaced by actual integers in a higher field.

Other writers have discussed the same question in special cases. Thus G. Fontené[6] has shown in the field $k(\sqrt{-5})$ that by adjoining to the integers of the field itself those of the form

$$\frac{2x+(1+\sqrt{-5})y}{\sqrt{2}},$$

where x and y denote rational integers, unique factorization is restored.

E. Cahen[7] has commented on the preceding, in particular calling attention to its relation to Klein's work.

Elizabeth R. Bennett[8] has proceeded similarly in the case of the field $k(\sqrt{-6})$.

A. E. Western[9] has treated in considerable detail certain related problems. Adopting Klein's representation of ideals, he deals particularly with imaginary quadratic fields in which there are just two classes of ideals, and discusses such questions as residues with respect to primary and secondary moduli, congruences, laws of reciprocity, generic characters, etc. He discusses also binary quadratic forms in which both the coefficients and the variables represent quadratic numbers.[10]

---

[5] Vorlesungen über Zahlentheorie von P. G. Lejeune Dirichlet, Braunschweig; 3rd ed., 1879, §175; 4th ed., 1894, §181; *Bull. des Sc. Math.*, (2), 1, 1877, 246.

[6] *Nouv. Ann. de Math.*, (4), 3, 1903, 209–214.

[7] *Ibid.*, 444–447.

[8] *Amer. Math. Monthly*, 15, 1908, 222–226.

[9] *Trans. Camb. Phil. Soc.*, 17, 1897–8, 109–148.

[10] Cf. Dickson's History of the Theory of Numbers, vol. 3, ch. vii.

Another direction in which the theory of quadratic fields has been extended is towards the development of asymptotic laws similar to those that are known to exist for rational integers. F. Mertens[11] appears to have been the pioneer in this class of work. Working in the field $k(\sqrt{-1})$, he obtained asymptotic values for each of the functions,

$$\Sigma\varphi(m), \quad \Sigma T(m), \quad \Sigma\psi(m),$$

where $\varphi(m)$ denotes the number of residues, mod. m, that are prime to m, $T(m)$ the number of divisors of m, $\psi(m)$ the number of divisors of m that are divisible by no square other than ± 1, and where in each case the sum is to be taken over all the integers m of the field whose norms do not exceed a given limit.

He obtained also an asymptotic expression for the sum of the reciprocals of the norms of all primes in the same field that are represented by $kt+l$, where k, l denote integers without a common divisor and t assumes all integral values in the field for which the expression denotes a prime whose norm does not exceed a given limit.

One of the results obtained by Mertens concerning the function $\Sigma T(m)$ was later obtained by E. Busche.[12]

For the same field J. W. L. Glaisher[13] has obtained some results concerning the function representing the sum of the primary integers that have a given norm and the function representing the sum of the squares of such integers.

The development of this subject is very largely due to L. Gegenbauer.[14] In several papers he determined asymptotic values for a large number of functions defined in the field $k(\sqrt{-1})$ similar to those discussed by Mertens. Some of his results are stated in terms of probabilities that a set of integers chosen at random would have certain properties. For example, he found the probability that two integers chosen at random would have no common divisor to be approximately 6000/9031 as compared with approximately 61/100 for ordinary rational integers.

Other results are stated in terms of mean values. For example, he found the mean value of the greatest common divisor of r arbitrarily chosen primary integers in this field. In all his work the Riemann ζ-function and other functions of a similar character play an important rôle.

Whereas in the main limited to the field $k(\sqrt{-1})$ some of his work

---

[11] *Jour. für Math.*, 77, 1874, 319–338.
[12] *Jour. für Math.*, 122, 1900, 262.
[13] *Quar. Jour. Math.*, 20, 1885, 97–167. For an extended report, see Dickson's History of the Theory of Numbers, vol. 2, 1920, 296–7.
[14] *Wien Denks.*, 50, I, 1885, 153–184; *Wien Berichte* 91, II, 1885, 1047–1058; 98, IIa, 1889, 635–646, 1036–1091; 101, IIa, 1892, 984–1012, 1143–1221.

in these papers deals with the "general Euclidean field," i. e. any algebraic field in which unique factorization holds without the introduction of ideals.

In another paper Gegenbauer[15] proves various theorems concerning the function representing the number of all integral complex numbers of the field $k(\sqrt{-1})$ whose norms do not exceed a given limit. Later he[16] gives a relation involving the function that represents the number of those sets of S primary integers in this field whose norms do not exceed a given limit and whose greatest common divisor is prime to a given integer. The relation is analogous to the summation theorem for the ordinary φ-function.

One of the more elementary topics to which a number of writers have given some study is the applicability of some analogue of Euclid's greatest common divisor algorithm to special types of quadratic fields. Thus L. Wantzel[17] showed that in the fields defined by cube roots and fourth roots of unity it is always possible in dividing two complex integers to make the norm of the remainder less than the norm of the divisor and hence that unique factorization is possible. In another paper he[18] extended his study to certain other quadratic fields.

C. Traub[19] made a much more lengthy investigation along similar lines for numbers $a+b\sqrt{D}$, $D=-1$, ± 2, ± 3, 5.

G. Vivanti[20] reviewed the known laws of divisibility in the field $k(\sqrt{-1})$, making use of the complex plane to give a geometrical significance to some of the relations.

I. Zignago[21] discussed the properties of the same field in their relation to the representation of numbers as the sum of two squares.

G. D. Birkhoff[22] showed that the only imaginary quadratic fields having the property that, given any number ξ, an integer α can always be found such that $|\xi-\alpha|<1$, are those for which the discriminant has one of the values -3, -4, -7, -8, -11.

R. Levavasseur[23] gave an elementary treatment of the laws of divisibility in the field defined by cube roots of unity preparatory to a discussion of cubic reciprocity (§9).

G. Meissner[24] determined by algebraic and geometric methods the nearest integer to an arbitrary number in the same field.

---

15 *Monats. für Math. und Phys.*, 1, 1890, 39–46.
16 *Monats. für Math. und Phys.*, 4, 1893, 184.
17 *Comptes Rendus*, Paris, 24, 1847, 430–434.
18 *Extraits des Procès-Verbaux des Séances*, Soc. Philomatique de Paris, 1848, 19–22. Cf. Dickson's History, vol. 3, Ch. I, Wantzel[46].
19 *Programm des Grossh. Lyceums*, Mannheim, 1868.
20 *Rivista di Mat.*, 2, 1892, 167–176.
21 *Rivista di Mat.*, 4, 1894, 151.
22 *Amer. Math. Monthly*, 13, 1906, 156–159.
23 *Ann. Univ. Lyon*, 21, 1908, 1–22.
24 *Mitt. Math. Gesell. Hamburg*, 4, 1909, 44. Cf. Gauss, Werke, II, 391–3.

J. Schatunowsky[25] determined the imaginary quadratic fields where it is always possible to choose an integral quotient of two integers such that the norm of the remainder is less than the norm of the divisor and showed that this is a sufficient condition for unique factorization. He also showed how the factors of an integer may be found in the fields where unique factorization exists by finding the factors of its norm.

G. Rabinowitsch[26] showed that a sufficient condition for unique factorization in a quadratic field is that for any pair of integers α, β, neither of which is divisible by the other, two integers ξ, η exist such that the norm of $\alpha\xi-\beta\eta$ is greater than 0 and less than the norm of β. He showed also that this condition is necessary in the case of any imaginary quadratic field with discriminant of the form $1-4m$. Among other results he showed that for this same type of quadratic field unique factorization holds for algebraic integers if, and only if, all the integers x^2-x+m $(x=1, 2, \cdots, m-2;\ m>2)$ are primes, and showed incidentally that, if such is the case, $(m-1)^2-(m-1)+m$ must also be prime.

Several authors have been interested in the type of abelian group determined by the multiplication of the residues with respect to and prime to an ideal modulus (§6). An early paper on this topic not referred to in Hilbert's report is one by J. J. Sylvester[27], who determined the number of incongruent residues with respect to a principal modulus in a quadratic field, and for the case where the modulus is not divisible by any rational integer noted that all the residues could be expressed as rational integers.

G. T. Bennett[28] discussed at considerable length the indices, generators, etc., of the residues with respect to a composite modulus in the field $k(\sqrt{-1})$. He gave also tables of indices for all moduli of this field whose norms do not exceed 100.

T. Takagi[29] proved Dirichlet's[30] result concerning the group of residue classes in the field $k(\sqrt{-1})$ with respect to a modulus that is a power of a rational prime.

A. Ranum[31] found a complete system of generators for the abelian group formed by classes of residues with respect to a composite ideal

[25] Der grösste gemeinschaftliche Teiler von algebraischen Zahlen zweiter Ordnung mit negativer Discriminante und die Zerlegung dieser Zahlen in Primfaktoren, Diss. Strassburg, 1911.

[26] *Jour. für Math.*, 142, 1913, 153–164; *Proc. Fifth Int. Congr. Math.*, Cambridge, 1912, I, 418–21. Cf. Dickson, *Bull. Amer. Math. Soc.*, 17, 1911, 534–7.

[27] *Quar. Jour. Math.*, 4, 1861, 94.

[28] *Phil. Trans. Royal Soc.*, London, 184A, 1893, 189–336.

[29] *Jour. College Sc.*, Tokio, 19, 1903, 13–15.

[30] Werke, I, 514–20; Berlin Abh., 1841, 141; Smith's Report, *Coll. Math. Papers*, I, 161–2.

[31] *Trans. Amer. Math. Soc.*, 11, 1910, 172–198.

modulus in a general quadratic field. In particular, those cases where primitive roots exist were determined.

A recent paper by Fl. Vasilescu[32] deals with primitive roots in the field defined by cube roots of unity.

The results of Vera Myller-Lebedeff[33] appear to be included in those of Ranum just referred to.

Other results concerning quadratic fields of a different character have been obtained. Thus a part of a paper by H. Weber[34] deals with "Ordnungen" in quadratic fields.

H. S. Vandiver[35] showed how the sign of the ambiguous residue in the congruence $[(p-1)/2]!\equiv\pm i \pmod{p}$, where p is a prime of the form $8k+5$, may be determined by use of complex residues, mod $a+bi$, where $i^2=-1$, $a^2+b^2=p$. The criterion is analogous to that obtained by Jacobi for the congruence $[(p-1)/2]!\equiv\pm 1 \pmod{p}$, where p is a prime of the form $4n+3$.

Three papers by A. Axer,[36] which have not been consulted, deal with the field defined by cube roots of unity.

A paper by W. P. Welmin,[37] to which access has not been obtained, deals with the decomposition into simple factors of the ideals of a quadratic field.

W. B. Carver[38] developed a method whereby, when two ideals of a quadratic field are each in canonic form, the canonic form of their product can be obtained. He also found necessary and sufficient conditions for a given ideal in canonic form to be a principal ideal.

A paper by M. Cipolla,[39] which has not been consulted, deals with the same subject.

L. E. Dickson,[40] after calling attention to the errors due to the assumption made by numerous authors that all the integral solutions of a homogeneous rational integral equation can be deduced at once from the formulas giving all the rational solutions, shows how the problem of finding all the integral solutions of equations of the type

$$x_1^2+ax_2^2+bx_3^2=x_4^2$$

can be attacked successfully by means of the ideal theory. He reduces this problem to that of solving the canonical equation $N=zw$, where

$$N=x^2-my^2 \text{ for } m\equiv 2, 3 \pmod{4};$$
$$=x^2+xy+\tfrac{1}{4}(1-m)y^2 \text{ for } m\equiv 1 \pmod{4}.$$

---

32 *Bull. de l'Académie*, Roumaine, 1919.
33 *Jour. de Math.*, (8), 2, 1919, 81–98.
34 *Math. Ann.*, 48, 1897, 451–462.
35 *Amer. Math. Monthly*, 11, 1904, 51–56.
36 *Wiad. Mat.*, Warsaw, 14, 1910, 1–66, 139–170; 15, 1911, 147–199.
37 Varsava Prot. Obšč. gest. (Proceedings of the Society of Naturalists of Warsaw), 23, 1911, 291–4.
38 *Amer. Math. Monthly*, 18, 1911, 81–87.
39 *Atti. Acc. Gionia Sc. Nat. in Catania* (5), 10, 1917, No. 20, (11 pp.).
40 *Bull. Amer. Math. Soc.*, 27, 1921, 312–319; 353–365.

For each of these cases he obtains the complete solution in integers for those values of m such that the class number of the realm $k(\sqrt{m})$ is unity. For other values of m he conjectures a theorem whereby all the solutions are obtained and proves it in several special cases.

Several text books have been published dealing in part with quadratic fields. H. Weber[41] has given an expository treatment of such subjects as the discriminant, relation between quadratic numbers and quadratic forms, ideals, "ordnungen," composition of forms and of ideals, genera, and class number. He takes up later the related questions of complex multiplication and class fields (§8).

L. J. Mordell[42] applied the theory of quadratic fields to the problems of finding integral solutions in rational integers of $x^2-y^3=k$. J. Sommer[42a] discusses at considerable length such topics as the unique factorization of ideals, units, ideal classes, genera for ideal classes, "Zahlringe," applications of the ideal theory to quadratic forms and to Fermat's Last Theorem, and the geometrical representation of ideals. After two chapters devoted to cubic fields he gives finally a table which contains for each quadratic field $k(\sqrt{m})$, where m is an integer between -97 and $+101$ having no square factor, representative ideals for each class together with the laws governing the multiplication of the classes and their genera.

A rather more elementary treatment of quadratic fields has been given by P. Bachmann,[43] containing, as noted above, a discussion of the representation of ideals by means of "lattice numbers."

L. W. Reid[44] has considered in great detail several particular quadratic fields together with the more general subjects of ideals, residues, units, and ideal classes in a general quadratic field.

L. E. Dickson[45] has given an elementary introduction to the ideal theory in connection with an account of the work on Fermat's Last Theorem, using as an example the field $k(\sqrt{-5})$. He has an account for general readers in the current number of the Italian journal *Scientia*.

As to solutions of congruences involving quadratic fields, cf. Amato[13] and Grosschmid[6] of §6.

For references on relative quadratic fields, see §8.

For other references on asymptotic expressions involving quadratic fields, see Poincaré,[2] Fanta,[3] Ondraczek,[12] and Axer[9] of §10.

---

[41] Elliptische Funktionen und Algebraische Zahlen, Braunschweig (2nd edition), 1908, 321–409 (issued as vol. 3 of Lehrbuch der Algebra).

[42] *Proc. London Math. Soc.*, (2), 13, 1914, 60–80.

[42a] Vorlesungen über Zahlentheorie, Leipzig and Berlin, 1907, 358 pp.; Introduction à la Théorie des Nombres Algébriques, Paris, 1911 (French translation).

[43] Grundlehren der Neueren Zahlentheorie, Leipzig, 1907, 270 pp. 2nd ed., 1921.

[44] The Elements of the Theory of Algebraic Numbers, The Macmillan Co., New York, 1910.

[45] *Annals of Math.*, (2), 18, 1917, 161–187; *Bull. Amer. Math. Soc.*, 13, 1907, 348–362.

2. Cubic Fields

L. Charve. *Ann. Sc. de l'École Norm. Sup.*, (2), 9, 1880, 143–152.
A. Markoff. *Comptes Rendus*, Paris, 112, 1891, pp. 780, 1049, 1123, 1288; *Mém. Acad. Sc. St. Pétersbourg*, (7), 38, 1892, 1–37.
J. J. Ivanoff. Die ganzen complexen Zahlen, St. Petersburg, 1891, 112 pp.
A. Markoff. *Mém. Acad. Sc. St. Pétersbourg*, (7), 38, 1892, No. 9, 1–37.
G. B. Mathews. *Proc. Lond. Math. Soc.*, 24, 1893, 319–327, 327–336.
G. Woronoj. Ueber die ganzen algebraischen Zahlen, die von einer Wurzel der Gleichung dritten Grades abhängen, St. Pétersburg, 1894, 150, 305.
Ph. Furtwängler. Zur Theorie der in Linearfactoren zerlegbaren, ganzzahligen ternären kubischen Formen, Diss., Gött. 1896, 64 pp.
L. W. Reid. Tafel der Klassenanzahlen für kubische Zahlkörper, Diss., Gött. 1899.
R. Dedekind. *Jour. für Math.*, 121, 1900, 40–123.
H. Minkowski. *Acta Math.*, 26, 1903, 333–351; *Gesammelte Abh.*, I, 357–371; *Dritte Internat. Math. Kongr.*, Heidelberg, 1904; *Gött. Nach.*, 1904, 311–355.
L. Kollross. Un Algorithme pour l'Approximation Simultanée à deux Grandeurs, Diss. Zürich, Geneva, Soullier, 1905.
W. Braun. Bestimmung der Körperdiskriminante in einem kubischen Zahlkörper, Diss. Strassburg, 1909.
A. Chatelet. *Comptes Rendus*, Paris, 152, 1911, 1290–1292.
F. Levi. Integritätsbereiche und Körper dritten Grades, Diss. Strassburg, 1911.
J. Westlund. *Deut. Math.-Ver.*, 22, 1913, 135–140.
W. E. H. Berwick. *Proc. London Math. Soc.*, (2), 12, 1913, 393–429.
F. Levi. *Leipziger Berichte*, Math.-Phys. Klasse, 1914, 26–37.
L. E. Dickson. *Bull. Amer. Math. Soc.*, (2), 25, 1919, 453–455.
B. Delaunay. *Comptes Rendus*, Paris, 122, 1921, 434–436.
J. Sommer's text was cited in note 42 of §1.
Landau[13] of §10.

3. Galois Fields

By a "Galois field" is meant here not the finite field[46] isomorphic with the residues with respect to a prime ideal modulus, to which the term is frequently applied, but an algebraic field defined by an equation the order of whose Galois group is equal to its degree. The following papers deal either wholly or in part with this subject, those prior to 1894 being listed because they are not cited in Hilbert's Report:

P. Bachmann. *Math. Ann.*, 18, 1881, 449–68.
G. Landsberg. Untersuchungen über die Theorie der Ideale, Diss. Breslau, 1890.
H. Minkowski. *Gött. Nachr.*, 1900, 90–93.
M. Bauer. *Jour. für Math.*, 132, 1907, 33–35; *Math. és termész. ért.*, 24, 30–33 (Hungarian).
G. Landsberg. *Jour. für Math.*, 132, 1907, 1–20 (cf. P. Bachmann, Zahlentheorie, V, 488–489).
F. Hüttig. Arithmetische Theorie eines Galoischen Körper, Diss., Marburg, 1907, 40 pp. See §35 below.
A. Speiser. *Math. Ann.*, 77, 1916, 546.
M. Bauer. *Math. Ann.*, 79, 1918, 321–2.
R. Fueter, *L'Enseignement Math.*, 20, 1918–9, 445–6.
A. Speiser, *Jour. für Math.*, 149, 1919, 174.
T. Rella. *Jour. für Math.*, 150, 1920, 157.
M. Bauer. *Jour. für Math.*, 150, 1920, 185; *Math. Ann.*, 83, 1921, 70, 74.
P. Bachmann, Zahlentheorie, V, Allgemeine Arithmetik der Zahlenkörper, Leipzig, 1905, 471–521 (expository).

[46]Dickson's History of the Theory of Numbers, vol. 1, pp. 233–252.

4. Abelian Fields

By an "Abelian field" is meant an algebraic field defined by an equation having an Abelian (commutative) group. In view of Kronecker's theorem that any Abelian field is a sub-field of a cyclotomic field, the latter topic is a closely related one. On the other hand it has also close contact with the subject of Galois fields (§3).

The following papers deal with Abelian fields, those by Kronecker being listed because they are not cited in Hilbert's Report:

L. Kronecker. *Berl. Ber.*, 1877, 845–51; *ibid.*, 1882, 1059, 1151.
E. J. Amberg. Ueber den Körper, dessen Zahlen sich rational aus zwei Quadratwurzeln zusammensetzen, Diss., Zurich, 1897, 50 pp.
M. Bauer. *Archiv. Math. Phys.*, 6, 1903, 218–9, 220, 221.
F. Mertens. *Wien Ber.*, 114, IIa, 1905, 105–148; *Jour. für Math.*, 131, 1906, 87–112.
H. Weber. *Jour. für Math.*, 132, 1907, 167–188; *Math. Ann.*, 67, 1909, 32–60; *ibid.*, 70, 1910–11, 459–470.
A. Chatelet. *Comptes Rendus*, Paris, 152, 1290–92.
F. Steinbacher. *Jour. für Math.*, 139, 1912, 85–100.
A. Chatelet. *Comptes Rendus*, Paris, 170, 1920, 651–3; 171, 1920, 658.

5. Units of a General Field

Relatively little has been done since the publication of Hilbert's Report in the way of advancing the theory of units in an algebraic field. The following papers appear to deal either wholly or in part with this subject:

H. Minkowski. *Gött. Nachr.*, 1900, 90–93.
D. A. Grave. *Suslov-Samml.*, 209–234; *Bericht der Phys.-math. Ges.*, 1910; Kiew Univ., 1912, 5, 1–25 (Russian).
O. Blumenthal, *Math. Annalen*, 56, 1903, 535–7.
H. Todd. *Proc. Cambr. Phil. Soc.*, 191, 1917, 111–116.
E. Landau. *Gött. Nachr.*, 1918, 86–95.
K. Waisata. *Oversigt af Finsk Vetenskaps Sc. Forhandlingar*, 61, 1918–19, 13, 18.
P. Bachmann. Zahlentheorie, V, Allgemeine Arithmetik der Zahlenkörper, Leipzig, 1905, 321–353 (expository).

6. Norms and Congruences in a General Algebraic Field

The term *residue class* will be used here in lieu of the German "Zahlklasse" (Dirichlet-Dedekind, Zahlentheorie, ed. 4, p. 508). We shall also employ the word indicator to mean the number of incongruent residue classes of an ideal modulus, the integers of the classes being prime to the modulus.

The classes of residues of a prime ideal modulus combine under addition, subtraction, multiplication and division in the same way as do the elements of a finite field as defined by E. H. Moore, Bull. New York Math. Soc., 3, 1893, p. 75.

The latter theory has been developed in Dickson's Linear Groups. The connection between the two theories noted above has not, in general, been taken into account by writers on algebraic numbers and consequently in a number of cases results have been developed at great length in lieu of which it would have sufficed to make a mere reference to the more general theorems of Moore or Dickson.

J. J. Sylvester[1] considered $x^r+px^{r-1}+\cdots+s=0$ with rational integral coefficients, and proved that the number of incongruent integral polynomials in x with respect to the modulus $\rho=\alpha_0+\alpha_1 x+\cdots+\alpha_{r-1}x^{r-1}$, the α's being rational integers, is the norm of ρ, The proof, depending on the theory of elimination, is carried out for the case $r=3$ only, but the method is general.

H. J. S. Smith[2] deduced the above result from a general criterion for the solubility of linear equations.

Smith[3] remarks that the methods which he gives for treating linear congruences in the rational field apply also to congruences involving complex numbers.

L. Stickelberger[4] considered linear dependence, with respect to a prime ideal modulus, of given algebraic integers in a field.

J. Westlund[5] found the solutions of $x^{\varphi(P)}\equiv 1 \pmod{P^n}$, where P is a prime ideal in a given field, in the form

$x\equiv\alpha[1+\mu_1 q_1(\alpha)]\cdots[1+\mu_{n-1}q_{n-1}(\alpha)] \pmod{P^n}$, α ranging over the incongruent roots of $x^{\varphi(P)}\equiv 1 \pmod{P}$, and $q_a(\alpha)$ is determined from the congruence $\alpha_a{}^{\varphi(P)}\equiv 1+\mu_a q_a(\alpha) \pmod{P^{a+1}}$, $\alpha_a{}^{\varphi(P)}\equiv 1 \pmod{P^a}$, μ_a being an algebraic integer divisible by P^a but not by P^{a+1}. Also $\varphi(P)$ is the indicator of P.

L. Grosschmid[6] gave an explicit representation of all rational solutions of $x^2\equiv D \pmod{p}$, D and p being rational integers prime to each other, by the use of ideal factors of p in the field $\Omega(\sqrt{D})$.

H. S. Vandiver[7] observed that the classes of residues of an ideal modulus form a particular type of finite algebra (see §43 below).

J. Klotz[8] treats the problem to find the number of solutions of the congruence in the x's,

$$\sum_{i,k}^{1,n} \alpha_{ik}\, x_i\, x_k \equiv \omega \pmod{j},$$

where $\alpha_{ik}=\alpha_{ki}$ and ω are given integers in an algebraic field prime to

[1] *Quar. Jour. Math.*, 4, 1861, 124–30.
[2] *Phil. Trans.*, 151, 1861, 326; *Coll. Math. Papers*, I, 406.
[3] *Phil. Trans.*, 151, 1861, 325; *Coll. Math. Papers*, I, 405.
[4] *Math. Ann.*, 37, 1890, 323–8.
[5] *Bull. Amer. Math. Soc.*, 10, 1903, 78.
[6] *Jour. für Math.*, 139, 1910, 101–5.
[7] *Trans. Amer. Math. Soc.*, 13, 1912, 295.
[8] *Vierteljahrschrift Naturfors. Gesell.*, Zürich, 58, 1913, 239–68.

an ideal in the field which is prime to 2. He shows that this depends n the number of solutions of $\Sigma\alpha_i' x_i^2 \equiv \omega$ (mod $\mathbf{P}^t$), where **P** is a prime leal in the field, the α_i' being integers in the field. This in turn de- ends on the congruence $\Sigma\, \beta_i\, x_i^2 \equiv \omega$ (mod **P**), where the β's are prime to '. The number of solutions of this is determined explicitly. In view f the fact, however, that the residue classes with respect to a prime leal modulus form a finite field, the latter result is only a statement, 1 the language of the theory of ideals of a result previously given by)ickson.[9]

L. Grosschmid[10] considered the solution of a quadratic congruence 1 an algebraic field by means of a prime ideal in a relative quadratic eld.

Vandiver[11] showed that if there is formed an integral homogeneous ymmetric function with the complete system of unit residues of an leal modulus **M**, in an algebraic field Ω, then the resulting integer is ivisible in Ω by **M**, unless the dimension of the function is divisible by ne of the integers $\varphi(\mathbf{P}_s)$, $s=1, 2, \cdots, k$, where $\mathbf{P}_1, \mathbf{P}_2 \cdots, \mathbf{P}_k$ are the istinct ideal prime factors of **M**, and $\varphi(x)$ denotes the indicator of . The theorem holds also if we replace the complete system of unit esidues by a complete system of residues modulo **M**.

Vandiver[12] proved that if **M** is an ideal in an algebraic field Ω, and $\mathbf{I} = \mathbf{P}_1^{\alpha_1}\mathbf{P}_2^{\alpha_2} \cdots \mathbf{P}_k^{\alpha_k}$, where $\mathbf{P}_1, \mathbf{P}_2, \cdots, \mathbf{P}_k$ are distinct prime ideals of orm $\neq 2$ in Ω, then

$$\text{1)} \qquad \Pi(x-U) = \sum_{s=1}^{k} \rho_s (x^{\varphi(\mathbf{P}_s)} - 1)^{\mathbf{M}} (\text{mod } \mathbf{M})$$

'here U ranges over all incongruent unit residues modulo **M**, $\mathbf{M} =$ $(\mathbf{M})/\varphi(\mathbf{P}_s)$, and the ρ's are defined by

$$\rho_s \equiv 1 (\text{mod } \mathbf{P}_s^{\alpha_s}),\ \rho_s \equiv 0 \left(\text{mod } \frac{\mathbf{M}}{\mathbf{P}_s^{\alpha_s}}\right),$$

$=1, 2, \cdots, k$. Further, x is an indeterminate, and $\varphi(k)$ is the indicator f k. For $x=0$, this gives a generalization of Wilson's theorem. Anal- gous results are found for the case in which U ranges over all in- ongruent residues modulo **M** in (1), and also for both cases in which he norm of a prime factor of the modulus is 2.

V. Amato[13] considers the solution of the congruence

$$x^n \equiv a \ (\text{mod } \mathbf{P})$$

'here **P** is a prime ideal in the quadratic field $\Omega(\sqrt{m})$ and a an integer

[9] Linear Groups, 1901, pp. 46–48.
[10] *Math. és termés értesitö* (Hungarian Academy of Sciences), 33, 1914, 524–32.
[11] *Annals of Math.*, (2), 18, 1917, 107–8.
[12] *Annals of Math.*, (2), 18, 1917, 115–9.
[13] *Palermo Rendiconti*, 42, 1917, 48–60.

in that field, n a divisor of the norm of **P** less one, and finds that **P** is of the second degree in Ω, then

$$x \equiv \sum_{k=0}^{\nu-1} A_k a^k, \quad A_k \equiv -n \sum_{c=1}^{\nu} \rho_c^{nk-1},$$

$\nu = (p^2-1)/n$, $\rho_1, \rho_2, \cdots, \rho_\nu$ being a set of integers in the field whos nth powers are incongruent modulo **P**. By means of the above relatic he finds different forms of the solution analogous to those given b Cipolla[14] for the solution of a quadratic congruence in the rational fiel

A. Wiman[15] showed that only the following types of ideals hav primitive roots.

1. All prime ideals.
2. All squares of prime ideals of the first degree.
3. All higher powers of a prime ideal π of the first degree, provide the norm of π is an odd prime not divisible by π^2.
4. The cubes of all prime ideals of the first degree whose squa divides 2.
5. Ideals which are the product of distinct prime ideal divisors 2, or of one of the ideals specified in cases 1–4, the indicators of sai ideals being prime to each other.

G. Wolff[16] examined the multiplicative group formed by the class of residues of an ideal (functional) modulus using Abelian group theor It is sufficient to consider the case where the modulus is a power of prime ideal, π^l. The order of the group is then $p^{(l-1)f}(p^f-1)$, and hen the group is the product of two groups, one of order p^f-1, and the oth of order $p^{(l-1)f}$. The first group is easily shown to be cyclic, and i basis is determined. The second case involves a complicated procedur but the author determines the basis and invariants for all cases exce that in which $e=m\ (p-1)$, where $p=\gamma\ \pi^e$, p being a rational intege and γ an integer in the field prime to π.

J. Westlund[17] derived the results of Wiman[15] in a bit different way.

T. Takenouchi[18] determined completely the basis and invarian of the multiplicative group formed by the residue classes of any ide modulus in an algebraic field, by a different method than th employed by Wolff.[16] If the modulus is $\mathbf{P}^n$, where **P** is a prime ideal i the field with the norm p^f, p a rational integer, and $\mathbf{P}^d$ is the highe power of **P** contained in p, then the rank r (i. e., the number of inva ants) of the group of order $p^{(n-1)f}$ is found to be

[14] *Math. Ann.*, 63, 1907, 54–61.

[15] *Ofversigt K. Ventenskaps-Akad. Förhandlingar*, Stockholm, 56, 1899, 879–885.

[16] Ueber Gruppen der Reste eines beliebigen Moduls im algebraischen Zahlkörpe Diss., Giessen, 1905.

[17] *Math. Ann.*, 71, 1911, 246–50.

[18] *Jour. of Coll. Sc.*, Tokio, 1913, 1–28. Abstract in *Proc. Imperial Acad. Tok* 1, 1912–14, 122–8.

$$r = fd + 1 \text{ or } fd, \text{ if } n > d + k,$$

according as the congruence $p + x^{p-1} \equiv 0 \pmod{p^{d+1}}$
as or has not a solution;

$$r = fd \text{ if } n = d + k;$$

$$r = f\left(n - \left[\frac{n}{p}\right]\right), \text{ if } 1 < n < d + k;$$

$$r = 1 \text{ if } n = 1,$$

here $[x]$ denotes greatest integer in x, and

$$\left[\frac{d}{p-1}\right] = k\,.$$

K. Hensel[19] gave, as new, known results (Wolff,[16] Takenouchi[18]) garding groups formed by residue classes with respect to an ideal odulus.

G. Metrod[20] arrived at known results regarding primitive roots of owers of a prime ideal modulus.

As to groups formed by classes of residues of an ideal modulus in quadratic field, cf. Ranum[31], Takagi[29], Vasilesco[32], Myller Lebedeff[33], f §1. On a similar problem for modular systems involving algebraic umbers, cf. Kircher [21] of §43.

Regarding asymptotic expressions for the indicator of an ideal, see Iertens,[11] Gegenbauer[14, 15] of §1, Landau,[15] Axer[22] of §11.

7. Classes of Ideals

For ideal classes in quadratic fields, cf. Dickson's History, Vol. 3, n the closely related topic of classes of quadratic forms; as well as abinowitsch[26] of §1.

Attention should be called to the fact that the finite expression given y Hilbert[1] for the class number of a cyclotomic field is incorrect, the rror occurring in the "second factor" of this number.

If Hilbert's expression is compared with that of Kummer,[2] it is ound that, whereas the first factor and the numerator of the second actor are the same, Hilbert's denominator R is $2^{(\lambda-3)/2}$ times Kummer's enominator Δ (Hilbert uses l instead of Kummer's λ). The reason or this difference is that, since all the conjugate fields are imaginary, ach element in the "regulator" R is the logarithm of the product of fundamental unit and the conjugate imaginary unit.[3] On the other

[19] *Jour. für Math.*, 145, 1914, 92–113; 146, 1916, 189–228; 147, 1917, 1–28.
[20] *Sphinx-Oedipe*, Nancy, 16, 1921, 147–50.
[1] *Bericht*, 376, 377; Encyclopädie (German ed.), I, 705. This expression is not iven in the French edition of the Encyclopaedia.
[2] *Jour. für Math.*, 40, 1850, 110.
[3] *Bericht*, 215, 221.

hand each element in Kummer's determinant Δ is the real logarithm of a real fundamental unit.[4]

Hilbert's expression is also in disagreement with that given by Dedekind.[5] While he uses the same definition of the regulator, and hence his R is the same as Dedekind's S', his numerator is different, each element in this determinant being one-half that in Dedekind's. Consequently, while the latter's expression is in essential agreement with Kummer's, the numerator and denominator being each multiplied by the same power of 2, Hilbert's expression is incorrect, as he has the same numerator as Kummer and the same denominator as Dedekind.

Finally it can be shown that Hilbert's[6] own expression for the class number in terms of infinite products is in disagreement with his two finite expressions.[7] The discrepancy can be removed by omitting the square root signs in the definitions of A_n and ϵ_g. (H. H. Mitchell.)

E. E. Kummer. *Monatsberichte,* Berlin, 1859, 734; 1870, 755–766, 856–880.
D. Mirimanoff. *Jour. für Math.*, 109, 1892, 82–88.
Ph. Furtwängler. *Gött. Nachr.*, 1895, 381–4.
R. Dedekind. *Jour. für Math.*, 121, 1900, 40–123.
L. W. Reid. *Amer. Jour. Math.*, 23, 1901, 68–84.
J. Westlund. *Trans. Amer. Math. Soc.*, 4, 1903, 201–212.
E. Landau. *Jour. für Math.*, 127, 1904, 162–174.
R. Fueter. *Gött. Nach.*, 1907, 288–298.
E. Landau. *Sitzungb. Wien,* 117, IIa, 1908, 1095–1107.
Furtwängler. *Jour. für Math.*, 134, 1908, 91–94.
F. Bernstein. *Gött. Nach.*, 1910, 420–424, 482–488, 507–516.
Furtwängler. *Gött. Nachr.*, 1910, 554–562.
E. Hecke. *Gött. Nach.*, 1910, 420–424, 619–625.
R. Fueter. *Rend. Circ. Mat. Palermo,* 29, 1910, 380–395.
Furtwängler. *Jour. für Math.*, 140, 1911, 29–32.
A. Verebrussov. Mémoire sur les classes des nombres complexes ideaux conjugués avec l'application à la démonstration du dernier théorème de Fermat, Paris, Gauthier-Villars, 1912, 18 pp.
J. Westlund. *Deut. Math.-Ver.*, 22, 1913, 135–140.
K. L. Jensen. *Nyt Tidsskrift for Matematik,* B, 26, 1915, 73–83.
R. Fueter. *Jour. für Math.*, 147, 1917, 174–183.
E. Hecke. *Naturf. Gesell. Basel,* 28, 1917, 363–372.
N. G. W. H. Beeger. *K. Akad. van Weten. Verslagen,* Amsterdam, 27, 1918, 324–336.
E. Landau. *Gött. Nach.*, 1918, 95–97; *Math. Zeitschrift,* 2, 1918, 52–154.
H. H. Mitchell. *Trans. Amer. Math. Soc.*, 19, 1918, 119–126.
N. G. W. H. Beeger. *K. Akad. van Weten. Verslagen,* Amsterdam, 28, 1919, 293–311, 427–446, 1021–1023; 29, 1919, 331–360; *K. Akad. van Weten. Proceedings,* Amsterdam, 21, 1919, 395–414.
H. S. Vandiver. *Ann. of Math.*, (2), 21, 1919, 73–80; *Bull. Amer. Math. Soc.*, (2), 25, 1919, 455–458; *Proc. Nat. Acad. Sciences,* 6, 1920, 416–421.
K. Reidemeister. *Abhandlungen aus dem Mathematischen Semin r der Hamburgischen Universität,* 1, 1921, 27–48.
Landau. 11, 15, 17, 20, 21, Hecke[16] of §10; Weber of §8; Reid of §2; Fueter[19] of §18.

[4] *Ibid.*, 100.
[5] *Dirichlet-Dedekind,* Zahlentheorie, 4th ed., §185, Braunschweig, 1894.
[6] *Bericht,* 375.
[7] *Bericht,* 376, 377. Cf. Got, *Ann. Fac. Sci. Toulouse,* (3) 3, 1911, 17-20. Error, p.20.

8. Relative Fields, Class Fields (Klassenkörper), Complex Multiplication of Elliptic Functions

L. Goering. Ueber die Theorie derjenigen complexen Zahlen welche aus drei quadrat Wurzeln gebildet sind, Diss. Gött., 1874.
L. Kronecker. *Berl. Monatsb.*, 1882, 1059, 1151.
D. Hilbert. *Deut. Math.-Ver.*, 6, 1897, 88–94.
H. Weber. *Math. Ann.*, 48, 1897, 433–473; 49, 1897, 83-100; 50, 1897, 1–28.
D. Hilbert. *Gött. Nach.*, 1898, 370–399; *M th. Ann.*, 51, 1898, 1–122.
A. Wiman. *Acta Univ. Lundensis*, 36, ——.
D. Hilbert. *Gött. Nach.*, 1900, 277–279.
K. S. Hilbert. Das allgemeine quad. Reciprocitätsgesetz in ausgewählten Kreiskörpern der zweiten Einheitswurzeln. Diss. Gött., 1900.
L. Sapolsky. Ueber die Theorie der relativ. Abelschen kubischen Zahlkörper, Diss. Gött., 1902.
D. Hilbert. *Acta Math.*, 26, 1902, 99.
R. Fueter. Der Klassenkörper der quadratischen Körper und die complexe Multiplication, Diss. Gött., 1903.
D. Bauer. Ueber den Teilungskörper der elliptische Funktionen mit singulären Modul und die zugehörigen Klassenkörper, Diss. Strassburg, 1904.
F. Bernstein. Ueber den Klassenkörper eines algebraischen Zahlkörpers, Diss. Halle, 1903.
F. Bernstein. *Gött. Nach.*, 1903, 46–58, 304–311.
D. Mirimanoff. *Math. Ann.*, 56, 1903, 115–128.
Ph. Furtwängler. *Gött. Nach.*, 1903, 203–217, 282–303.
A. Wiman. *Acta Math.*, 27, 1903, 163–176.
T. Takagi. *Tokyo Jour. Coll. Sci.*, 19, 1903, 42.
F. Bernstein. *Deut. Math.-Ver.*, 13, 1904, 116–119.
Ph. Furtwängler. *Gött. Nach.*, 1904, 173–195.
R. Fueter. *Jour. für Math.*, 130, 1905, 197–237.
H. Weber. *Jour. für Math.*, 129, 1905, 35–62.
Ph. Furtwängler. *Math. Ann.*, 63, 1906, 1–37; *Gött. Nach.*, 1906, 417–434.
R. Fueter. *Jour. für Math.*, 132, 1907, 255–269; *Gött. Nach.*, 1907, 288–298.
Furtwängler. *Gött. Nach.*, 1907, 1–24.
H. Bresslau. Dirichlets Satz von der Arithmetischen Reihe fur den Körper der Dritten Einheitswurzeln, Diss. Strassburg, 1907.
F. Mertens. *Sitzungsb. Wien*, 117, 1908, 3–7, 116, 1907, 1343.
A. Speiser. Die Theorie der binären quadratischen Formen mit Koeffizienten und Unbestimmten in einem beliebigen Zahlkörper, Diss. Gött., 1909.
E. Hecke. Zur Theorie der Modulfunktionen von zwei Variabeln und ihrer Anwendung auf die Zahlentheorie, Diss. Gött., 1910.
E. Hecke. *Gött. Nach.*, 1910, 619–623.
R. Fueter. *Deut. Math.-Ver.*, 20, 1911, 1–47.
Furtwängler. *Gött. Nach.*, 1911, 293–317.
E. Hecke. *Math. Ann.*, 71, 1912, 1–37.
J. Cameron. Ueber die Zerlegungen, etc., Diss. Marburg, 1912, 39 pp. Cf. (22) of §27.
R. Fueter. *Gött. Nach.*, 1913, 331–334.
E. Hecke. *Math. Ann.*, 74, 1913, 465–510.
R. Fueter. *Math. Ann.*, 75, 1914, 177–255.
T. Takagi. *Tokyo Math. Gesell.*, (2), 7, 1914, 414–417.
Furtwängler. *Monatsh. Math. Phys.*, 27, 1916, 1–15.
T. Takenouchi. *Tokyo Jour. Coll. Sci.*, 37, 1916, 70 pp.
R. Fueter. *Naturf. Gesell. Zürich*, 62, 1917, 67–72.
E. Hecke. *Gött. Nach.*, 1917, 90–95.
Furtwängler. *Sitzungb. Wien*, 128, 1919, 247–280; 129, 1920, 161. Cf. (56) of §38.

T. Rella. *Math. Zeitsch.*, 5, 1919, 11–16.
A. Speiser. *Jour. für Math.*, 149, 1919, 174–188.
T. Takagi. Zur Theorie der relativ abelschen Zahlkörper, Tôkyô Sûgaku Butsurigakkwai Kyi (Proceedings of the Tôkyô Mathematical and Physical Society), (2), 8, 1915–1916, 154–162.
T. Takagi. Zur Theorie der komplexen Multiplikation der elliptischen Funktionen, Tôkyô Sûgaku Butsurigakkwai Kyi, (2), 8, 1915–1916, 386–393.
R. Tambs Lyche. *Skrifter Videnskabsselskab Forhandlingar*, 1919, II, No. 5, Christiania.
T. Takagi. *Jour. College of Sci. Tokyo*, 41, 1920.
L. Koshmieder. *Math. Ann.*, 83, 1921, 280–285.
K. Reidemeister. *Abhandlungen aus dem Mathematischen Seminar der Hamburgischen Universität*, 1, 1921, 27–48.
See Weber[17] of §1, and references to Dickson's History immediately following Nagel[17] of §20.

9. Higher Reciprocity Laws and Kummer Fields

G. Eisenstein. *Jour. für Math.*, 39, 1850, 281.
X. Stouff. *Comptes Rendus*, Paris, 123, 1896, 486–488; 126, 1898, 812–4; Sur les lois de réciprocité, Paris, Herrmann, 1898, 31 pp. *Ann. l'Ecole Normale*, (3), 10, 1893 295; *Ann. Faculté Sci. Toulouse*, (1), 4, 1890, No. 16; (1), 5, 1891, No. 3; (1), 6, 1892, No. 7; (1), 8, 1894, No. 4.
D. Hilbert. *Gött. Nach.*, 1898, 370–399; *Math. Ann.*, 51, 1898, 1–122.
H. Dörrie. Das quadratische Reciprocitätsgesetz im quadratischen Zahlkörper mit der Klassenzahl 1, Diss. Gött., 1898.
D. Hilbert. *Gött. Nach.*, 1900, 276.
Ph. Furtwängler. *Gött. Abh.*, 1902; *Math. Ann.*, 58, 1904, 1–50.
W. Lietzmann. Ueber das biquadratische Reciprocitätsgesetz im algebraischen Zahlkörpern, Diss. Gött., 1904.
W. Lietzmann. *Math. Ann.*, 60, 1905, 263–284.
St. Bohniĉek. *Math. Ann.*, 63, 1905, 85–144; *Agram. Akad. Proc.*, 165, 1906, 1–49, 94–210.
F. Mertens. *Sitsungsb. Wien*, 114, IIa, 1905, 1359-68.
A. E. Western. *Proc. London Math. Soc.*, (2), 6, 1908, 16–28, 265–297.
St. Bohniĉek. *Agram. Akad. Proc.*, 177, 1909, 1–96.
Furtwängler, *Math. Ann.*, 67, 1909, 1–31.
E. E. Kummer. Festschrift zur Feier des 100 sten Geburtstages Edouard Kummers, *Abh. Gesch. Math.*, 29, 1910, 81–2, 89–90, 96–7.
J. Westlund. *Trans. Amer. Math. Soc.*, 11, 1910, 388–392; *Bull. Amer. Math. Soc.*, (2), 16, 1910, 398.
St. Bohniĉek. *Agram. Akad. Proc.*, 185, 168–193.
Lietzmann. *Math. Ann.*, 68, 1910, 119.
R. Fueter. *Deut. Math.-Ver.*, 20, 1911, 1–47.
J. Westlund. *Bull. Amer. Math. Soc.*, (2), 17, 1911, 344–347.
Furtwängler. *Math. Ann.*, 72, 1912, 346–386.
St. Bohniĉek. *Sitsungsb. Wien*, 121, IIa, 1912, 712.
O. Selberg. *Archiv für Math.*, 33, 1912, No. 4, pp. 29.
P. Welmin. Zur Theorie der Reste achten Grades in den algebraischen Zahlkör pern, Warsaw, XXI+229 pp.
Furtwängler. *Math. Ann.*, 74, 1913, 413–429.
F. Mertens. *Wiener Bericht*, 126, IIa, 1917, 1337–1343.
T. Takagi. *Tokyô Sûgaku Butsurigakkwai Kyi*, (2), 9, 1917-18, 166–169.
H. S. Vandiver. *Bull. Amer. Math. Soc.*, 25, 1919, 221–3.
L. J. Mordell. *Proc. London Math. Soc.*, (2), 20, 1921, 289.
Sapolsky of § 8, Hensel of § 34, § 36, § 37.

10. Distribution of Prime Ideals

R. Dedekind[1] proved the convergence for any real $s>1$(or $s=\sigma+ti$, $\sigma>1$) of

$$\zeta_\kappa(s)\equiv\sum_\alpha\frac{1}{N(\alpha)^s}=\prod_{\mathbf{P}}\left[1-\frac{1}{N(\mathbf{P})^s}\right]^{-1}=\sum_{m=1}^{\infty}\frac{F(m)}{m^s},$$

the first summation extending over all ideals α of an algebraic number field κ, and the product extending over all prime ideals of κ. Here N (α) denotes the norm of α, and F (m) denotes the number of distinct ideals of κ whose norm is the positive integer m. He proved that when s approaches 1 through larger values, $(s-1)$ ζ_κ (s) has a finite limit $\neq 0$, which he evaluated to compute the number of classes of ideals of κ.

H. Poincaré[2] extended to complex primes $a+bi$ theorems by Tchebychef (*ibid.*, 17, 1852, 366-390), investigating the sum $\Theta(x)$ of the logarithms of the norms of all *prime* ideals whose norm does not exceed the norm of x, and the corresponding sum T (x) for all ideals, besides evaluating asymptotically the number of complex primes whose norms are under a given limit.

E. Fanta[3] proved that, if L and M are relatively prime integers of the field F defined by $\sqrt{-3}$, $L+Mz$ is a prime in F for an infinitude of integral numbers of F.

G. Torelli[4] failed[5] in his extension of Poincaré's results to ideals in the field defined by a pth root of unity, where p is any prime >2.

E. Landau[6] investigated Dedekind's zeta function for complex values of s, extended to a general field κ the results of Poincaré[2] for complex numbers $a+bi$, extended to κ the properties and asymptotic laws of Euler's φ-function, the number of divisors, and other number-theoretic functions, and investigated Kronecker's limit formula involving binary quadratic forms.

Landau,[7] by means of results in his preceding paper, proved the "prime ideal theorem": the number of prime ideals of norm $\leqq x$ of any algebraic number field is asymptotically $x/\log x$, whence in two arbitrary fields there are asymptotically equally many prime ideals.

---

[1] Dirichlet-Dedekind, Zahlentheorie, ed. 3, 8179, 578–9; ed. 4, 1894, 610–1.
[2] *Jour. de Math.*, (4), 8, 1892, 25–68.
[3] *Monatshefte Math. Phys.*, 12, 1901, 1–44.
[4] *Rendiconti del Circolo Mat. di Palermo*, 16, 1902, 100–3.
[5] Since he employed two asymptotic formulas of his historical report on the distribution of primes, Atti Accad. Sc. fis. Mat. Napoli, (2), 11, 1903, 215 pp., which contains (p. 157, lines 9–10) a false conclusion, which cannot be rectified in the opinion of Landau, Fortschritte Math., 1902, 214.
[6] *Jour. für Math.*, 125, 1903, 64–188.
[7] *Math. Annalen*, 56, 1903, 665–670.

Landau[8] proved that, for an arbitrary algebraic number field,

$$\lim_{x=\infty} \frac{\log^m x}{x} \sum_{N(\alpha)=1}^{x} \mu(\alpha)=0,$$

where $\mu(\alpha)$ is defined by $\mu(1)=1$, $\mu(\alpha)=0$ if α is divisible by the square of an ideal $\neq 1$, $\mu(\alpha)=(-1)^\rho$ if α is the product of ρ distinct prime ideals. There are obtained various asymptotic relations involving $\mu(\alpha)$, as well as $\lambda(\alpha)$ which is $+1$ or -1 according as is the product of an even or odd number of prime ideals, while $\lambda(1)=1$.

A. Axer[9] studied various number theoretic functions and their asymptotic and mean values in the domain κ defined by a cube root of unity, including the number $A(n)$ of primary numbers of norm $\leqq n$, the zeta function $\zeta_\kappa(\alpha)$, the number of primary divisors of a number of κ, and the analogues of Euler's and Möbius' functions φ and μ.

M. Schleser[9a] supplemented the work of Axer[9].

Landau[10] generalized to an arbitrary field κ the theory of the distribution of primes by employing only the elements of the theory of functions, especially Cauchy's integral theorem, avoiding Dedekind's zeta function since it is not known to exist over the whole plane. The prime ideal theorem[7] is proved.

Landau[11] proved that in every class of ideals of an algebraic field κ for which $\Sigma 1/Np$ is divergent (where p ranges over all prime ideals of the principal class in the narrow sense), there are asymptotically equally many prime ideals. A more general theorem includes also his asymptotic theorem on the infinitude of primes in an arithmetical progression.

H. Ondraczek's[12] paper was not available for report.

Landau[13] gave an asymptotic expression for the number of primes $\leqq x$ which are representable by a primitive binary quadratic form $au^2+buv+cv^2$, a, b, c being rational integers. The second part is on Dedekind's zeta function $\zeta_\kappa(s)$ for a pure cubic field κ.

E. Hecke[14] proved that, if $\zeta_\kappa(s)$ is Dedekind's zeta function for an arbitrary algebraic number field κ, $(s-1)\zeta_\kappa(s)$ is an integral transcendental function of s, so that $\zeta_\kappa(s)$ is regular in the whole plane except at the pole $s=1$ of the first order. Let n be the degree of κ and Δ its discriminant. Of the conjugate fields, let r_1 be real and r_2 pairs be imaginary, so that $n=r_1+2r_2$. Put $A=2^{-r_2}\pi^{-n/2}\sqrt{|\Delta|}$. Then the function

$$Z(s)\equiv s(1-s)A^s\Gamma(s)^{r_2}\Gamma(\tfrac{1}{2}s)^{r_1}\zeta_\kappa(s)$$

---

[8] *Sitzungsber. Akad. Wiss. Wien* (Math.), 112, IIa, 1903, 554–570.
[9] *Monatshefte Math. Phys.*, 15, 1904, 239–291.
[9a] *Ibid.*, 21, 1910, 61–102.
[10] *Sitzungsber. Akad. Wiss. Wien* (Math.), 115, IIa, 1906, 589–632.
[11] *Math. Annalen*, 63, 1907, 145–204.
[12] Der Dirichletsche Satz über die linearen Funktionen in Zahlenkörper der Determinant +5, Diss., Wien, 45 pp.
[13] *Math. Abh.* H. A. Schwartz 50 Doktorjubiläum, Berlin, 1914, 244–273.
[14] *Göttingen Nachr.*, 1917, 77–89.

is an integral function which is not altered by the interchange of s with $1-s$, so that $\zeta_\kappa(s)$ satisfies a functional equation.

E. Landau[15] applied Hecke's[14] functional equation to obtain an asymptotic formula for the number of ideals of a field (or a class) of norm $\leqq x$ (see Walfisz[26]).

Hecke,[16] by extending his[14] method to the function

$$L(s)=\sum_{n=1}^{\infty}\chi(n)n^{-s},$$

where χ is a character, proved the following theorem closely related [Landau[21]] to Dirichlet's theorem on the infinitude of primes in any arithmetical progression: If $\mathbf{f}$ is an ideal of any algebraic field, $\mathbf{r}$ any ideal prime to $\mathbf{f}$, there exist in the ideal class (under wider equivalence) determined by $\mathbf{r}^{-1}$ an infinitude of prime ideals $\mathbf{p}$ such that the number $\mathbf{pr}$ is congruent to a unit modulo $\mathbf{f}$. Taking $\mathbf{r}$ to be a principal ideal $[\rho]$ prime to $\mathbf{f}$, we see that there exist infinitely many prime numbers π of the field for which $\pi\equiv\rho(\text{mod } \mathbf{f})$.

Landau[17] obtained superior and inferior bounds for the number of classes of ideals of an imaginary quadratic field. There exists a positive constant a such that $L(s)$ has a zero $s=\sigma+ti$ in the rectangle $\frac{1}{2}\leqq\sigma<1$, $|t|\leqq a$. There is proved a similar theorem for fields of order >2.

Landau[18] obtained an approximation to $\Sigma\chi(\alpha)$, where α ranges over all ideals whose norm is $\leqq x$ of any field, χ being a character not a principal one.

E. Hecke[19] defined a function (called a character) $\lambda(A)$ of any algebraic number A or ideal A of any algebraic number field κ by means of the units of κ. For example, if κ is a real quadratic field with the class number h and fundamental unit ϵ, and if α denotes the hth power of any ideal A, and α' the conjugate to α, then

$$\lambda(A)=e^t,\ t\equiv\frac{\pi i}{\log|\epsilon|}\log\left|\frac{\alpha}{\alpha'}\right|.$$

Then new types of zeta functions and L-functions are defined by

$$\zeta(s;\lambda)=\sum_x\frac{\lambda(x)}{N(x)^s},\quad L(s;\lambda,\chi)=\sum_x\frac{\lambda(x)\,\chi(x)}{N(x)^s},$$

summed for all integral ideals x of the field. Here the real part of the complex number s exceeds 1, and $\chi(x)$ is an ordinary character.

[15] *Göttingen Nachr.*, 1917, 102–111. Cf. Landau,[20] p. 131, p. 135.
[16] *Göttingen Nachr.*, 1917, 299–318.
[17] *Math. Annalen*, 79, 1918, 388–401.
[18] *Göttingen Nachr.*, 1918, 478–88.
[19] *Math. Zeitschrift*, 1, 1918, 357–376. See Hecke.[28]

E. Landau[20] gave in 25 pages an elementary account of algebraic numbers and ideals as far as a proof of the main theorem that every ideal of an algebraic number field is expressible uniquely as a product of prime ideals. The next 29 pages are devoted to norms and bases of ideals, Hurwitz's proof of Minkowski's theorem on limits to n linear forms for integral values of the n variables, classes of ideals, and Bachmann's proof of Dirichlet's theorem on units. This first part furnishes a brief, attractive introduction to algebraic numbers and ideals, available to readers acquainted with the elements of the theory of equations.

In the second part is proved Hecke's[14] fundamental theorem on Dedekind's zeta function and by means of it the prime ideal theorem[7] and new related facts. The elements of the theory of functions of a complex variable are presupposed, but no analytic number theory.

Landau[21] noted that the final result quoted in the report on Hecke[16] becomes for the case of the field of rational numbers the fact that, for relatively prime positive integers r and f, the two arithmetical progressions $fx+r$ and $fx-r$ together contain infinitely many primes, and not Dirichlet's theorem that $fx+r$ alone does. The latter is contained in Landau's present theorem that if $[\rho]$ is a principal ideal relatively prime to the ideal $\mathbf{f}$, there exist infinitely many, not associated, numbers π of positive norm for which $[\pi]$ is a prime ideal and $\pi\equiv\rho(\text{mod } \mathbf{f})$. This theorem and its generalization are obtained by employing narrow equivalence of ideals. There are numerous further new theorems on the analytic theory of ideals, including the number of ideals of norm$\leqq x$ of a class.

Landau[22] proved for Hecke's[19] zeta function that

$$\frac{1}{|\zeta(1,\chi)|}<\lambda_1 \log^n k(\log\log k)^{3n/8},$$

for an arbitrary complex character χ modulo $\mathbf{f}$, while $k=|\Delta|N\mathbf{f}$, Δ being the discriminant of the field of order n.

Hecke[23] noted that his[19] former types of zeta functions having a representation as a product are exhaustive for fields all of whose conjugates are real. There is here a generalization covering all fields. As an example of the applications, x^2+y^2 and x^2-2y^2 each represents an infinitude of primes for integers x, y giving points within an arbitrary angle with vertex at the origin, and the number of these primes $<t$ is asymptotically proportional to the angle measured with respect to the quadratic form as by Cayley and Klein. The work is simplified by

---

[20] *Einführung in die elementare und analytische Theorie der algebraischen Zahlen und der Ideale*, 1918, Teubner, 143 pp.
[21] *Math. Zeitschrift*, 2, 1918, 52–154.
[22] *Math. Zeitschrift*, 4, 1919, 152–162.
[23] *Math. Zeitschrift*, 6, 1920, 11–51.

xtending the field to one in which every ideal is a principal ideal, hence an ideal may be replaced by an individual number.

H. Cramér[24] obtained, by means of Hecke's[14] functional equation satisfied by $\zeta_\kappa(s)$, expressions for $\Sigma e^{\rho z}$, summed for the complex roots $=\beta+\gamma i$, $\gamma>0$, of $\zeta_\kappa(s)=0$, and stated that it is possible to deduce heorems on prime ideals analogous to those on prime numbers in the rst three chapters.

L. Bianchi[25] gave an exposition of the theory of algebraic numbers ncluding the older and recent investigations of Dedekind's zeta function.

A. Walfisz[26] wrote $H(x)$ for the number of all ideals of norm $\geqq x$ of field κ of degree $n\geq 2$, h for its class-number, $h\lambda$ for the residue of Dedekind's $\zeta_\kappa(s)$ for $s=1$, $P(x)$ for $H(x)-h\lambda x$, and proved the existence f a positive constant K, depending on the field, such that each of $P(x)>Kx^t$, $P(x)<-Kx^t$ is satisfied by values of x surpassing all limit, where $t=\frac{1}{2}-\frac{1}{2}n^{-1}$. This extends Landau's[15] result that $P(x)=O(x^y)$ for o $y>t$.

Let $F(x)$ be the number of ideals of κ of positive norm x, but $F(x)=0$ f x is not an integer >0, and define A as by Hecke,[14] and $F(x)$ as by Dedekind.[1] Then

$$H(x)-\tfrac{1}{2}F(x)=h\lambda x+\zeta_\kappa(0)+A\sqrt[n]{\frac{x}{A^2}}\sum_{j=1}^{\infty}\frac{F(j)}{j^{1-1/n}}\,J_{r1,r2}\left(2n\pi\sqrt[n]{\frac{jx}{|\Delta|}}\right),$$

where the J generalizes Bessel's functions.

C. Siegel[27] employed the Cauchy integral theorem to prove the functional equation for Dedekind's function $\zeta_\kappa(s)$ for a total real algebraic ield κ, and that it may be continued analytically over the half plane $\sigma>-1$, where $s=\sigma+ti$. He[28] gave another proof without the use of Dirichlet's theorem on the units of a field.

11. Miscellaneous

E. Selling[1] considered the numbers formed by taking algebraic unctions with rational coefficients of the n roots of an equation $a_0x^n+a_1x^{n-1}+\cdots+a_n=0$, irreducible in the rational field, the a's being rational integers. Extending Kummer's method of defining ideals in the field defined by a primitive kth root of unity, he defined ideal factors of these numbers and gave a number of their properties.

[24] *Arkiv för Mat., Astr., Fysik*, 15, 1921, No. 5, Ch. IV.
[25] Lezioni sulla teoria dei numeri algebrici, Pisa, 1921.
[26] Über die summatorischen Funktionen einiger Dirichletscher Reihen, Diss. Göttingen, 1922, 56 pp.
[27] *Math. Annalen*, 85, 1922, 123–8.
[28] *Göttingen Nachr.*, 1922, 25–31.
[1] *Zeitschrift für Math. u. Phys.*, 10, 1865, 17–47.

G. Zolotareff[2] defines a complex integer as $\varphi(x_0)=b_0+b_1x_0+\cdots+b_{n-1}x_0^{n-1}$ where x_0 satisfies the equation $F(x)=x^n+a_1x^{n-1}+a_2x^{n-2}+\cdots+a_{n-1}x+a_n=0$ the a's and b's being rational integers. He defined the norm of $\varphi(x_0)$ in the usual way. He examined the divisibility of complex integers and ideals are defined in such a way that if p is a rational prime and $F(x)=V^mV_1^{m_1}\cdots V_h^{m_h}+pM(x)$, where the V's and $M(x)$ are polynominals in x with integral coefficients, the V's being irreducible modulo p, then $p=\mathbf{P}^m\mathbf{P}_1^{m_1}\mathbf{P}_2^{m_2}\cdots\mathbf{P}_h^{m_h}$, the **P**'s being prime ideals. As to this definition Cf. Dedekind.[3]

H. Poincaré[4] established between ideals and quadratic forms a correspondence less precise than that given by Dedekind.[5]

Poincaré[6] sought all ideals with a given norm.

A. S. Hathaway[7] gave an exposition of Dedekind's theory of ideals.

J. Sochocki[8] developed a theory of divisibility of algebraic numbers.

J. J. Iwanow[9] treated the connection between the theories of ideals given by Dedekind and Zolotareff.[2]

R. Fricke[10] examined the connection between algebraic numbers and automorphic functions.

D. Hilbert[11] proved that if ν, μ are any integers of an algebraic field k, $\nu\xi^2+\mu\eta^2=1$ is solvable in numbers ξ, η of k if the congruence $\nu\xi^2+\mu\eta^2\equiv 1$ with respect to every prime ideal of k and every power of a prime is solvable in integers of k.

H. Minkowski[12] gave a criterion for algebraic numbers of degree n. Write

$$\xi=x_1+x_2a+\cdots+x_na^{n-1},$$

where $x_1,\cdots,x_n$ are rational integers. Choose any positive integer r and give to each x_i the values $0, \pm1,\cdots,\pm r$, such that not all the x_i are 0. Let $x_1=p_{11},\cdots,x_n=p_{n1}$ be such a system for which the absolute value of ξ is as small as possible and the last non-vanishing p is positive. Select a second system $x_1=p_{12},\cdots,x_n=p_{n2}$ independent of the first

[2] Théories des nombres entiers complexes, avec une application an calcul integral, St. Petersburg, 1874; *Bull. St. Petersburg*, 5, 1879; *Jour. de Math.*, (3), 6, 1880, 51–84, 129–66.

[3] *Gott. Abh.*, 23, 1878.

[4] *Jour. école polyt.*, t. 28, cah. 47, 1880, 177–245 (Part V). Cf. his obscure remarks in *Comptes Rendus*, Paris, 89, 1879, 344–6.

[5] Dirichlet-Dedekind, Zahlentheorie, ed. 4, 1894, 585, 655.

[6] *Bull. Soc. Math. France*, 13, 1885, 169–194.

[7] *Amer. Jour. Math.*, 9, 1887, 162–79.

[8] The principle of the greatest common divisor and its application to the theory of algebraic numbers, St. Petersburg, 1893, (Russian). *Prace mat.-fiz* 4, 1893, 95–153. (Polish). Cf. Fortschritte der Math. 25, 1893, 297–301.

[9] On Complex Integers, Magisterthese, St. Petersburg, 1891, 112 pp.; *Abh. der Akad.*, St. Petersburg, 72, (Russian.)

[10] *Jahresbericht. Deutsche Math. Verein.* 6, 1897, 94–95.

[11] *Math. Annalen*, 51, 1899, 124–5.

[12] *Göttingen Nachrichten*, 1899, 77.

nd for which $|\xi|$ is as small as possible; etc., until we reach an nth ystem $p_{1n},\cdots, p_{nn}$, independent of the earlier systems. For these ystems let $\alpha_1,\cdots,\alpha_n$ be the values of ξ. Then $|\alpha_1|\leqq\cdots\leqq|\alpha_n|$, and he substitution

$$P: \qquad x_k=p_{k1}z_1+\cdots+p_{kn}z_n \ (k=1,\cdots,n)$$

s of determinant $\neq 0$ and replaces ξ by $\alpha_1z_1+\cdots+\alpha_nz_n$. This substitution P is said to belong to the number r. Let P_1 belong to $r_1=1$; f it does not belong to every r, let r_2-1 be the greatest r to which it elongs. Let P_2 belong to r_2, etc. Then $P_1, P_2,\cdots$ form a "chain" of ubstitutions and replace ξ by $\chi_1, \chi_2,\cdots$. Write $\sigma=1$ if a is real, $=2$ if a is complex, and take $n>\sigma$. We have the criteria:

(I) If a is not an algebraic number of degree $\geqq n$, the chain $P_1, P_2,\cdots$ s infinite and the equations $\chi_1=0, \chi_2=0,\cdots$ are all distinct.

(II) If a is an algebraic number of degree n, the chain is infinite, only finite number of $\chi_1=0,\cdots$ are distinct, and all coefficients in each χ_k are not zero.

(III) If a is an algebraic number of degree $n-m>\sigma$, $m>0$, the chain s infinite, only a finite number of $\chi_1=0,\cdots$ are distinct, and in the χ_k, rom a certain one on, the first m coefficients are zero and the others re not zero.

(IV) If a is algebraic of degree σ, the chain is finite.

J. Westlund[13] treated the decomposition of rational primes in a biquadratic field defined by an equation whose discriminant is a prime.

M. Bauer[14] considered properties of rational primes whose ideal factors in a given algebraic field were of the first degree.

E. Landau[15] found asymptotic expressions for $\sum_n \varphi(n)$, n ranging over all ideals whose norms are less than a given integer, $\sum_n 1/\varphi(n)$, $\sum_n \psi(n)$, $\sum_n \Theta(n)$, where $\Theta(n)$ represents the number of ideal divisors of n and $\psi(n)$ is the number of decompositions of n into two factors prime to each other.

L. E. Dickson[16] evaluated certain determinants arising when we form the product of any two numbers of a field of degree n.

O. Meissner[17] proved that if r is the real mth root of a positive rational number z and if m is odd, then every number of the field $F(r)$ is a sum of $4m$ squares of the field. All numbers of $F(i\sqrt{z})$ are sums of 5 squares in the field of which 4 are real.

Meissner[18] proved that if $\alpha-\beta\sqrt{n}>0$, $\alpha+\beta\sqrt{n}$ is a sum of five

---

[13] *Indiana Acad. Sc. Proc.*, 1900, 105.
[14] *Archiv. der Math. u. Phys.*, 6, 1903; *Math. Ann.*, 77, 1915–16, 353–6.
[15] *Jour. für Math.*, 125, 1903, 153–161.
[16] *Bull. Amer. Math. Soc.*, 11, 1904–5, 482–6.
[17] *Archiv. Math. Phys.*, (3), 7, 1904, 266–8.
[18] *Ibid.*, (3), 9, 1905, 202–3.

squares $(\alpha_i+\beta_i\sqrt{n})^2$. If $r=\sqrt[3]{n}$, every number $\alpha+\beta r+\gamma r^2$ is a su■ of 12 squares in $F(r)$, since $r=n/r^2$. For $F(\omega r)$, where $\omega^2+\omega+1=$ ■ 24 squares suffice.

G. Humbert[19] proved that if $\rho=\frac{1}{2}(1+\sqrt{5})$ and M and P are intege■ (positive, negative, or zero) of the same parity, the number of decom■ positions of $4M+3+(4P+3)\rho$ into a sum of three squares $[2m_i-(2n_i+1)\rho]^2$ is double the number of its decompositions into

$$(2\mu_1+2\nu_1\rho)^2+(2\mu_2+1+2\nu_2\rho)^2+[2\mu_3+1+(2\nu_3+1)\rho]^2.$$

Also two similar theorems for $4M+3+8P\rho$ and $8M+6+(4P+1)\rho$.

A. Thue[20] discussed fractions approximating to $\sqrt[r]{k}$.

Thue[20a] proved that if ρ is a positive root of an equation of degre■ $r>1$ with integral coefficients, and if c,k are any given positive number■

$$\left|\rho-\frac{p}{q}\right|<c/q^{k+\frac{1}{2}r+1}$$

does not have infinitely many solutions in positive integers p, q.

H. Minkowski[21] proved that if $\xi=\alpha x+\beta y$, $\eta=\gamma x+\delta y$ have any com■ plex coefficients of determinant $\Delta\neq0$, there exist integers x, y, not bot■ zero, of the field defined by an imaginary cube root of unity for whic■ $|\xi|\leq|\sqrt{\Delta}|$, $|\eta|\leq|\sqrt{\Delta}|$. For the field defined by $i=\sqrt{-1}$, the correspond■ ing limit is the square root of $\Delta\sqrt{2}/(3-\sqrt{3})$. He made an extende■ application of point lattices to algebraic numbers and ideals.

D. A. Grave[21a] gave an exposition of the elements of the theor■ of algebraic fields.

A. Axer[22] found that if $\varphi(r)$ is the number of integers in an algebrai■ field of degree k which are incongruent with respect to an ideal modulu■ r, and $N(r)$ is the norm of r, then $\varphi(r_\lambda)$ is represented asymptotically b■

$$\frac{N(r_\lambda)}{\alpha e^c \log\log N(r_\lambda)}$$

where r_λ is the product of the first λ prime ideals, arranged according t■ their norms, c is Euler's constant, and α is a certain constant dependin■ on the field considered. His method of derivation is an extensio■ and simplification of that employed by Landau[23].

[19] *Comptes Rendus*, Paris, 142, 1906, 537–541; *Jour. de Math.*, (6), 2, 1906, 329–355 for the same and analogous theorems in $\sqrt{2}$, $\sqrt{3}$.

[20] *Videnskabs-Selskabets Skrifter*, Christiania, 1908, No. 3, 34 pp.

[20a] *Jour. für Math.*, 135, 1909, 284–305.

[21] Diophantische Approximationen, 1907, 200–233.

[21a] Lectures on Elementary Theory of Numbers (Russian), Kiew, 1909; 2nd edi tion, Kiew, 1913. First edition appeared also in Bull. Kiew Univ., 1909–1910. Cf *Fortschritte der Math.*, 40, 1909, 234–5; 1913, 207–8.

[22] *Prace Math. & Fiz.*, 21, 1910, 37–41. (Polish.)

[23] *Archiv. Math. u. Phys.* (3), 5, 1903, 86–91; Handbuch der Verteilung der Prim■ zahlen 1, 217–9. Cf. also Landau, *Prace Math. & Fiz.*, 21, 1910, 97–177, abstract i■ *Bull. des Sci. Math.* (2), 37, 1913, 44–8.

R. Fueter[24] gave an introduction to the theory of algebraic fields.

A. Axer[25] considered the number $\chi_\lambda(\alpha)$ of factors of an ideal α of a iven algebraic field such that α is not divisible by the λth power of n ideal for $\lambda \geq 2$, and the number $\chi_{\lambda,\nu}(\alpha)$ of decompositions of α into wo factors, the first factor not being divisible by the λth power of an leal and the second factor not divisible by a νth power, where $\lambda \geq 2$, >2, and found asymptotic expressions for the means

$$\Sigma\chi_\lambda(\alpha),\ \Sigma\chi_{\lambda,\nu}(\alpha),$$

ımmed for the ideals α whose norms do not exceed x.

G. Frobenius[26] showed that if A and B are two algebraic fields of egrees a and b having the greatest common divisor Δ of degree d, and ıe least common multiple of degree m, then if one of the fields A and B relative Galoisian $dm=ab$.

E. Landau[27] wrote $T_k(n)$ for the number of representations of a ositive rational integer n as the norm of a product of k ideals of any umber field, and found an asymptotic expression for

$$\sum_{n=1}^{x} T_k(n)n^{-s}=\Sigma N(\alpha_1\ldots\alpha_k)^{-s},$$

ımmed for all sets of numbers $\alpha_1,\cdots,\alpha_k$ of the field, the norm N of hose product is $\leqq x$. For $s=0$, we get an asymptotic expression for he number of solutions of $N(\alpha_1\cdots\alpha_k)\leqq x$.

G. Szegö[28] considered greatest common ideal divisor of all n^2 minors of ertain determinants.

Ph. Furtwängler[29] derived criteria that a number is an algebraic umber of the nth degree by means of extension of ideas involving ontinued fractions expansions in case of quadratic irrationalities due o Minkowski. Cf. also, Minkowski.[12]

A. Speiser[30] discussed the problem of finding the simplest algebraic eld in which a given finite group of linear substitutions can be repreented rationally. A special case leads to theorem 90 in Hilbert's eport (on numbers of a relative cyclic field which are exact powers).

C. L. Siegel[32] improved Thue's[20a] result by showing that

$$\left|\rho-\frac{p}{q}\right| \geqq 1/q^{2\sqrt{r}}$$

[24] *Verh. Schweiz. Natf. Gesell.* 93, 1910. (Proc. verb. 339–40.)
[25] *Prace Matemat.-fiz.*, 22, 1911, 73-102 (Polish and German); review in *Bull. des* :. *math.*, (2), 38, II, 1914, 11-13.
[26] *Math. Ann.*, 70, 1911, 457–458.
[27] *Trans. Amer. Math. Soc.*, 13, 1912, 1–21.
[28] *Archiv. der Math. u. Phys.* (3), 24, 1915, 86–7.
[29] *Wiener Bericht*, 162, IIa, 1917, 299–309.
[30] *Math. Zeitschrift*, 5, 1919, 1–6. Cf. I. Schur, *ibid.*, 7–10.
[32] *Math. Zeitschrift*, 10, 1921, 173–213.

has only a finite number of positive integral solutions p, q. This hol also when the exponent $2\sqrt{r}$ is replaced by

$$\underset{\lambda=1,\ldots,r}{\text{Minimum}}\left(\frac{r}{\lambda+1}+\lambda\right)+\epsilon, \qquad \epsilon>0.$$

There is given the generalization that

$$|\rho-\zeta|\leqq 1/H(\zeta)^{2\sqrt{r}}$$

has only a finite number of solutions ζ which are primitive numbers an algebraic number field K, ρ being of degree r with respect to and $H(\zeta)$ being the maximum of the absolute values of the relative prime integral coefficients of the irreducible equation satisfied by Hence if $U(x, y)$ is a homogeneous form of degree d with coefficients in field K_0 of degree h_0, if K is a field containing K_0 and of degree h wit respect to the field of rational numbers, if $d>2h(2h-1)$, and if $V(x,$ is a polynomial, prime to U and with coefficients in K_0, whose dimensio is $<d-hm$, where m is the minimum of $\lambda+d/(\lambda+1)$ for $\lambda=1,\cdots,$ then $U(x, y)=V(x, y)$ has only a finite number of solutions in integr numbers of K. Other applications are to the prime ideal divisors of polynomial $f(x)$ with algebraic coefficients and to the finiteness of th solutions of $W(x, y)=0$ in integral numbers of a field whose prim divisors belong to a given finite set of ideals.

Siegel[33] proved the conjecture of Hilbert that every total positiv number of any algebraic number field K is expressible as a sum of fo squares of K. There is made an auxiliary study of ternary quadrati forms whose coefficients are integral numbers of K. Every tot positive number of K is a sum of a fixed number (independent of but dependent on m) of m the powers of total positive numbers of The proof is simpler than Hilbert's proof of Waring's theorem sinc use is made of powers of numbers not necessarily integers of K.

H. Hancock[34] solved $\xi^2+\eta^2=\zeta^2$ in quadratic algebraic numbers.

L. Bianchi [35] defined an absolute primary ideal A to be an ideal whos norm coincides with the least rational integer in A. They include a prime ideals of the first degree. Every A is a product of such prim ideals. There are found all A's whose norm is a given rational intege Every field contains an infinitude of prime ideals of the first degree.

[33] *Ibid.*, 11, 1921, 246–75 E. Landau, *Göttinger Nachr.*, 1919, 392–6, prove Hilbert's conjecture for every quadratic field.

[34] *Jour. de Math.*, (8), 4, 1921, 321–341.

[35] *Jour. de Math.*, (9), 1, 1922, 1–18.

Chapter II

CYCLOTOMY

12. Properties of the Function $F_n(x)$, where $F_n(x)=0$ is the Equation for the Primitive nth Roots of Unity

A. L. Cauchy[1] proved that, if $a, b, c, \cdots$ are the distinct prime factors of n,

$$F_n(x)=\frac{(x^n-1)\Pi(x^{n/ab}-1)\dots}{\Pi(x^{n/a}-1)\ \Pi(x^{n/abc}-1)\dots}$$

N. Trudi[2] proved that, if ρ is a primitive nth root of unity and α is a positive integer not divisible by n, then

$$n/(\rho^\alpha-1)=\rho^\alpha+2\rho^{2\alpha}+\cdots+(n-1)\rho^{(n-1)\alpha}.$$

If n' denotes the product of the distinct prime factors of n, $F_n(x)\equiv F_{n'}(x^{n/n'})$. If n is odd, $F_{2n}(x)=F_n(-x)$. Next, $x^n-1=\Pi F_d(x)$, where d ranges over all the divisors of n. Also, $F_n(1)=p$ if n is a power of a prime p, but $=1$ if n is not a power of a prime.

R. Rubini[3] proved Trudi's first result.

E. Catalan[4] obtained the polynomial expansions of

$$\frac{(1-x^{pq})\,(1-x)}{(1-x^p)\,(1-x^q)},\quad \frac{(1-x)^2\,(1-x^{pqr})}{(1-x^p)\,(1-x^q)\,(1-x^r)},$$

where p, q, r are relatively prime.

A. Migotti[5] wrote P for the product of the distinct primes $p_1, \cdots, p_\nu$ dividing n, n' for n/P, and S_k for the sum of the kth powers of the roots of $F_n(x)=0$. If k is not divisible by n', every $S=0$. In the contrary case,

$$S_k-\Sigma S_{k/p_1}+\Sigma S_{k/(p_1p_2)}-\cdots+(-1)^\nu S_{k/P}=0 \text{ or } (-1)^\lambda k,$$

according as P is not or is divisible by k/n', where λ is the number of the primes dividing n/k. If p and q are distinct odd primes, the coefficients of $F_{pq}(x)$ are all $0, \pm 1$, as proved by means of

$$F_{pq}(x)=F_q(x^p)/F_q(x).$$

A. S. Bang[6] proved the final result of Migotti and the fact that, if

[1] *Exercices de Math.*, 4, 1829, 231–3; Oeuvres, (2), 9, 1891, 275–7.
[2] *Atti Accad. Napoli*, 3, 1866–8, No. 6, pp. 20–29; *Annali di Mat.*, (2), 2, 1868–9, 160–2.
[3] *Giornale di Mat.*, 5, 1867, 184–9.
[4] *Bull. Acad. R. Belgique*, (2), 29, 1870, 182–198.
[5] *Sitzungsber. Akad. Wiss. Wien. (Math.)*, 87, II, 1883, 7–14.
[6] *Nyt Tidsskrift for Math.*, VI, B, 1895, 6–12.

$n=pqr$, where p, q, r are primes, $r<q<p$, no coefficient of $F_n(x)$ exceeds $r-1$ or $r-2$, according as r is odd or even.

L. Kronecker[7] discussed the irreducible factors of x^n-1. In particular, the g. c. d. of $F_m(x^n)$ and $F_n(x^m)$ is $F_{mn}(x)$, if m, n are relatively prime. The last restriction was removed by E. Netto.[8]

I. Amaldi[9] developed $F_n(x)$ in a series in two ways and found the sum of the kth powers of its roots (cf. Netto, Algebra, I, §304).

L. E. Dickson[10] proved that, if $n=\nu p^r$, where ν is not divisible by the prime p,

$$F_n(x)=F_\nu(x^{p^r})/F_\nu(x^{p^{r-1}}),$$

and used this recursion formula to obtain Cauchy's expression for $F_n(x)$. He gave theorems on the prime factors of $F_n(x)$ when x is an integer.

J. W. L. Glaisher[11] evaluated the sum of the rth powers of the primitive nth roots of unity. In Cauchy's form of the equation for them, write $\delta=n/(ab\cdots)$, $\xi=x^\delta$. When $n=a^\alpha b^\beta$, we get,

$$\frac{(\xi-1)(\xi^{ab}-1)}{(\xi^a-1)(\xi^b-1)}.$$

The explicit polynomial form of the latter is obtained [Catalan[4]].

An anonymous writer[12] stated that $\Pi F_d(1)=n$, where d ranges over the divisors of n. Also that the value of $F_n(-1)$ is 2 if n is a power of 2, $F_p(1)$ if n is double an odd prime p; but is 1 in all remaining cases.

S. Szilárd[13] expressed $F_n(x)$ as a determinant.

13. Irreducibility of the Equation $F_n(x)=0$ for the Primitive nth Roots of Unity

C. F. Gauss[1] was the first to prove that, if p is an odd prime,

$$X\equiv x^{p-1}+x^{p-2}+\cdots+x+1=0 \tag{1}$$

is irreducible, i. e., X is not the product of two polynomials in x with rational coefficients. He employed the lemma (Art. 42) that if a polynomial $x^n+ax^{n-1}+\cdots$ with integral coefficients is divisible by $x^m+Ax^{m-1}+\cdots$, whose coefficients are rational, the latter coefficients $A, \cdots$ are all integers. Let X have a factor $P(x)$ of degree λ First, let the

[7] *Vorlesungen über Zahlentheorie*, 1901, 169, 281–98, 375–82, 440–2.
[8] *Archiv Math. Phys.*, (3), 4, 1902, 65–67.
[9] *Giornale di Mat.*, 40, 1902, 31–36.
[10] *Amer. Math. Monthly*, 12, 1905, 86–89. Cf. R. D. Carmichael, 17, 1910, 120, for a related unsolved problem.
[11] *Messenger Math.*, 39, 1909–10, 81–85.
[12] *L' intermédiaire des math.*, 24, 1917, 5–6 (no reply in 1917–9).
[13] *Math. és Phys. Lapok*, 26, 1917, 81–88.
[1] *Disquisitiones Arithmeticae*, 1801, Art. 341; Werke, 1, 1863, 417–9. Maser's German transl., pp. 402–4.

reciprocal of each root of $P=0$ be a root of $P=0$; then P is a product of factors

$$x^2-2x\cos\omega+1=(x-\cos\omega)^2+\sin^2\omega,$$

and $P(x)$ is positive for every real x. Let $P_\alpha(x)=0$ be the equation whose roots are the αth powers of the roots of $P=0$. From

$$\prod_{\alpha=1}^{p-1} P_\alpha(1)=p^\lambda,\quad \Sigma P_\alpha(1)\equiv 0 \pmod{p},$$

and the fact that each $P_\alpha(1)$ is a positive integer, we have a contradiction. The case in which $P=0$ is not a reciprocal equation was treated separately.

A. M. Legendre[2] noted that we need treat only the first case of Gauss since each root of $P_\alpha(x)=0$ is imaginary, being a root of $X=0$, whence $P_\alpha(1)>0$. He gave another proof of Gauss' lemma.

L. Kronecker[3] noted that $X=f(x)\phi(x)$ implies $p=f(1)\phi(1)$. Hence we may take $f(1)=1$. One of the roots $\alpha, \cdots, \alpha^{p-1}$ of $X=0$ satisfies $f(x)=0$, whence α is a root of $P(x)\equiv f(x)f(x^2)\cdots f(x^{p-1})=0$. Expand this product and give to x the values $1, \alpha, \cdots, \alpha^{p-1}$, and add. The sum of the values of x^n is zero unless n is divisible by p and then the sum is p. Hence

$$0\equiv f(1)^{p-1}+(p-1)f(\alpha)f(\alpha^2)\cdots f(\alpha^{p-1}) \pmod{p}.$$

But $P(\alpha)=0$, $f(1)=1$. Hence we have a contradiction.

Th. Schönemann[4] employed the evident fact that a function is algebraically irreducible if it is irreducible modulo m, and proved that (1) is irreducible with respect to any prime modulus m which is a primitive root of p. But if r is one primitive root of p, there occur among the primitive roots $r+yp$ an infinitude of primes (by Dirichlet's theorem on arithmetical progressions).

Schönemann[5] deduced a second proof from the fact that $(x-a)^n+pF(x)$ is irreducible modulo p^2 (and hence algebraically irreducible) if and only if $F(a)\not\equiv 0 \pmod{p}$. But

$$X=\frac{x^p-1}{x-1}=(x-1)^{p-1}+pF(x),\quad F(1)=1.$$

The first fact with $a=0$ implies that a polynomial is irreducible if the coefficient of the highest power of x is unity, all remaining coefficients are integers divisible by p, and the constant term is not divisible by p^2. This implication was not stated explicitly.

[2] *Théorie des nombres*, ed. 2, 1808, pp. 438–40.
[3] *Jour. für Math.*, 29, 1845, 280; Werke, I, 1–4. French transl., *Nouv. Ann. Math.*, 8, 1849, 419–21. Reproduced in P. Bachmann's Kreistheilung, 1872, 34.
[4] *Jour. fur Math.*, 31, 1846, 325 (reprint of Progr., Brandenburg, 1844, §50).
[5] *Ibid.*, 32, 1846, 100, §61 (40, 1850, 188 for priority to Eisenstein[6]).

G. Eisenstein[6] stated explicitly the last result and gave a very simple proof of it. To convert X into such a polynomial, write $x=z+1$ [Schönemann[5]].

E. Prouhet[7] readily proved by Fermat's theorem that, if x is an integer $\not\equiv 1 \pmod p$, every divisor of X is $\equiv 1 \pmod p$. Hence, if $\phi(x)$ is a factor of X, $\phi(x)-1\equiv 0 \pmod p$ has the roots $0, 2, 3, \cdots, p-1$, whose number $p-1$ exceeds the degree of ϕ.

J. A. Serret[8] extended Kronecker's[3] proof to the irreducibility of

$$(2) \qquad \frac{x^{p^\mu}-1}{x^{p^{\mu-1}}-1}\equiv \sum_{j=0}^{p-1} x^{jp^{\mu-1}}=0,$$

whose roots are the primitive p^μth roots of unity. He stated that it follows readily that F_n is irreducible when n is arbitrary; this had been stated without proof by A. L. Cauchy.[9]

Serret[10] extended Eisenstein's[6] proof to (2).

L. Kronecker[11] proved that, if n is any integer, $F_n(x)=0$ is irreducible; nor can it be decomposed into factors whose coefficients are rational functions of a root of an irreducible equation with integral coefficients (that of the highest power being unity) whose discriminant is prime to n. In particular, since the discriminant of $x^m=1$ is m^m, the irreducible factors of x^n-1 remain irreducible after the adjunction of a primitive root of unity whose exponent is prime to n, but not in the contrary case.

R. Dedekind[12] abbreviated Kronecker's[11] proof by use of the theory of algebraic numbers.

L. Kronecker[13] showed that if a factor $\phi(x)$ of (1) vanishes for $x=\omega$,

$$P(x)\equiv\phi(x^{m_1})\phi(x^{m_2})\cdots\phi(x^{m_{p-1}})$$

has the factor X, where $km_k\equiv 1 \pmod p$. Hence $P(1)$ is divisible by p, whereas $\phi(1)=\pm 1$, so that $P(1)=1$. The proof applies also to (2).

R. Dedekind[14] gave a simple proof of the irreducibility of F_n for any

---

[6] *Ibid.*, 39, 1850, 166–7. Reproduced by Serret[10]; Mathews, Theory of Numbers, 1892, 186–9; Bachmann, Kreistheilung, 1872, 36–37.

[7] *Nouv. Ann. Math.*, 9, 1850, 348–9. Repeated by E. Cahen, *ibid.*, (4), 11, 1911, 70; Birkhoff and Vandiver, Annals of Math., (2), 5, 1904, 180.

[8] *Jour. de Math.*, 15, 1850, 296.

[9] *Comptes Rendus*, Paris, 24, 1847, 407; Oeuvres, (1), 10, 1897, 234.

[10] Cours d'algèbre supérieure, ed. 2, 1854, 516–21; ed. 5, 1885, I, 242–7; ed. 6, 1910, I, 244.

[11] *Jour. de Math.*, 19, 1854, 177–192; Werke, I, 75–92. Summary in Bachmann's Kreistheilung, 1872, 40–43, and in Weber.[27] New proof by F. Mertens, *Sitzungsber Akad. Wiss. Wien (Math.)*, 116, IIa, 1907, 1337-42.

[12] *Zeitschr. Math. Phys.*, 18, 1873, Lit., 17–19.

[13] *Jour. de Math.*, (2), 1, 1856, 399–400; Werke, I, 99–102. Reproduced by Bachmann, Kreistheilung, 1872, 35–36. Simplified by Dickson in Miller, Blichfeldt and Dickson's Theory and Application of Finite Groups, 1916, 310.

[14] *Jour. für Math.*, 54, 1857, 27–30. Reproduced by H. Weber, Algebra, ed. 2, I, 1898, 596–600.

n by use of the following fact due to Schönemann. If p is a prime and if the polynomial $f(x)$ has integral coefficients and if $f_1(x)=0$ is the equation whose roots are the pth powers of the roots of $f(x)=0$, then $f_1(x)\equiv f(x) \pmod{p}$, identically.

F. Arndt[15] employed the last fact to prove the irreducibility of F_n, where $n=p^a n'$ and n' is not divisible by p, granting the irreducibility of $F_{n'}$.

V. A. Lebesgue[16] gave a modification of Arndt's[15] proof.

R. Dedekind[17] proved the irreducibility of (1) very simply by use of algebraic numbers.

L. Kronecker[18] proved that if $F(x)$ is a polynomial with integral coefficients and if ν_p denotes the number of equal or distinct roots of $F(x)\equiv 0 \pmod{p}$, the limit for infinitely small positive values of w of the series $\Sigma \nu_p p^{-1-w}$, summed for all primes p, is the product of log $1/w$ by the number of irreducible factors of $F(x)$. This is used to prove the irreducibility of (1). The method is said to apply to any F_n.

Kronecker[19] employed principles of his arithmetical theory of algebraic quantities (*ibid.*, 92, 1882) to prove the irreducibility of (2) and of $(x-1)^n+p\Phi(x)$, where $\Phi(x)$ is a polynomial with integral coefficients of degree $n-1$ such that $\Phi(1)$ is not divisible by p (cf. Schönemann[5]).

N. W. L. A. Gravelaar[20] proved that F_n is irreducible by showing that x^n-1 contains only one irreducible factor F_n not a divisor of $x^k-1 (k=1, \cdots, n-1)$, while $x^n-1=\Pi F_d$, d ranging over the factors of n.

D. Hilbert[20a] used algebraic numbers to prove $F_n(x)$ irreducible.

M. Mandl[21] proved the irreducibility of (2) by applying the following method of testing the reducibility of any polynomial $f(x)$ with integral coefficients. Let h be an integer exceeding the upper limit to the positive real parts α of the roots $\alpha+\beta i$ of $f=0$. Then $F(y)\equiv f(y+h)$, as well as each real factor, has all its coefficients positive. The problem to express $F(y)=\Sigma c_r y^r$ as a product of $\Sigma a_k y^k$ and $\Sigma b_j y^j$ reduces to the solution of

$$c_r=\sum_{k=0}^{r} a_k b_{r-k} \qquad (r=0, 1, .., n)$$

in positive integers. First choose all pairs of positive integers a_0, b_0

---

[15] *Jour. für Math.*, 56, 1859, 178–81. Reproduced by Bachmann, Kreistheilung, 38–40, and by Weber.[27]

[16] *Jour. de Math.*, (2), 4, 1859, 105–110; *Annali di Mat.*, 2, 1859, 232–8. His statement that $F_n(1)=1$ when n is not a power of a prime was proved by J. J. Sylvester, *Phil. Mag.*, (4), 18, 1859, 281–3.

[17] Dirichlet-Dedekind, Zahlentheorie, Suppl. XI, ed. 3, 1879, ä179, pp. 581–3; ed. 4, 1895, §185, pp. 613–4. This proof was incorrectly ascribed to Kummer by Ruthinger,[32] p. 103.

[18] *Monatsber. Akad. Wiss.*, Berlin, 1880, 155–62; Werke, II, 83–93.

[19] *Jour. für Math.*, 100, 1887, 79–82; Werke, III_1, 243.

[20] *Nieuw Archief voor Wiskunde*, 20, 1893, 7–25.

[20a] *Jahresb. Deut. Math.-Vereinig.*, 4, 1894–5, 331–2.

[21] *Jour. für Math.*, 113, 1894, 252–261.

whose product is c_0. For each pair, seek all pairs of positive integral solutions a_1, b_1 of $a_0b_1+a_1b_0=c_1$. For each set a_0, b_0, a_1, b_1, seek all pairs of positive integral solutions a_2, b_2 of $a_0b_2+a_2b_0=c_1-a_1b_1$; etc.

L. Königsberger[22] proved that if p is a prime, if r is relatively prime to n, if the a_i are any integers such that neither a_0 nor a_n is divisible by p, and if $[t]$ is the largest integer $\leqq t$, then

$$a_0x^n+\sum_{j=1}^{n-1} p^{[jr/n]+1}a_jx^{n-j}+p^ra_n$$

is irreducible. For $r=1$ this becomes the theorem of Schönemann[5] and Eisenstein.[6] He treated also the case in which the coefficients have two prime factors. Other generalizations were given by E. Netto,[23] W. F. Kahan,[24] O. Perron,[25] and H. Blumberg.[26]

H. Weber[27] erred in his first proof of the irreducibility of F_n, and gave[28] a new proof by use of infinite arithmetical progressions and algebraic ideals.

L. Königsberger[29] noted that the irreducibility of (2) is a special case of the following theorem. If the coefficients, other than the first, of $F(x)$ are all divisible by the prime p, and if $f(x)$ has the same property and is a factor of $F(x)$, and if the exponent of the highest power of p which divides the constant term of $F(x)$ exceeds by unity that of $f(x)$, then F/f is irreducible. If F_a and F_b are irreducible when a and b are any two relatively prime integers, then F_{ab} is irreducible. After the adjunction of the square root of $(-1)^{\frac{1}{2}(q-1)}q$, where q is a prime, F_p reduces or remains irreducible, according as the prime p is or is not equal to q.

A. Thue[30] assumed that $U(x)$, given by (1), has the factors $P(x)$, $Q(x)$. We may take $P(1)=1$, $Q(1)=p$. Write $x-1=y$. Then

$$U(x)=\frac{(y+1)^p-1}{y}=y^{p-1}+pR(y).$$

Take the nth derivative, where $n<p-1$. Thus $U^{(n)}(1)=pR^{(n)}(0)$. By

---

[22] *Sitzungsber. Akad. Wiss.*, Berlin, 1894, 1135–9; 1898, 735–41; *Jour. für Math.*, 115, 1895, 53–78; 121, 1900, 320–59. Simpler proof by M. Bauer, *Jour. für Math.*, 128, 1905, 298–301.

[23] *Oberhessische Gesell. für Natur.-u. Heilkunde*, Giessen, 30, 1895; 31, 1896, 113; Algebra, I, 1896, 56–64; *Math. Annalen*, 48, 1897, 81–88. Cf. M. Bauer, *Jour. für Math.*, 132, 1907, 32; 134, 1908, 29.

[24] *Math. Soc.*, St. Petersburg, 1899, 114–6 (*Fortschritte Math.*, 30, 1899, 100).

[25] *Math. Annalen*, 60, 1905, 448–458; *Jour. für Math.*, 132, 1907, 288–307.

[26] *Trans. Amer. Math. Soc.*, 17, 1916, 517–544.

[27] *Algebra*, ed. 1, I, 1895, 419; error noted in II, 1896, 768–76, where are given the proofs by Arndt[15] and Kronecker.[11]

[28] *Algebra*, ed. 1, II, 1896, 777–82; ed. 2, II, 1899, 728–33.

[29] *Jour. für Math.*, 121, 1900, 344–54.

[30] *Archiv for Math. og Naturv.*, 25, 1904, No. 3.

this and $Q(1)=p$, the successive derivatives of $U=PQ$ show that $Q'(1), \cdots, Q^{(n)}(1)$ are all divisible by p. Thus all coefficients of $Q(x)$ are divisible by p, whereas the leading coefficient is unity.

F. Mertens[31] simplified Dedekind's[14] proof by showing that $F_n(x^m)$ is divisible by $F_n(x)$ if m is prime to n.

M. Ruthinger[32] reproduced many of the above proofs with personal coloring.

F. Mertens[33] wrote ν for the degree $\phi(n)$ of F_n, P for the product of the primes $<2^\nu\nu$, r for the largest factor prime to n of P, and a for any integer prime to n. Let m be a positive solution of $m\equiv a(\text{mod } n)$, $m\equiv 1(\text{mod } r)$. Let p be a prime factor of m. Suppose that F_n has a factor $f(x)$ which vanishes for $x=\alpha, \beta, \cdots$. Then $f(\alpha^p)/p, f(\beta^p)/p, \cdots$ are algebraic integers whose absolute values are $<1/\nu$, whence their elementary symmetric functions are <1 and, being integers, are zero, whence $f(\alpha^p)=0$, etc. Starting with $\alpha^p, \beta^p, \cdots$ in place of $\alpha, \beta, \cdots$, we see similarly that, if q is a prime factor of m/p, $f(\alpha^{pq})=0, \cdots$, and finally that $f(\alpha^m)=f(\alpha^a)=0$. Thus f has all the roots of F_n.

M. Bauer[34] proved that (2) is irreducible.

14. Irreducibility of Polynomials

Further references on irreducible polynomials in one or two variables not mentioned in the two reports in the Encyclopédie des sc. math., tome I, vol. 2, pp. 205–232, 252–4:

Paul Halcke. Mathematisches Sinnenconfect, 1719, 1835. Cf. B. Meth, *Progr.*, Berlin, 1902; *Fortschritte der Math.*, 33, 1902, 102–3.

D. Sélivanoff. *Bull. Soc. Math. France*, 13, 1885, 119–31; *Acta Math.*, 19, 1895, 73–91.

I. Bendixson. *Öfversigt K. Vetenskaps-Akad. Förhandlingar*, Stockholm, 49, 1892, 189–93.

L. Königsberger. *Math. Annalen*, 53, 1900, 49–53.

G. Charasoff. Arithmetische Untersuchungen über Irreduktibilität, Diss., Heidelberg, 1902, 67 pp.

M. Bauer. *Math. Naturwiss. Berichte aus Ungarn*, 20, 1902 (1905), 30–33, 39–42; *Math. es Phys. Lapok*, 13, 1904, 92–95, 319–22.

F. Mertens. *Sitzungsber. Akad. Wiss. Wien*, 120, IIa, 1911, 1485–1502.

G. Pólya. *Jahresbericht d. Deutschen Math.-Vereinigung*, 28, 1919, 31–36.

Th. Skolem. *Videnskapsselskapets Skrifter (Math.)*, 1921, No. 17.

For the reducibility of x^n-a, see *Encyclopédie*, pp. 230–1, and

K. Th. Vahlen, *Acta Math.*, 19, 1895, 195.

D. Mair, *Proc. Edinburgh Math. Soc.*, 19, 1901, 33.

G. Chrystal, *ibid.*, 46–49.

F. Mertens, *Sitzungsber. Akad. Wiss. Wien*, 114, IIa, 1905, 1297–9.

F. Gomes Teixeira. *Revista Sociedad Mat. Española*, 4, 1914–5, 65–66.

---

[31] *Sitzungsber. Akad. Wiss. Wien (Math.)*, 114, IIa, 1905, 1293–4.

[32] Die Irreducibilitätsbeweise der Kreisteilungsgleichung, Diss. Strassburg, 1907, 117 pp.

[33] *Sitzungsber. Akad. Wiss. Wien (Math.)*, 117, IIa, 1908, 689–90.

[34] *Archiv Math. Phys.*, (3), 25, 1916–7, 131–4.

15. Equation for the e Periods of pth Roots of Unity

C. F. Gauss. Disquisitiones Arithmeticae, 1801, Arts. 355–366; Werke, I, 1863, 412–63 (Maser's transl., 397–448). Posth. MS, Werke, II, 243–65 (235); Maser, 630–52, 678–82 (624).
A. M. Legendre. Theorie des nombres, ed. 2, 1808, 435–80; ed. 3, 1830, II, 166–330, 369–90 (Maser's transl., II, 161–323, 359–80).
V. A. Lebesgue. *Comptes Rendus*, Paris, 5, 1837, 722–50; *Jour. de Math.*, 3, 1838, 113–144; *Comptes Rendus*, Paris, 18, 1844, 696; 51, 1860, 9–13.
J. Frischauf. *Sitzungsber. Akad. Wiss. Wien* (*Math.*), 55, II, 1867, 113–20.
C. G. Reuschle. $e=3, 4$, Tafeln Complexer Primzahlen, 1875.
A. Cayley. $e=3, 4$, *Proc. London Math. Soc.*, 11, 1879–80, 4–17; $e=5$, *ibid.*, 12, 1880–1, 15–16; 16, 1884–5, 61–63.
H. J. S. Smith. $e=6$, *Assoc. franç. av. sc.*, 1880, 190–1.
J. J. Sylvester. $e=3, 4$, *Assoc. franç. av. sc.*, 1880, 96–98; *Johns Hopkins University Circulars*, 1, 1881, 150–1. See his papers 6, 7 of §20.
A. E. Pellet. *Comptes Rendus*, Paris, 93, 1881, 838–40; *Bull. Soc. Math. France*, 15, 1887, 86–96; *Assoc. franç. av. sc.*, 1900, I, 125.
A. Migotti. *Sitzungsber. Akad. Wiss. Wien* (*Math.*), 87, II, 1883, 7–14.
C. A. Scott. $e=4, 5$, *Amer. Jour. Math.*, 8, 1886, 261–4.
H. W. Lloyd Tanner. $e=5$, *Proc. London Math. Soc.*, 18, 1886–7, 214–34; general theory, *ibid.*, 20, 1889, 63–87, 258–296.
H. Scheffler. Beiträge zur Zahlentheorie, 1891 (not reliable).
G. B. Mathews. Theory of Numbers, 1892, 195, 219.
F. S. Carey. $e=3, 4, 5, 6$, *Quar. Jour. Math.*, 26, 1893, 322–71.
X. Stouff. *Comptes Rendus*, Paris, 125, 1897, 859–60.
J. C. Glashan. *Amer. Jour. Math.*, 21, 1899, 270–85.
P. Heidke, Ueber Kreisteilungsgleichungen, Diss., Greifswald, 1899.
J. Schumacher. *Zeitschr. Math. Naturw. Unterricht*, 41, 1910, 425–47.
W. Burnside. $e=5$, *Proc. London Math. Soc.*, (2), 14, 1915, 251–9.
O. Upadhyaya. $e=5, 7$, *Bull. Calcutta Math. Soc.*, 12, 1920–1, 29–32, 33–36.

16. Cyclotomic Function as a Binary Quadratic Form

C. F. Gauss[1] employed the two periods of the imaginary nth roots of unity, where n is an odd prime, to prove that

$$(1)\qquad 4\left(\frac{x^n-1}{x-1}\right)=Y^2\mp nZ^2,\quad n\equiv\pm1 \pmod 4,$$

where $Y=2x^m+x^{m-1}+\cdots$, $Z=x^{m-1}+\cdots$ are polynomials in x with $m=(n-1)/2$, which he tabulated for $n=3, 5, 7, 11, 13, 17, 19, 23$.

Sophie Germain[2] stated in her first letter to Gauss, Nov. 21, 1804, that she had two proofs of the existence of polynomials Y_1, Z_1 such that

$$4\left(\frac{x^{n^s}-1}{x-1}\right)=Y_1^2\mp nZ_1^2\quad (n \text{ a prime}).$$

She[3] gave the following proof when $s=2$. In (1) change x to x^n,

[1] *Disquisitiones Arithmeticae*, 1801, Art. 357; Werke, 1, 1863, pp. 443–4; German transl. by H. Maser, 1889, p. 427. Proof slightly modified by J. A. Serret, Algèbre, ed. 2, 1854, 522–32; ed. 5, II, 1885, 573–82.

[2] *Oeuvres philosophiques de S. Germain*, Paris, 1879, 298. Cinq lettres de S. Germain à C. F. Gauss, Berlin, 1880, 24 pp. Reproduced in *Archiv Math. Phys.*, 65, 1880, *Litt. Bericht* 259, pp. 27–31; 66, 1881, *Litt. Bericht* 261, pp. 3–10.

[3] *Jour. für Math.*, 7, 1831, 201–4.

Y to y, Z to z and multiply the resulting relation by (1). Thus

$$Y_1=\tfrac{1}{2}(yY\pm nzZ),\ Z_1=\tfrac{1}{2}(yZ+zY).$$

A. M. Legendre[4] noted that $Y\equiv 2x^m(1-1/x)^{-\frac{1}{2}}$ (mod n), $m=(n-1)/2$. Legendre[5] gave a simpler rule. Since $x^n-1\equiv(x-1)^n$ (mod n),

$$4(x-1)^n\equiv(x-1)Y^2,\ Y\equiv 2(x-1)^{\frac{1}{2}(n-1)}\ (\text{mod } n).$$

Hence Y is found by developing the final binomial and reducing the coefficients to values numerically $<\frac{1}{2}n$ by omitting multiples of n.

C. G. J. Jacobi[6] noted that Legendre's last rule holds only for small primes n. The correct values of Y and Z are given by known formulas which express the coefficients of an equation in terms of sums of powers of its roots, these sums being here $\frac{1}{2}(t-1)$ or $\frac{1}{2}(-t-1)$, where $t^2=\pm n$.

Legendre[7] developed at length the method suggested by Jacobi.

V. A. Lebesgue[8] showed that (1) holds for specified polynomials Y and Z in x whose coefficients are expressed in terms of symbols giving the numbers of sets of solutions of

$$x_1^2+\cdots+x_k^2\equiv 1,\ 0,\ \nu\ (\text{mod } n).$$

G. L. Dirichlet[9] proved (1) and applied it to solve $t^2-nu^2=1$ in integers. He noted that the discussion by Gauss can be readily extended to the case in which n is any composite number and stated the following result when n is a product of two distinct primes: There exist polynomials Y and Z with integral coefficients such that

$$\frac{4(x^{pq}-1)(x-1)}{(x^p-1)(x^q-1)}=Y^2\mp pqZ^2\ ,\ pq\equiv\pm 1(\text{mod } 4).$$

Dirichlet[10] employed a product P of distinct odd primes, and

$$A(x)=\Pi(x-\theta^a),\ B(x)=\Pi(x-\theta^b),\ \theta=\cos 2\pi/P+i\sin 2\pi/P,$$

where a and b range over the positive integers $<P$ and prime to P for which $(a/P)=+1$, $(b/P)=-1$, respectively, in Jacobi's quadratic

[4] *Théorie des nombres*, ed. 2, 1808, pp. 467–9; ed. 3, 1830, II, pp. 192–4, German transl. by Maser, II, pp. 186–8.

[5] *Ibid.*, ed. 2, second supplément, 1825, p. 34; ed. 3, 1830, II, pp. 194–5 (Maser, II, p. 188).

[6] Letter to Legendre, July 2, 1830; Jacobi's Werke, 1, 1881, 453–4; *Ann. sc. école norm. sup.*, 6, 1869, 171; *Jour. für Math.*, 80, 1875, 271–2; *Bull. des. sc. math. astr.*, 9, 1875, 133–6. In his reply, Oct. 1, 1830, l.c., Legendre admitted his error.

[7] *Mém. Acad. Sc. l'Institut de France*, 11, 1832, 81–99.

[8] *Comptes Rendus*, Paris, 5, 1837, 722–5; *Jour. de Math.*, 3, 1838, 128–131.

[9] *Jour. für Math.*, 17, 1837, 286–290; Werke, I, 343–350 Reproduced by P. Bachmann, Die Lehre . . . Kreistheilung, 1872, 294–9. Full report in Dickson's History of the Theory of Numbers, II, 371.

[10] *Jour. für Math.*, 21, 1840, 153–5; Werke, I, 493–6. Amplified in his Zahlentheorie, 1863, §140; ed. 2, 1871, 359–365; ed. 3, 1879, 363–370; ed. 4, 1894, 363–370. For proofs of theorems in the latter, see P. C. Maria, *Giornale di Mat.*, 4, 1866, 345; S. Szilárd, *Math. és phys. lapok*, 26, 1917, 81–88.

residue symbols. Thus $AB=X$, where $X=0$ is the equation for the primitive Pth roots of unity. Making use mainly of Newton's identities, it is shown that

$$2A(x)=Y-j\sqrt{P}Z,\ 2B(x)=Y+j\sqrt{P}Z,\ j=i^{\frac{1}{4}(P-1)^2},\ i=\sqrt{-1},$$

where Y and Z are polynomials in x with integral coefficients. Thus

$$4X=Y^2-(-1/P)PZ^2.$$

To compute the coefficients of Y and Z, note that the sum of the kth powers of the roots of $X=0$ equals $(-1)^r\phi(Q)$, where ϕ is Euler's function and Q is the g.c.d. of k and $P=QR$, while r is the number of prime factors of R.

A. L. Cauchy[11] stated that the theory of alternate functions of the primitive nth roots of unity yields the following generalization of the theorems of Gauss[1] and Dirichlet[9]: If the odd prime factors of n are distinct and the power of 2 factor (if it exists) is 4 or 8, and if the equation for the primitive nth roots of unity is $X=0$, then $4X=Y^2\pm nZ^2$, where Y and Z are polynomials in x with integral coefficients.

Cauchy[12] employed an integer n whose odd prime factors are distinct and the power of 2 factor (if it exists) is 4 or 8. Let ρ be a primitive root of $x^n=1$ and write $\Delta=\Sigma\rho^h-\Sigma\rho^k$, where h and k range over the integers $<n$ and prime to n for which $(h/n)=+1$, $(k/n)=-1$. Then $\Delta^2=+n$ if $n=4\alpha+1$, $4(4\alpha+3)$ or $8(4\alpha+1)$. But $\Delta^2=-n$ if $n=4\alpha+3$ or $4(4\alpha+1)$ or $8(4\alpha+3)$, and then

$$\Sigma \sin 2h\pi/n-\Sigma \sin 2k\pi/n=\sqrt{n}.$$

J. Liouville[13] prove that in $4X=Y^2\mp pZ^2$, where p is an odd prime,

$$U\equiv Y+Z\sqrt{\pm p}=2\sqrt{X}e^t,\ t=\tfrac{1}{2}\sqrt{\pm p}\sum_{m=1}^{\infty}\left(\frac{m}{p}\right)\frac{1}{mx^m}.$$

This result may be used to compute U, the coefficient of whose general term is expressed in terms of gamma functions. He proved that

$$Z\frac{dY}{dx}-Y\frac{dZ}{dx}=\frac{2}{x(x-1)}\left\{\left(\frac{1}{p}\right)x^{p-1}+\left(\frac{2}{p}\right)x^{p-2}+\dots+\left(\frac{p-1}{p}\right)x\right\}.$$

G. K. C. von Staudt[14] gave an elementary, but long, proof of (1). He computed the first six coefficients of both Y and Z.

N. Trudi[15] treated Dirichlet's problem by an analogous method,

---

[11] *Comptes Rendus*, Paris, 10, 1840, 181; Oeuvres, (1), 5, 1885, 84.
[12] *Mém. Acad. Sc. Institut de France*, 17, 1840, 665–699, Note XII; Oeuvres, (1), III, 359–361.
[13] *Jour. de Math.*, (2), 2, 1857, 413–423; *Comptes Rendus*, Paris, 44, 1857, 798.
[14] *Jour. für Math.*, 67, 1867, 205–217.
[15] *Annali di Mat.*, (2), 2, 1868–9, 150–166.

writing n for P, U for $2A(x)$, V for $2B(x)$. Let S_r denote the sum of the rth powers of the primitive nth roots of unity, and write

$$Y=2x^m+a_1x^{m-1}+\cdots+a_m,\ Z=b_1x^{m-1}\cdots+b_{m+1}x,\ m=\tfrac{1}{2}\phi(n).$$

By Newton's identities for $U=0$, $V=0$, he proved the recursion formulas

$$2ra_r=-[2S_r+a_1S_{r-1}+\ldots+a_{r-1}S_1]\pm n\left[\left(\frac{r-1}{n}\right)b_1+\ldots+\left(\frac{1}{n}\right)b_{r-1}\right],$$

$$2rb_r=-[\qquad b_1S_{r-1}+\ldots+b_{r-1}S_1]+$$
$$\left[2\left(\frac{r}{n}\right)+\left(\frac{r-1}{n}\right)a_1+\ldots+\left(\frac{1}{n}\right)a_{r-1}\right].$$

His criticism of Cauchy[11] was shown to be invalid by A. Genocchi,[16] who noted that, while Cauchy[11] did not give a proof, the principles in his paper in the same volume and in Cauchy[12] lead easily to a direct proof. Cauchy proved that $\Delta^2=\pm n$. Then the method of Gauss yields $4X=Y^2\pm nZ^2$. Trudi found a different formula when n is even, but failed to note that $4X$ can be represented by two or more quadratic forms.

G. Zolotareff[17] employed a prime p and

$$S(x)=\sum_{i=1}^{p-1}\left(\frac{i}{p}\right)x^i,\ X=\frac{x^p-1}{x-1}.$$

In the development of S/X as a continued fraction, let f_μ/ψ_μ be the last convergent the degree of whose denominator is $<m\equiv\frac{1}{2}(p-1)$. Then

(2) $$\phi_\mu(x)\equiv S(x)\cdot\psi_\mu(x)-Xf_\mu(x)$$

is of degree $\leqq m$. There exists a rational constant λ such that

$$Z=\pm\lambda\psi_\mu(x),\ Y=\lambda\phi_\mu(x).$$

The coefficients of ψ are computed from linear equations obtained from the decomposition into partial fractions of

$$\frac{S\psi}{X}-f=\frac{\phi}{X}=\Sigma\frac{A_i}{x-r^i},$$

where r is a primitive pth root of unity. The expansion of the final sum as a series in x must lack the terms x^{-j} $(j=1,\cdots,m-1)$, since ϕ/X is of degree $-m$. Hence $\Sigma r^{ki}A_i=0$ $(k=0,1,\cdots,m-2)$. When ψ (and hence Z) is found, we obtain ϕ from (2), and hence V, as the remainder when $S\psi$ is divided by X.

[16] *Ibid.*, 216–8; *Comptes Rendus*, Paris, 67, 1868, 1035–7.

[17] *Math. Sbornik*, 6, 1872, 83–96 (Russian). French Transl. with new numbering of formulas, *Nouv. Ann. Math.*, (2), 11, 1872, 539–549.

H. J. S. Smith[18] solved the problem proposed by G. Eisenstein[19] to find the primes n for which (1) has more that one set of solutions Y, Z. If $n\equiv 3 \pmod 4$, there is a single solution if $\pm X, \pm Y$ are regarded as one solution, except for $n=3$, where it has three solutions. If $n\equiv 1 \pmod 4$, there is an infinitude of solutions.

E. Lucas[20] employed the two recursion formulas of Trudi[15] to compute the coefficients of Y and Z when n is an odd integer $\leqq 41$ without a square factor and when $n=61$. Given

$$4X_n = Y^2-(-1/n)nz^2Z^2,$$

where n is odd and without square factors, and the factor z of the second polynomial has been placed in evidence, let X_n, Y, Z become X_n', $A+B\sqrt{z}$, $A'+B'\sqrt{z}$ when z is changed to $\sqrt{z}$. Write X_n'' for X_n with z changed to $-\sqrt{z}$. Since $X_m'X_n''=X_n$, we get[21]

$$16X_n=\left[A^2-B^2z+\left(\frac{-1}{n}\right)nz(A'^2B'^2z)\right]^2-4\left(\frac{-1}{n}\right)nz(AA'-BB'z)^2.$$

Replacing z by $-z^2$, we obtain Cauchy's[11] formula for the case $4n$. The coefficients of the resulting Y_1, Z_1 are tabulated for 21 values of n. Similarly from the case $4n$, we may deduce the case $8n$ by changing z to $\pm zi$ and taking the product; the coefficients of the resulting Y_2, Z_2 are tabulated for 18 values of $2n$. A. Cunningham[22] listed errata in these three and the related tables by Lucas.[23]

E. Catalan[24] and E. de Jonquières[25] made minor remarks of no interest.

K. Schwering[26] stated that a slight change in Legendre's[5] rule for Y gives correct values, but gave details only for a related problem.

H. Weber[26a] gave a method of deriving from (1) an expansion of $\Pi(x-r^a)$, where a ranges over all the quadratic residues of the prime n, and r is a primitive nth root of unity.

L. J. Rogers[27] stated the most practical method of determining Y and Z is to use the series reversing them:

$$y=2+x+c_2x^2+c_3x^3+\cdots,\quad z=x+f_2x^2+f_3x^3+\cdots.$$

---

[18] *Messenger Math.*, 5, 1876, 143–4; *Proc. London Math. Soc.*, 7, 1875–6, 273–8; *Coll. Math. Papers*, 2, 1894, 132.

[19] *Jour. für Math.*, 27, 1844, 88, Prob. 11.

[20] *Assoc. franç. av. sc.*, 7, 1878, 164–173.

[21] For n a prime, Lucas, *Atti R. Accad. Sc. Torino*. 13, 1877–8, 271–2.

[22] *Messenger Math.*, 46, 1916–7, 62–65.

[23] *Bull. Bibl. Storia Sc. Mat. e Fis.*, 11, 1878, 786.

[24] *Atti Accad. Pont. Nuovi Lincei*, 37, 1883–4, 98–101; *Bull. Accad. R. Sc. Belgique*, (3), 6, 1883, 264.

[25] *Comptes Rendus*, Paris, 98, 1884, 1358–62 (correction, 1515).

[26] *Jour. für Math.*, 110, 1892, 49.

[26a] Algebra, ed. 2, I, 1898.

[27] *Proc. London Math. Soc.*, 30, 1898–9, 23–30.

By the known reciprocal properties of Y, Z, $y=e_1Y$, $z=Z$, $e_1=(-1/p)$, while from Liouville's[13] final formula we obtain similarly

$$e_1(x^{p-1}+e_2x^{p-2}+\ldots+e_{p-1}x)=x+e_2x^2+\ldots+e_{p-1}x^{p-1}=\tfrac{1}{2}x\,(x-1)(zy'-yz'),$$

where $e_k=(k/p)$ if $k>1$. Eliminating z' by means of (1), we obtain a linear relation between y, z, y'. There is a similar relation involving z'. Hence the initial series lead to two equations in x with integral coefficients which serve to determine in succession $c_2, f_2, c_3, f_3, \cdots$.

N. Teege[28] employed Dirichlet's[10] notations and proved that

$$x^{P-1}+\left(\frac{2}{P}\right)x^{P-2}+\cdots+\left(\frac{P-1}{P}\right)x=-\tfrac{1}{2}x(x^P-1)\left(YZ'-ZY')\frac{\Pi(x^{\mu_2}-1)}{\Pi(x^{\mu_1}-1)}\right).$$

When P is a prime p, this becomes Liouville's[13] final result, whence

$$\sum_{\alpha=1}^{\frac{1}{2}(p-1)}\left(\frac{\alpha}{p}\right)=-Z'(-1)\ ,\ p=4n+3.$$

The same sum equals $(2/p)Z'(-1)$ if p is a composite number $4n+3$.

C. E. Bickmore[29] proved that, if $2m+1$ is >3 and prime to 3,

$$\frac{(x^{6m+3}-y^{6m+3})(x-y)}{(x^{2m+1}-y^{2m+1})(x^3-y^3)}=P^2-xyQ^2,$$

$$P=(x+y)Q+x^my^m,\quad Q=\frac{(x-y)(x^m-y^m)(x^{m+1}-y^{m+1})}{x^3-y^3}.$$

H. Holden[30] gave a new proof of (1).

Holden[31] proved that, if p is an odd prime or a product of distinct odd primes, Z_p is divisible by Z_{17}, Z_{11}, Z_5, Z_7 for $p\equiv 1, 3, 5, 7 \pmod 8$, respectively, and similar results.

A. Cunningham[32] proved that, if $n\equiv 3 \pmod 4$,

$$X^n-Y^n=\frac{x^3-y^3}{x-y}$$

has an infinitude of solutions in positive integers.

Several[33] expressed $(x^{14}+x^7+1)/(x^2+x+1)$ in the forms A^2+3B^2 and C^2+7D^2.

Several[34] expressed by a quadratic form

$$\frac{x^{17}-1}{x-1},\ \frac{(x^{3p}-1)(x-1)}{(x^p-1)(x^3-1)}\ (p=5 \text{ or } 11),\ \frac{(x^{15}-y^{15})(x-y)}{(x^5-y^5)(x^3-y^3)}-mxy\left(\frac{x^7-y^7}{x-y}\right).$$

---

[28] Ueber die $\frac{1}{2}(p-1)$ Gliedrigen Gaussischen Perioden . . . , Diss., Kiel, 1900, 31–38.

[29] *Math. Quest. Educ. Times*, 73, 1900, 68–69.

[30] *Quar. Jour. Math.*, 34, 1903, 235–240.

[31] *Messenger Math.*, 37, 1908, 130–9.

[32] *L'intermédiaire des math.*, 20, 1913, 66–68.

[33] *Mathesis*, (4), 4, 1914, 79–82.

[34] *Math. Questions and Solutions* (contin. of Educ. Times), 5, 1918, 95; 6, 1918, 50–51, 65.

Pandit Oudh Upadhyaya[35] verified that Legendre's[5] rule holds good up to $p=37$, but fails for $p=41$. Mathews (Theory of Numbers, 1892, p. 218) had noted that it fails for $p=61$.

17. Miscellaneous Results on Cyclotomy

J. L. Lagrange[1] found algebraically the roots of $x^\mu=1$, where μ is a prime. Let r be a root $\neq 1$ of $r^\mu=1$, a a primitive root of μ, and $\alpha^{\mu-1}=1$. Write

$$t=r+\alpha r^a+\alpha^2 r^{a^2}+\cdots+\alpha^{\mu-2}r^{a^{\mu-2}}.$$

We readily compute the value Θ of $t^{\mu-1}$. Using the $\mu-1$ roots of $\alpha^{\mu-1}=1$, we have as many linear equations which yield $r, r^a, \cdots$. Lagrange (p. 310) spoke of his method as a simplification of that of Gauss. But Gauss[2] remarked that this simplification is only apparent and introduces a difficulty which he had avoided.

N. H. Abel[3] noted that the radicals Θ should be prefixed by $(\mu-1)th$ roots of unity, and removed the resulting ambiguity in the formulas.

A Genocchi[4] employed an imaginary nth root r of unity, n a prime, and

$$a_i=hi+h_1\frac{i(i+1)}{1.2}+\ldots+h_m\frac{i(i+1)\ldots(i+m)}{1.2\ldots(m+1)}-\frac{i(i+1)\ldots(i+m+1)}{1.2\ldots(m+2)},$$

where $h, h_1, \cdots, h_m$ are integers, and proved that $a_1 r+\cdots+a_{n-1}r^{n-1}$ is divisible by $(1-r)^{n-m-3}$, and the sum of the coefficients of the quotient is of the form $kn-1$.

M. Roberts[5] gave a determinant Δ of order n such that $\Delta=0$ is the equation for the squares of the difference of the roots of $x^n=1$.

J. W. L. Glaisher[6] proved that, if x is any primitive nth root of unity and (y) denotes $(1-x^y)^k$, and if all the sets of r elements that can be formed from (1), (2), $\cdots$, $(n-1)$ be written according to any rule with regard to sequences and breaks, the sum of all these sets is rational. For example, if $n=7$, $r=3$, $k=1$, the sets having a sequence of two and one break (i. e., two consecutive numbers and one non-consecutive) are 124, 125, 126, 134, 145, 156, 235, 236, 245, 256, 346, 356. Then $(1-x)(1-x^2)(1-x^4)+\cdots+(1-x^3)(1-x^5)(1-x^6)$ is rational.

J. Hermes[7] treated cyclotomy for the case of primes $p=2^m+1$ with

[35] *London Math. Soc.*, Records of Proceedings, Nov. 17, 1921.

[1] Traité de la résolution des équations numériques, ed. 2, 1808, Note XIV; ed. 3, 1826, 273–310.

[2] Werke, II, 1863, 249 (Maser's transl., 636).

[3] *Jour. für Math.*, 4, 1829, 131–156; Oeuvres, I, 1881, 478–507. Cf. V. A. Lebesgue, *Comptes Rendus*, Paris, 38, 1854, 914–6.

[4] *Jour. de Math.*, 19, 1854, 281–8.

[5] *Nouv. Ann. Math.*, 20, 1861, 139. Proof by E. Beltrami, (2), 3, 1864, 64–6.

[6] British Assoc. Report for 1875 (1876), *Trans. of Sec.*, 13–14.

[7] *Jour. für Math.*, 87, 1879, 84–113; *Archiv. Math. Phys.*, (2), 4, 1886, 207–17.

application to regular polygons and the decomposition of p into sums of squares.

K. Schwering[8] found the number of terms in the expansion of $\Pi(a_1\alpha+a_2\alpha^{\delta}+\cdots+a_m\alpha^{\mu})$, where α ranges over the pth roots of unity.

A. Pellet[9] noted that $X=x^{p-1}+\cdots+1$ decomposes after the adjunction of $\sqrt{p}$ into two factors of like degree with the discriminants δ and δ_1, where δ is of the form

$$\delta=\pm(bp-a\sqrt{p})p^k(a-b\sqrt{p})^{2k_1},$$

a, b being the least solution of $a^2-b^2p=-1$. The discriminant of X is $p^{p-2}=d^2\delta\delta_1$, where d is rational. A like theorem is true of any Abelian equation of even degree.

H. Vogt[10] discussed the algebraic solution of $x^p=1$, p a prime.

W. Burnside[11] proved that if ω is a primitive mth root of unity, χ is any polynomial in ω with integral coefficients, and χ' the conjugate imaginary to χ, then $\Sigma\chi\chi'=0$ or $\pm\phi(m)$, where the latter is Euler's ϕ-function and the summation extends over the $\phi(m)$ primitive mth roots of unity.

R. D. von Sterneck[12] employed for an odd prime p and $q=\frac{1}{2}(p-1)$

$$\prod_{i=0}^{q-1}\left(x-\rho^{g^{2i}}\right)\equiv x^q+M_1x^{q-1}+\cdots+M_q,\quad \rho=\cos\frac{2\pi}{p}+i\sin\frac{2\pi}{p}$$

and proved by means of quadratic congruences that

$$2iM_i=\sum_{\lambda=1}^{i}\left\{1-\left(\frac{\lambda}{p}\right)\left(\sqrt{\left(\frac{-1}{p}\right)p}\right)\right\}M_{i-\lambda},$$

which serves as a recursion formula for the computation of the M's. By changing the sign before the radical, we get a relation between the coefficients of the equation for the q roots in the second period of Gauss. Next, if $p=3q+1$ is a prime, $(x^p-1)/(x-1)$ is the product of three factors

$$\Pi(x-\rho^r),\quad \Pi(x-\rho^m),\quad \Pi(x-\rho^n),$$

where r ranges over the cubic residues of p, and m (or n) over the cubic non-residues whose qth powers are $\equiv b$ (or b^2), where $1+b+b^2\equiv 0$.

G. Rados[13] gave a very elementary method of finding the discriminant of the equation for the primitive nth roots of unity. The method in Hilbert's report (p. 333) employs general theorems proved by use of ideals.

---

[8] *Acta Math.*, 11, 1887–8, 265–96.
[9] *Comptes Rendus*, Paris, 112, 1891, 1196–7, 1249–53.
[10] *Revue de Math. spéc.*, 6, 1896, 417–425.
[11] *Proc. London Math. Soc.*, (2), 1, 1903, 112.
[12] *Sitzungsber. Akad. Wiss. Wien (Math.)*, 114, IIa, 1905, 724–732, 743–4.
[13] *Jour. für Math.*, 131, 1906, 49–55; Math. és. termés. ért., 22, 1904, 115–22.

G. Rados[14] proved that, except for $x^2-1=0$, an equation $x^2+\omega x+\tau=0$ with real coefficients has roots of unity as its roots if and only if ω is an algebraic integer whose conjugates are all real and comprised between -2 and $+2$, and if $\tau=1$. An upper limit is obtained for the number of equations of degree n all of whose roots are roots of unity and whose coefficients belong to a domain of rationality of degree ρ. The example $x^2+(\sqrt{5}-3)x+1=0$ shows that an equation with integral algebraic coefficients, the leading coefficient being unity, need not have exclusively roots which are roots of unity.

M. Cipolla[15] proved that an equation $f(x)=0$ whose coefficients are real algebraic integers of an algebraic field F, and leading coefficient unity, will have all its roots imaginary roots of unity if and only if the equation is a reciprocal equation of even degree, and its transform by $y=x+1/x$ as well as all the conjugates of this transform with respect to F have exclusively real roots between -2 and $+2$. Removing the condition that the coefficients be real, he found the criterion to be that norm $f(x)=0$ be a reciprocal equation not having a root ± 1 and that its transform by $y=x+1/x$ have all its roots real and between -2 and $+2$.

J. Schumacher[16] proved that if α is a primitive nth root of unity, n an odd prime,

$$(1+\alpha^2)(1+\alpha^4)\cdots(1+\alpha^{n-1})=(-\alpha)^e,\ e=\tfrac{1}{8}(n^2-1).$$

A. E. Pellet[17] proved that, if p is a prime >2, and g is a primitive root of p^ν, $\nu>1$, then

$$x+x^{g^2}+x^{g^4}+\cdots+x^{g^e}\quad (e=p^{\nu-1}(p-1)-2)$$

is divisible by $(x^{p^\nu}-1)/(x^{p^{\nu-1}}-1)$.

G. Pólya[18] proved that, if ρ is a root of unity and N is rational, it is impossible to find positive integers a_i for which

$$(1-\rho)^{a_1}(2-\rho)^{a_2}\cdots=\sigma N,\quad \sigma^\kappa=1.$$

J. G. Van der Corput[19] discussed the prime divisor of $x^\kappa-1$.

T. Nagel[20] found the discriminant of the equation for the primitive nth roots of unity.

---

[14] *Rendiconti Circolo Mat. Palermo*, 36, 1913, 299–304; Math. és termés. ért., 26 1908, 167–174, 260–1.
[15] *Rendiconti Circolo Mat. Palermo*, 38, 1914, 370–5.
[16] *Archiv Math. Phys.*, (3), 23, 1914–5, 80–81.
[17] *Nouv. Ann. Math.*, (4), 16, 1916, 470–1.
[18] *Archiv for Math. og Naturw.*, 35, 1917, No. 5.
[19] *Proc. Akad. Wetenschappen*, Amsterdam, 21, 1918, 262–270.
[20] *Norsk Matematisk Tidsskrift*, 1, 1919, 99–101.

The following papers were not available for report:

S. Giermann. Spaczinsky's Bote, 226, 1896 (Russian).
K. Wilske. Zur Kreisteilung, Bromberg, 1899, 25 pp.
H. Wallin. Om Cirkeldelnings Ekvationerna, Diss. Upsala, 1900, 30 pp.
W. P. Thysen. *Wiskundig Tijdschrift*, 15, 1918–9, 58–61, 177–180.

Elementary known results were given by

S. Réalis. *Nouv. Ann. Math.*, 2, 1843, 5–16, 147–56.
V. Mollame. *Rendiconto Accad. Sc. Fis. Mat. Napoli*, 31, 1892, 179–183.
F. Giudice. *Periodico di Mat.*, 27, 1912, 161–9.
J. J. C. Westendorp, *Wiskundig Tijdschrift*, 10, 1913, 15–22.

Expositions of the theory of cyclotomy have been given by

U. Scarpis. Il problema della divisione della circonferenza, Savona, 1891, 72 pp.
G. B. Mathews. Theory of Numbers, 1892, 184–228.
E. Netto. Algebra, I, 1896, 345–385.
H. Weber. Algebra, I, 1895, 554–94; II, 1896, 63–113, 705–44; ed. 2, I, 1898, 596–643; II, 1899, 69–120, 736–821.
E. Terradas é Illa. *Revista trimestral de Mat.*, 4, 1904, 193–213.

18. Norms, Units, Ideals, Divisibility, Discriminants of Cyclotomic Fields

For third and fourth roots of unity see §1.

C. F. Gauss[1] considered an integer in the field defined by $\epsilon^5=1$, multiplied it by its conjugate imaginary, and treated properties of the product. He also considered special properties of congruences in this field with moduli which are powers of $1-\epsilon$.

G. Eisenstein[2] examined properties of the field formed by an 8th root of unity.

J. A. Gmeiner[3] obtained results of no novelty regarding fields defined by a 5th root of unity.

J. Ouspensky[4] examined factorization of primes in the field defined by a primitive 5th root of unity. Ouspensky[5] employed for the same field the form of a norm of an integer given by Gauss[1], and proved the analogue of Euclid's process for rational fields by showing that, if m is a number in the former field, then it is always possible to find an integer μ in the field such that norm$(m-\mu)<1$.

H. W. Lloyd Tanner[6] gave a method of decomposing integers in a field Ω defined by a primitive fifth root of unity, which is different from that employed by Kummer (*Berlin Monats.*, 1870) and probably

[1] *Werke*, 2, 394.
[2] *Jour. für Math.*, 39, 1850, 281.
[3] Programm des Staats Gymn. in Pola, 6, 1896; *Monatshefte für Math.*, 9, 1898, 184–206; 11, 1900, 1–27.
[4] *Matem. Sborn*, Moscow (Moskau Math. Sammlung), 26, 1906, 1–17.
[5] *Math. Annalen*, 66, 1909, 109.
[6] *Proc. London Math. Soc.*, 24, 1893, 223–72.

different from that employed by Reuschle[9] in constructing his Table. He then gave a table containing a prime factor in Ω of all rational primes $<10{,}000$ which are of the form $10n+1$ and several larger primes of this form.

E. E. Kummer[7] treated the decomposition of rational integers into prime factors in various special cyclotomic fields. He listed actual factors in the field defined by a primitive λth root of unity contained in rational primes <1000 of the form $k\lambda+1$, λ a prime $\leqq 23$.

A. Cayley[8] in his first paper cited observes that Kummer obtained a factor of 47, viz., $A=\alpha^{10}+\alpha^{13}+\alpha^{8}+\alpha^{15}+\alpha^{7}+\alpha^{16}$, where $\alpha^{23}=1$, and inquires if A^3 can be expressed as the product of two conjugate imaginary complex factors, and apparently shows that this is impossible. But in the second paper Cayley quotes a letter from Kummer in which it is shown that $E(\alpha)A^3=F(\alpha)F(\alpha^{-1})$, where $F(\alpha)=\alpha^4+\alpha^5+\alpha^9+\alpha^{10}+\alpha^{16}-\alpha^{20}+\alpha^{22}$, and $E(\alpha)$ is the unit

$$(\alpha+\alpha^{21})\div(\alpha^8+\alpha^{15})(\alpha^9+\alpha^{14})(\alpha^{10}+\alpha^{13})^2(\alpha^{11}+\alpha^{12})\ ,$$

indicating that Cayley had not considered the possibility of unit factors.

C. G. Reuschle[9] gave an extended table of prime factors in cyclotomic fields of rational primes.

C. E. Bickmore and O. Western[10] gave a table of complex prime factors of all rational primes of the form $8n+1$ which are <25000 in the field defined by a primitive 8th root of unity, ζ, and listed each factor in the form $\pi=a_0+a_1\zeta+a_2\zeta^2+a_3\zeta^3$, $a_0\equiv 1$, $a_1\equiv a_2\equiv a_3\equiv 0 \pmod 2$. The values of the a's were computed with the aid of Cunningham's tables of quadratic partitions (London, 1904).

Gauss[11] considered the product of an integer in the field of an nth root of unity by its conjugate imaginary. Put $f(\epsilon)=a+a'\epsilon+a''\epsilon^2+\cdots+a^{(n-1)}\epsilon^{n-1}=m$, $D=f(\epsilon)f(\epsilon^2)\cdots f(\epsilon^{n-1})$, $f(\epsilon)f(\epsilon^{n-1})=-b'(\epsilon+\epsilon^{n-1})-b''(\epsilon^2+\epsilon^{-2})-b'''(\epsilon^3+\epsilon^{-3})+\cdots$.

Then it is found that

$$2b'=(a-a')^2+(a'-a'')^2+(a''-a''')^2+\cdots$$
$$2b''=(a-a'')^2+(a'-a''')^2+(a''-a'''')^2+\cdots,\cdots$$

He called b', b'', b''', etc., the partial measures (*Partialmensuren*) of m, and Σb the general measure, and found

$$\Sigma b>\frac{n-1}{2}\cdot D^{\frac{2}{n-1}}.$$

[7] Diss., Breslau, 1844; reprinted in *Jour. de Math.*, 12, 1847, 185–212.

[8] *Jour. für Math.*, 55, 1858, 192; 56, 1859, 186; Collected Math. Papers, IV, 70–1, 78–9.

[9] Tafeln der Complexer Primzahlen, welche aus Wurzeln der Einheit gebildet sind, Berlin, 1875, 671 pp. Reuschle had published parts of this table previously as follows: *Berlin Monatsberichte*, 1859, 488; 1859, 694; 1860, 190, 735. See comments on these tables by Kummer, *Berlin Monatsberichte*, 1860, 735; Kronecker, *ibid.*, 1875, 236–8; Cayley, Report British Assoc., 1875, 332–6; Smith, Collected Papers, I, 138–9.

[10] *Messenger Math.*, (2), 41, 1911, 52–64.

[11] Werke, 2, 395.

Kummer[12] introduced ideals into the theory of complex numbers formed by pth roots of unity, p a prime.

Cauchy[13] investigated polynomial radicals with integral coefficients, i. e., polynomials in a primitive nth root of unity; stated false theorems on their norms (called factorials), and concluded falsely that unique factorization into primes and other laws of divisibility hold for these polynomial radicals, the errors being admitted at the end of his final theorem. The application intended was to Fermat's last theorem. In a continuation of this study, Cauchy[14] obtained results most of which are included in Kummer's general theory of cyclotomic numbers.

Gauss[15] stated that it is possible to prove by his theory of the "general measure" (Gauss[11]) that if $E(\alpha)$ is a real unit in the field of a λth root of unity α, λ a prime, then $E(\alpha)=\alpha^t E(\alpha^{-1})$, a result previously published by Kummer.

F. Mertens[16] gave a new proof of Kronecker's theorem that if ω is a primitive nth root of unity and $E(\omega)$ is a unit in the field defined by ω, then $E(\omega)/E(\omega^{-1})=f(\omega)$ is an nth root of unity or a $2n$th root of unity according as n is even or odd. He shows first that $f(\omega^p)=f(\omega)^p$ n not divisible by p, a prime, making use of a known theorem that if the absolute value of a unit is 1, then the unit is a root of unity. The method is then extended to show that $f(\omega)^m=f(\omega^m)$, m being any integer prime to n. Setting $m=n+1$ or $2n+1$ according as n is even or odd, we obtain $f(\omega)^n=1$ or $f(\omega)^{2n}=1$, from which the above theorem is readily obtained.

H. Scheffler[17] treated ideal theory and cyclotomy, but many of his results are erroneous.

M. Bauer[18] proved that if all the rational primes which contain only ideal divisors of the first degree in an algebraic field are in arithmetic progression, then the field is cyclotomic.

R. Fueter[19] gave an extended exposition of the theory of cyclotomic fields.

Ch. Hermite[20] stated without proof that if p is a divisor of the norm of any complex number formed with the complex mth roots of unity, we can always find an integral power of p which is represented by this norm.

---

[12] *Berlin Monatsb.*, 1846, 87–96.

[13] *Comptes Rendus*, Paris, 24, 1847, 347, 407, 469, 516, 578, 633, 661, 996, 1022; Oeuvres, (1), X, 224–6, 231–285, 296–308. Detailed report in Dickson's History of the Theory of Numbers, Vol. II, 740.

[14] *Comptes Rendus*, Paris, 25, 1847, 37, 46, 93, 132, 177, 242, 285; Oeuvres, (1), X, 324–351, 354–371.

[15] Werke, II, 396.

[16] *Wiener Bericht*, 115, 1906, 481–84.

[17] Beitrage zur Zahlentheorie insbesondere zur Kreis und Kreisteilung mit einen Nachtrage zur Theorie der Gleichungen, Leipzig, 1891, F. Foerster. Cf. Fortschritte der Math., 1891, 74, regarding errors.

[18] *Archiv. Math. Phys.*, (3), 6, 1903, 221–4.

[19] Synthetische Zahlentheorie, Berlin and Leipzig, 1917, 97–268.

[20] *Jour. de Math.*, 14, 1849, 452.

19. The Lagrange Resolvent and the Jacobi ψ Number

For applications to quadratic forms and quadratic reciprocity, see Dickson's History of the Theory of Numbers, III, Ch. 2; to Gauss sums, IV; to cubic forms, III, Ch. 12; to the congruence $ax^p+by^p+1\equiv 0$ (mod n), and Fermat's Last Theorem, II, Ch. 26.

A. L. Cauchy[1] investigated at length the cyclotomic resolvent function of Lagrange. His applications to the solution of $x^2+\Delta y^2=p^k$ or $4p^k$, where p is a prime, are cited in Ch. II (on that topic) of Vol. III of Dickson's History of the Theory of Numbers. In the last reference p. 362 cited, he stated a result regarding Fermat's last theorem, which indicates that he was familiar with a theorem equivalent to the decomposition of the Jacobi ψ number into ideal factors. Cf. Kummer,[2] relation (3) for $k=1$.

Kummer[2] considered the number

$$(\alpha,x)=x+\alpha x^g+\alpha^2x^{g^2}+\cdots+\alpha^{p-2}x^{g^{p-2}}, \tag{1}$$

where $x^p=1$, $\alpha^\lambda=1$, $x\neq 1$, $\alpha\neq 1$, $p=\mu\lambda+1$, and λ and p are primes, g being a primitive root of p. The number (α, x) is termed the Lagrange resolvent. The function of α only, found by Jacobi,[3]

$$\psi_k(\alpha)=\frac{(\alpha, x)(\alpha^k, x)}{(\alpha^{k+1}, x)} \tag{2}$$

will be called the Jacobi ψ number, where $k+1\not\equiv 0 \pmod{\lambda}$.* Using the expression for the residue of $\psi(g)$, modulo λ, as found by Jacobi[3] (p. 166), Kummer derived

$$\psi_k(\alpha)=\pm\alpha^r\prod_h f(\alpha^{m_h}) \tag{3}$$

where h ranges over the integers $<\lambda$ such that $h+[kh]>\lambda$, the symbol $[kh]$ being the least positive residue of kh, and $hm_h\equiv 1$ (mod. λ.)

Further, $f(\alpha)$ is a prime ideal factor of p which belongs to the substitution $\alpha=u$, where $g^{(p-1)/\lambda}\equiv u \pmod{p}$. By means of this result he obtained from the relation (due to Jacobi[3])

$$(\alpha,\ x)^\lambda=p\psi_1(\alpha)\psi_2(\alpha)\cdots\psi_{\lambda-2}(\alpha)$$

the decomposition

$$(\alpha,\ x)^\lambda=\pm\alpha^s f(\alpha)^{m_1}f(\alpha^2)^{m_2}\cdots f(\alpha^{\lambda-1})^{m_{\lambda-1}},\ 0<m_h<\lambda.$$

---

[1] *Bull. sc. math. astr. phys. chim.* (ed. Férussac), 12, 1829, 205; *Mém. Acad. Sc. Inst. France,* (2), 17, 1840; Oeuvres, (1), III.
Comptes Rendus, Paris, 9, 1839, 519; Oeuvres, (1), IV, 506–513; *ibid.*, 10, 1840, 51, 85, 178, 181, 229, 437, 560, 594, 719; Oeuvres, (1), V, 52–111, 135–180, 199–212; *ibid.*, 25, 1847, 93, 177; Oeuvres, (1), X, 344–351, 360–6.

[2] *Jour. für Math.*, 35, 1847, 361–3.

[3] *Jour. für Math.*, 30, 166–82; Werke, VI, 254.

* For the symbolism $\not\equiv 0$ (mod λ), read "is not congruent to zero, modulo λ," and similarly throughout the report.

Kummer[4] had proved by a different method the above results in the case where p is the product of $\lambda-1$ actual complex integers.

Kummer[5] generalized the Lagrange resolvent. Let p be an odd prime, g a primitive root of p^a, β any root of $\beta^\pi=1$, $\pi=p^{a-1}(p-1)$, z a primitive root of $z^{p^a}=1$. We may set $\beta=\omega z^{rp}$, where $\omega^{p-1}=1$ and r is any integer. Then

$$(\beta, z)=z+\beta z^g+\beta^2 z^{g^2}+\cdots+\beta^{\pi-1}z^{g^{\pi-1}}=(\omega z^{rp}, z)=\sum_{h=0}^{\pi-1}\omega^h z^{rph+g^h}.$$

This becomes the Lagrange resolvent if $a=1$, a special case which is excluded here. If r is a multiple of p, $(\omega z^{rp}, z)=0$. If r is prime to p, let ρ be determined by the congruence $e'g^\rho\equiv r \pmod p$, where $e'=(g^{p-1}-1)/p$. He then proved that

$$(\omega z^{rp}, z)=\pm(-1)^{\frac{1}{4}(p-1)}p^{a/2}\omega^\rho z^{rp\epsilon+g},$$

whence

$$(\omega z^{rp},z)(\omega^{-1}z^{-rp},z^{-1})=p^a.$$

Lebesgue[6] simplified proofs by Cauchy[1] (notes 1 and 5 of Memoire) of elementary properties of (1) and (2) in the case where α is a primitive λth root of unity, and λ is composite.

Kummer[7] generalized the Jacobi ψ number. Let q be an odd* prime, λ an odd prime and $q^t\equiv 1 \pmod\lambda$. Set

$$\psi(\alpha)=\sum_h \alpha^{-(r+1)h+\text{ind}(g^h+1)},$$

where $\alpha^\lambda=1$, $\alpha\neq 1$, r is an integer such that r and $r+1$ are each $\not\equiv 0 \pmod\lambda$, g is a primitive root of $f(\alpha)$, a prime ideal factor of q, such that $g^{(q^t-1)/\lambda}\equiv\alpha \pmod{f(\alpha)}$, and ind x is defined by $g^{\text{ind } x}\equiv x \pmod{f(\alpha)}$. Furthermore, h ranges over the integers 0, 1, 2, $\cdots$, q^t-1, excepting $\frac{1}{2}(q^t$-1). He proved (pp. 110–11) by direct multiplication that

$$\psi_r(\alpha^{-1})\psi_r(\alpha)=q^t,$$

which gives for t even (p. 112),

$$\psi_r(\alpha)=q^{\frac{1}{2}t}.$$

He then determined the ideal factors of $\psi_r(\alpha)$, where t is odd, by extending the method previously employed by him (Kummer[2]) for the case $t=1$. To carry this through he attempted to prove a lemma

---

[4] De numeris complexis qui radicatus unitatis et numeris integris constant, Programm zur Jubelfeier der Universität Königsberg, 1844 (Diss. Breslau). Reprinted in *Jour. de Math.*, (1), 12, 1847, 185–212. Cf. in particular pp. 209–11.

[5] Atti dell Accad. Pontif Nuovi Lincei, 6, 1852, 237–41.

[6] *Jour. de Math.*, (1), 19, 1854, 289–96.

[7] *Jour. für Math.*, 44, 1852, 106–121.

* Although Kummer did not state that q must be odd, his ψ function has no meaning for $q=2$. See definition of ψ given by Mitchell.[12]

(p. 115) regarding the rational integral factors of binomial coefficients, which argument was shown to be inaccurate by Mitchell,[12] who corrected it.

Schwering[8] considers various special properties of the Lagrange resolvent and the Jacobi ψ function. Kronecker stated that Jacobi had thought perhaps that $(\alpha, x)^\lambda$ could always be expressed as the product of ψ functions, one being given and the others being conjugates of it. Kronecker verified this conjecture for all λ's up to 83, but found it false for $\lambda=83$. Schwering (p. 72) checks Kronecker's statement as to $\lambda=83$, and remarked that Wolfskehl had also checked the same.

Stickelberger[9] generalized the Lagrange resolvent.

C. Cellerier[10] arrived at known results regarding the Lagrange resolvent and Jacobi ψ number.

Mertens[11] considered the decomposition of the Lagrange resolvent using Kummer's theory of ideals. Let $L(\alpha)=\sum_s \alpha^{-\text{ind } s}r^s$, $s=1, 2, \cdots, p-1$; $g^{\text{ind } s}\equiv s \pmod{p}$, g a primitive root of p, r a primitive p^{th} root of unity, p a prime, while α is a primitive λ^{th} root of unity, λ a prime, $p\equiv 1 \pmod{\lambda}$. He took $X=1+x+x^2+\cdots+x^{p-1}$, $G(x)=\sum_s \alpha^{-\text{ind} s}x^s$, where x is an indeterminate. Taking $nn'\equiv 1 \pmod{\lambda}$, and using a prime ideal divisor $P(\alpha)$ of p such that $g^\nu\equiv\alpha \pmod{P(\alpha)}$, where $\nu=(p-1)/\lambda$, he found the relation

$$G(x)\equiv\frac{d_0{}^l}{dv^l}X(xe^v) \pmod{P(\alpha^n)},$$

where $l=(\lambda-n')\nu$, and the symbol $d_0{}^l/dv^l$ means that the differentiation is to be carried out and $v=0$ substituted in the result. Whence

$$G(x)\equiv\frac{d_0{}^l}{dv^l}(1-xe^v)^{p-1} \pmod{P(\alpha^n)}.$$

By transforming the value of $G^\lambda(x)$ from this congruence it is found that

$(L(\alpha))^\lambda\equiv 0 \pmod{P(\alpha^n)^{n'}}$, $n=1, 2, \cdots, \lambda-1$.

Since the norm of $[L(\alpha)]^\lambda$ is $p^{\frac{1}{2}\lambda(\lambda-1)}$, we have

$$(L(\alpha))^\lambda=\prod_n P(\alpha^n)^{n'}.$$

He then considered the generalized Lagrange resolvent due to Stickelberger and found its decomposition in an analogous way. If $(P(\alpha))^H$

[8] *Jour. für Math.*, 102, 1888, 56.

[9] *Math. Annalen*, 37, 1890, 321–67. See account of these results in Encyc. des Sc. Math. t. 1, v. 3, 440–2.

[10] *Mémoires de la Société de physique et d'Historie Naturelle de Genève*, 32, 1894–7, No. 7, 61 pp.

[11] *Wiener Bericht*, 114, IIa, 1905, 1359–68.

is the least power of P which is a principal ideal, he proved that

$$(L(\alpha))^{\lambda H}=E\prod_{s=1}^{\lambda-1} f(\alpha^s)^{s'},\ ss'\equiv 1 \pmod{\lambda},$$

where λ is now any prime different from p, $f(\alpha)$ is an integer in $\Omega(\alpha)$, and

$$E=(-1)^H\left(\frac{f(1)}{\lambda}\right),$$

the symbol on the right being Legendre's quadratic residue symbol.

H. H. Mitchell[12] considered an extension of Kummer's ψ function. Let

$$\psi_{-a,\,-b}(\alpha)=\sum_h \alpha^{-bh+(a+b)\operatorname{ind}(g^h+1)},$$

where α is a primitive λth root of unity, λ any integer, a and b integers such that $a\not\equiv 0$, $b\not\equiv 0$, $a+b\not\equiv 0 \pmod{\lambda}$, q a prime, $q^t\equiv 1 \pmod{\lambda}$, g a primitive root in the Galois field of order q^t, and let h range over the values $0, 1, \cdots q^t-2$, excepting $(q^t-1)/2$ when q is odd and zero if $q=2$. This is Kummer's function when λ is an odd prime and t the exponent to which q belongs modulo λ. He proved by a new method that $\psi(\alpha)\psi(\alpha^{-1})=q^t$. He determined the ideal prime factors of ψ by extending the method employed by Kummer for the special ψ. On p. 171 there is corrected an error of the latter in the proof of a lemma involving factors of binomial coefficients. There is obtained the Theorem: *If* $(q^t-1)/\lambda=\nu$, *and* $g^\nu\equiv\alpha \pmod{\mathfrak{q}}$, $\mathfrak{q}$ *being a prime ideal divisor of* q, *then the number of times the ideal* $\mathfrak{q}_i$ *is contained in* $\psi(\alpha)$ *is equal to the number of the expressions* $|aiq^{t-j}|+|biq^{t-j}|$, $j=0, 1, 2, \cdots t-1$, *whose values exceed* λ, *where* i *assumes* $\varphi(\lambda)/t_1$ *values prime to* λ *such that the quotient of no two of them is congruent*, mod λ, *to a power of* q. *Here* t_1 *is the exponent to which* q *belongs modulo* λ *and* $|x|$ *is the least positive residue of* x, *mod* λ. Also, $\mathfrak{q}_i$ is the ideal obtained from $\mathfrak{q}$ by the substitution (α^k/α), $ki\equiv 1 \pmod{\lambda}$. By using this result he obtained a relation between the ψ function for a Galois field q^t and the ψ function for a field q^{t_1}. Also he proved that $\psi(\alpha)=(-1)^{s-1}q^t$, where q belongs to the exponent $2t_1$, modulo λ, and $q^{t_1}\equiv -1 \pmod{\lambda}$, $s=t/t_1$.

20. Cyclotomic Sub-fields and the Normal Basis, or Cyclotomic Periods

On the theory of quadratic sub-fields, see §16, and Gauss Sums, Dickson's History, III. On elementary properties of the periods, see §15.

T. Schönemann[1] considered the solution of the congruence,

(1) $$[x-f(g^k)]\,[x-f(g^{k+1})]\cdots[x-f(g^{2k-1})]\equiv 0 \pmod{p}$$

[12] *Trans. Amer. Math. Soc.*, 17, 1916, 165–77. Cf. also Stickelberger.[9]

[1] *Jour. für Math.*, 19, 1839, 306–8.

p and $f(g^s)$ being defined as follows. Let g be a primitive root of n, where n is prime, $\alpha^n=1$, $\alpha\neq 1$. Let p be a prime for which $x^k\equiv p$ (mod n), $n-1=km$. Then $f(g^k)$ is a symmetric function, with rational integral, coefficients, of α^g, α^{g^k}, $\cdots$, $\alpha^{g^{(m-1)k}}$. Raising the f's to the pth power and making use of $x^k\equiv p\equiv g^{sk}$ (mod n), where s is an integer, we have

$$f(g^a)^p=f(g^a)+p\varphi(g^a),\quad a=k,\ k+1,\cdots,\ 2k-1.$$

Whence $\sum_a f(g^a)=k+p\frac{A}{B}$, A and B integers. He proved that $A\equiv 0$ (mod B), aside from a special case treated separately. Similarly, $\sum_c f(g^a)^{c(p-1)}\equiv k$ (mod p), $c=2, 3, \cdots, p-1$. By means of a theorem previously proved (p. 293) he deduced from the last relation that (1) has k integral roots i.e., $\Pi(x-f(g))$ decomposes into linear factors modulo p, provided $p\overline{\gtrless}k$.

E. E. Kummer[2] essayed to prove the theorem that, if $\varphi(y)=(y-\eta)(y-\eta_1)\cdots(y-\eta_{e-1})$, $\eta_i=x^{g^i}+x^{g^{i+e}}+\cdots+x^{g^{(f-1)e+i}}$, $x^p=1, x\neq 1, g$ being a primitive root of the prime $p=ef+1$, then $\varphi(y)$ decomposes into e linear factors modulo q, where q is congruent to the eth power of an integer modulo p. (This theorem is the basis of his theory of ideals.) He employed first the identical congruence

$$(y-\eta_k)\ (y-1-\eta_k)\cdots\ (y-q+1-\eta_k)\equiv(y-\eta_k)^q-(y-\eta_k)\ \ (\text{mod } q).$$

Using $(y-\eta_k)^q\equiv y-\eta_{k+r}$ (mod q), where $q\equiv g^r$ (mod p), and letting k range over the values 0, 1, 2, $\cdots$, $e-1$, there is obtained

$$(2)\quad \varphi(y)\varphi(y-1)\ \cdots\ \varphi(y-q+1)\equiv(\eta-\eta_r)\ (\eta_1-\eta_{r+1})\cdots\ (\eta_{e-1}-\eta_{r+e-1})\ (\text{mod } q).$$

In particular, if $r\equiv 0$ (mod e), we have

$$(3)\qquad \varphi(y)\varphi(y-1)\cdots\varphi(y-q+1)\equiv 0\ (\text{mod } q^e).$$

Kummer erroneously (Smith,[5] Dirichlet[14]) drew the conclusion from (3) that $\varphi(y)$ factors completely into linear factors modulo q, or as expressed by him, the congruence $\varphi(y)\equiv 0$ (mod q) has e real roots. If

$$P_r=(\eta-\eta_r)\ (\eta_1-\eta_{r+1})\cdots(\eta_{e-1}-\eta_{r+e-1})$$

he stated that P is a symmetric function (?) of the periods and therefore an integer independent of q, and drew the conclusion that $\varphi(y)$, if y takes on arbitrary integral values, will have as prime factors only primes such that $q\equiv g^{ea}$ (mod p), aside from the primes which divide P_r, $r=1$, 2,$\cdots$, $e-1$.

[2] *Jour. für Math.*, 30, 1846, 107–116, reproduced in *Jour. de Math.*, (1), 16, 1851, 408–9.

A. L. Cauchy[3] employed a polynomial (**H**) in a primitive pth root θ of unity, where p is a prime. When θ is replaced by the remaining primitive roots, let **H** take n distinct values, the roots of $f(x)=0$. If q is a prime $>n$, q not a divisor of the discriminant of $f(x)$, and if the polynomial in θ of degree $p-2$ which is equal to $\mathbf{H}^q-\mathbf{H}$ has all its coefficients divisible by q, then the congruence $f(x)\equiv 0 \pmod{p}$ has n distinct roots.

Kummer[4] rigorously established certain relations between his ideals and the congruences formed by period equations, which include the result above as to the e roots of $\varphi(y)$.

H. J. S. Smith[5] in reporting on Kummer's[2] work filled the gap in the latter's proof that $\varphi(y)$ decomposes into e linear factors modulo q. In Kummer's notation he found

$$\varphi(y)\varphi(y-1)\cdots\varphi(y-q+1)\equiv(y^q-y)^e \pmod{q}$$

and since

$$y^q-y\equiv(y-1)\ (y-2)\cdots(y-q+1) \pmod{q},$$

then $\varphi(y)$ factors into linear factors modulo q.

J. J. Sylvester[6] considered functions

$$\psi_k(u)=\prod_\lambda(u-(\omega^\lambda+\omega^{-\lambda}))=\prod_\lambda\left(u-2\cos\frac{2\lambda\pi}{k}\right),$$

where λ ranges over the integers less than $k/2$ and prime to it, k being any integer. He proved that if u is an integer, all the divisors of $\psi_k(u)$ are of the form $kr\pm 1$, and $\psi_k(u)$ may be divisible by any power of $kr\pm 1$, aside from those which divide k, the former statement having been proved by Kummer[2] (p. 113) for k a prime. In the latter case he indicated a proof (p. 334) that if k has the form $p^i(p\mp 1)/m$, where p is a prime, then $\psi_k(u)$ is divisible by p, but not by p^2. He listed (p. 327) a table of all these $\psi_k(u)$ for $k<37$. He also considered the general functions $(x-\eta_1)\ (x-\eta_2)\cdots(x-\eta_n)$, where the η's are the period's formed by the kth roots of unity, n being a divisor of $\varphi(k)$ as defined by Kummer,[6a] and listed a number of special functions of this type (p. 338). He also stated without proof, that those divisors d of such functions for x integral, which are prime to the index, satisfy the congruence $d^{\varphi(k)/n}\equiv 1 \pmod{k}$. This statement is incorrect as may be seen by the example which Kummer[2] (p. 112.) gives.

---

[3] *Comptes Rendus*, Paris, 44, 1857, 77–80; Oeuvres, (1), XII, 401–5.
[4] *Jour. für Math.*, 53, 1857, 142–8.
[5] Report of British Assoc., 1860, 128, footnote; *Coll. Math. Papers*, I, 103–4 footnote.
[6] *Amer. Jour. Math.*, 2, 1879, 357–81; 3, 1880, 179–81; *Coll. Math. Papers*, III, 325–39.
[6a] *Berlin Abh.*, 1856, 4–5.

Sylvester[7] gave without proof several results regarding divisors of a general cyclotomic function which are either included in Sylvester[6] or in Kummer[2]. In a footnote to the last reference cited he also stated without proof that the function $(x-\eta)\ (x-\eta_1)\cdots(x-\eta_e)$, in the notation of Kummer,[2] may be divisible by any power of a prime which is an eth power residue modulo p.

T. Pepin[8] proved a statement of Sylvester,[6] namely, that all the prime divisors of $x^3-3x\pm1$ are 3, or primes of the form $18l\pm1$ exclusively.

E. Lucas[9] pointed out that the special cyclotomic functions formed by periods of two terms, treated by Sylvester,[6] differ only by change in variable from the simply periodic numerical functions of Lucas, since the product of the proper divisors of $(a^n-b^n)/(a-b)$, where a and b are roots of $z^2-zx+1=0$, is exactly the cyclotomic function of Sylvester. The latter's law had already been treated by Lucas[10] under the name of the law of apparition and repetition of primes in recurrent series. Also, Pepin's proof differs only in form from that of Lucas. Cf. also Dedekind.[11]

A. S. Hathaway[12] gave without proof obscure results relating to cyclotomic periods.

T. Vahlen[13] considered the function

$$F(x, y)=\prod_{\alpha,\eta}(\alpha x-\eta y)=x^{e\varphi(m)}+\cdots,$$

where α ranges over all the primitive mth roots of unity and η ranges over the e periods corresponding to $p=ef+1$. The properties of this function are used to obtain the result that there is an infinity of primes of the form $mz+1$.

G. L. Dirichlet[14] in a letter to Liouville, dated Feb. 1857, stated that Dedekind had pointed out the error of Kummer[2] and had given a method for correcting it. This method is the same as that employed by Smith.[5]

I. Schur,[15] designated the $n=\varphi(k)$ primitive roots of $x^k=1$ by $\epsilon_1=\epsilon^{a_1}$ $\epsilon_2=\epsilon^{a_2}, \cdots \epsilon_n=\epsilon^{a_n}$, where the a's are the integers less than and prime to k. Let $h(x)$ be a polynomial in x with rational integral coefficients, and among the quantities $h(\epsilon_\lambda)$, $\lambda=1, 2, \cdots, n$, suppose that r are equal

---

[7] *Comptes Rendus*, Paris, 90, 1880, 287–9; *Coll. Papers*, III, 428–32. *Amer. Jour. Math.*, 3, 1880, 392; *Coll. Papers*, III, 448. *Comptes Rendus*, Paris, 92, 1881, 1084; *Coll. Papers*, III, 479.

[8] *Comptes Rendus*, Paris, 90, 1880, 287–9.

[9] *Comptes Rendus*, Paris, 90, 1880, 855.

[10] *Amer. Jour. Math.*, 1, 1878, 210, 290–300.

[11] *Comptes Rendus*, Paris, 90, 1880, 1205.

[12] *Johns Hopkins Univ. Circular*, 1, 1880–1, 67, 131.

[13] Schriften der Physikalisch—Ökonomischen Gesell. Königsberg, 38, 1897, 72; *Sitzungsberichte*, p. 47.

[14] *Bull. des. Sc. Math.*, (2), 33, 1909, 53–6, E. Cahen, *ibid.*, p. 157.

[15] *Sitzungs. Berlin Math. Ges.*, 11, 1912, 40–50.

to $\eta=h(\epsilon)$, so that $\eta=h(\epsilon^{l_1})=h(\epsilon^{l_2})=\cdots=h(\epsilon^{l_r})$, $l_1=1$. The distinct $h(\epsilon_\lambda)$ are designated by $\eta_1=\eta=h(\epsilon^{m_1})$; $\eta_2=h(\epsilon^{m_2}), \cdots, \eta_s=h(\epsilon^{m_s})$, $m_1=1$. Then $rs=\varphi(k)$ and $H(x)=\prod_{u=1}^{s}(x-\eta_u)$ is a function of x with rational integral coefficients. He gave the theorem:

If x is a rational integer then every prime factor of $H(x)$, which is prime to the discriminant of $H(x)$ and to k, is contained in one of the progressions

$$kz+l_1,\ kz+l_2,\ \cdots,\ kz+l_r.$$

For proof, let p be a prime divisor of $H(x)$ and $\mathbf{P}$ a prime ideal divisor of p, in the field $\Omega(\epsilon)$. If a is a rational integer such that $H(a)=\Pi(a-\eta_u)$ is divisible by p then we may assume that $a\equiv h(\epsilon) \pmod{\mathbf{P}}$. If p is prime to k, then $h(\epsilon^p)\equiv(h(\epsilon))^p\equiv a^p\equiv a\equiv h(\epsilon) \pmod{\mathbf{P}}$ is one of the numbers $\eta_1, \eta_2 \cdots, \eta_s$. If $h(\epsilon^p)$ is different from $h(\epsilon)$ then one of the numbers $\eta_2-\eta_1, \eta_3-\eta_1, \cdots \eta_s-\eta_1$, is divisible by $\mathbf{P}$ and therefore the discriminant D of $H(x)$ is divisible by p. Assuming then that p is prime to both D and k, then $h(\epsilon^p)=h(\epsilon)$ and therefore p is congruent to $l_1, l_2, \cdots, l_r$, modulo k. A second proof of the theorem is given, depending on the Galois (finite) field theory. Schur gave a second theorem which is included in known results due to Kummer.[4,6a]

G. Rados [16] filled gaps in arguments of Kummer.[2]

T. Nagel [17] stated two theorems on the forms of the divisors of the irreducible cyclotomic function for the primitive nth roots of unity.

Further results on divisors of cyclotomic functions may be found in references in Dickson's history, vol. I, p. 245, reference (83); 383, (21); 384, (29, 33, 34, 36); 388, (66); 366, (75); 367, (81); 406, (89); 400, (38, 39); 405, (76).

Kummer[2] of §19, pp. 110–112, gave results which are, in effect, theorems concerning the divisor of the discriminant of a cyclotomic sub-field.

E. Netto [18] showed that the essential divisor (*wesentliche Theiler*) of the discriminant of the field defined by one of the e periods formed by pth roots of unity, p a prime, $p=ef+1$, is p^{e-1}.

J. Westlund [19] considered an equation of the form $y^3-3py-pA=0$, where $4p=A^2+27B^2$, $A\equiv1 \pmod 3$, $p\equiv1 \pmod 6$, which is satisfied by $y=3\eta+1$, $\eta=r+r^{g^3}+r^{g^6}+\cdots+r^{g^{(2n-1)3}}$, r a primitive pth root of unity and g a primitive root of the prime p. He discussed methods of decomposing rational primes into their prime ideal factors in $k(\eta)$. He found that the prime p is equal to the third power of a prime ideal of the first degree. The prime 2 is a prime ideal of the third degree

[16] *Math. és termés értesitö* (Hungarian Acad. of Sc.), 35, 1917, 593–604.
[17] *Norsk Matematisk Tidsskrift*, 1, 1919, 77.
[18] *Math. Ann.*, 24, 1884, 579–87.
[19] *Deutsche Math.-Verein.*, 22, 1913, 135–40.

or equal to the product of three prime ideals of the first degree according as B is odd or even. Every odd prime factor of B is equal to the product of three prime ideals of the first degree. If B is not divisible by 3, the prime 3 is a prime ideal of the third degree. Any odd prime q which is prime to $3pB$ is a prime ideal of the third degree or equal to the product of three prime ideals of the first degree according as $z^3-3pz+pA\equiv 0 \pmod{q}$ is not solvable or is solvable. He also tabulated factorizations into prime ideal factors of all rational primes $q<2\sqrt{\Delta}/9$, Δ being the discriminant of $k(\eta)$ for all values of $p<100$. Compare the general theorem of Dedekind.[11]

Chapter III

HENSEL'S p-ADIC NUMBERS

21. Rings in General

A ring[1] is a set of elements closed under the operations addition, subtraction, and multiplication; but division is not always possible due to the presence of elements which are called divisors of zero. An element b is called a divisor of zero when there exists an element $a \neq 0$ such that $ab=0$. If zero is the only such element which exists in the ring, the ring is a field.

An element of a ring which is not a divisor of zero is called a regular element. Division by regular elements is always possible.

If a is divisible by b, and b is not divisible by a, then b is called a proper divisor of a. If a is divisible by b and b by a, then a and b are said to be equivalent.

A prime divisor of zero is one which aside from regular elements has no proper divisor.

A simple ring is one in which all prime divisors of zero are equivalent.

A separable ring is one whose elements satisfy the following condition: If $a\,b$ is divisible by c, then there exist two elements c_1 and c_2 such that $c_1\,c_2=c$ and a is divisible by c_1 and b by c_2.

A ring R which contains n non-equivalent prime divisors of zero can be separated into n simple rings $R_1, R_2, \cdots, R_n$ such that each simple ring contains only elements of R; no element excepting zero is contained in more than one of the simple rings; the product of two elements from two different rings R_i and R_j is zero; and finally each element of R can be represented as the sum of n elements, one from each of the simple rings.[2]

Fraenkel[3] has also investigated sub-sets of rings and the extensions of rings formed by the adjunction of new elements both algebraic and transcendental.

A general study of rings and the ideals of a ring has been made by Masazo Sono.[4]

22. The Rational g-adic Numbers

By a rational g-adic number[5] we understand any series of the form $a_\rho g^\rho + a_{\rho+1} g^{\rho+1} + \cdots$, in which ρ is a rational integer, positive, negative,

---

[1] Fraenkel, *Jour. für Math.*, 145, 1914–15, 139–76.

[2] Fraenkel, *Jour. für Math.*, 145, 1914, 139–76; Über gewisse Teilbereiche und Erweiterungen von Ringen, Berlin, B. G. Teubner, 1916.

[3] Fraenkel, text[2], and *Jour. für Math.*, 151, 1921, 121–67.

[4] *Mem. Coll. of Sc.*, Kyoto, 2, 1917, 203–26; 3, 1918, 113–49, 189–97.

[5] Hensel, *Zahlentheorie*, Göshen, Leipzig u. Berlin, 1913, Chaps. 4 and 5.

or zero; g is a rational integer greater than 1; and the coefficients a_ρ, $a_{\rho+1}, \cdots$ are rational numbers which are integers with respect to the modulus g.

If $A=a_\rho g^\rho+a_{\rho+1}g^{\rho+1}+\cdots$, $B=b_\rho g^\rho+\cdots$, we define addition, subtraction, and multiplication of the g-adic numbers by the following equations:

$$A\pm B=(a_\rho\pm b_\rho)g^\rho+(a_{\rho+1}\pm b_{\rho+1})g^{\rho+1}+\cdots,$$
$$A\,B=a_\rho b_\rho\cdot g^{2\rho}+(a_\rho b_{\rho+1}+a_{\rho+1}b_\rho)g^{2\rho+1}+\cdots,$$

and hence the g-adic numbers constitute a ring which shall be denoted by $R(g)$.

If, however, we attempt to find an x such that Ax shall give B, we find, due to the restriction that the coefficient be integers with respect to the modulus g, that this is not always possible and therefore $R(g)$ is not a field.

If we further restrict the coefficients of the powers of g in a g-adic number to take only positive integral values less than g, we have what is known as a reduced g-adic number.

If $A=a_\rho g^\rho+a_{\rho+1}g^{\rho+1}+\cdots$ is any g-adic number, then the finite sum

$$\mathrm{A}_\kappa=a_\rho g^\rho+a_{\rho+1}g^{\rho+1}+\cdots+a_\kappa g^\kappa$$

is called the κth convergent of A.

Two g-adic numbers A and B are said to be equal with respect to g when for every ν there exists a λ such that, for all $\kappa\geqq\lambda$, $A_\kappa\equiv B_\kappa$ mod. g^ν, where A_κ and B_κ are the κ convergent of A and B respectively. From this definition of equality it follows that every g-adic number is equal to a uniquely determined reduced g-adic number.

Any ordinary rational number n which is an integer mod. g satisfies a congruence of the form

$$n\equiv a_\rho g^\rho+\cdots\cdot+a_\kappa g^\kappa \text{ mod. } g^{\kappa+1},$$

and the sequence of coefficients may be computed as far as is desired. We thus have a g-adic number which we shall consider as the representation of n in $R(g)$.

If n is a fraction mod. g, we can by multiplying both numerator and denominator by some properly chosen number reduce n to the form ν/g^s where ν is an integer mod. g and not divisible by g; whence expending ν as above and dividing by g^s we have for n the following representation

$$a_{-s}g^{-s}+a_{-s+1}g^{-s+1}\cdots+a_0+a_1g+a_2g^2+\cdots.$$

We thus have a g-adic representation for all rational numbers. It must, however, be observed that all g-adic numbers are not the representations of rational numbers.

The lowest power of g which occurs in the reduced g-adic representation is the power of g which is contained in the number as a factor and the exponent is called the order of the number. A g-adic number is an integer of $R(g)$ when and only when its order is positive or zero. The order of the sum of two numbers is greater than or equal to the smallest of the orders of the two numbers. The order of a product is equal to the sum of the orders.

The ring $R(g)$ is a separable ring. If $g=P\cdot Q$ it is evident that every g-adic number can be written as a P-adic or a Q-adic number. Thus with respect to P or Q every number of $R(g)$ is equal[6] to a number in $R(P)$ or $R(Q)$.

If $P\cdot Q=g$ and P and Q are relatively prime, and if A_P is an arbitrarily chosen number from $R(P)$ and A_Q an arbitrarily chosen number from $R(Q)$, then there exist[7] in $R(g)$ a uniquely defined number A such that $A=A_P$ with respect to P and $A=A_Q$ with respect to Q. These equalities shall be expressed in the form

$$A=A_P(P),\ A=A_Q(Q).$$

Hence if we have $A=1(P)$, $A=0(Q)$ and $B=0(P)$, $B=1(Q)$, then $A\neq 0(g)$, and $B\neq 0(g)$, but $A\cdot B=0(g)$, and hence $R(g)$ contains divisors of zero which are different from zero.

Corresponding to each one of the distinct prime factors of g there is then a simple ring $R(p)$, and the ring $R(g)$ can be separated into simple rings according to the general theorem regarding separable rings.[8] Each of the simple rings thus defined contains only one prime divisor of zero and in this case it is zero itself and hence $R(p)$ is a field and shall as such be denoted by $k(p)$.

A number of $R(g)$ whose order is zero and whose first coefficient is relatively prime to g has the property that its reciprocal is also a g-adic integer and hence it is called a unit of $R(g)$. Thus in $R(p)$ all numbers whose orders are zero are units.

23. Polynomials in $k(p)$

For a clear understanding of the applications of p-adic numbers to the development of the theory of algebraic numbers a few definitions and theorems from the theory of polynomials[9] will be necessary. The ordinary theory of resultants and discriminants of polynomials is easily extended to the polynomials in $k(p)$.

---

[6] Cf. Masazo Sono: *Mem. College Science*, Kyoto, 2, 1917, 203–26.
[7] Hensel, *Zahlentheorie*, p. 79.
[8] Hensel, *Zahlentheorie*, Chap. 5, §4.
[9] Hensel, *Jahresbericht d. Deut. Math.-Ver.*, 6, 7, 1896–8, 83–88; 16, 1907, 299–319; 8–393; 473–496; *Jour. für Math.*,127, 1904, 51–84; *Theorie der Alg. Zahlen.* Dumas, *ur. de Math.*, (6), 2, 1906, 191–258.

A polynomial whose coefficients are integers of $R(p)$ and of which at least one is not divisible by p is called a primitive polynomial.

An Eisenstein polynomial is one in which all the coefficients except that of the highest power of x are divisible by p.

I. A polynomial with p-adic coefficients can be resolved into the product of irreducible polynomials in only one way.

II. If the discriminant of the polynomial $F(x)$ is of order δ, then $F(x)$ is in $R(p)$ the product of factors of lower degree when and only when the δth convergent $F^{(\delta)}(x)$ is reducible mod. $p^{\delta+1}$; and to the factorization $F^{(\delta)}(x)\equiv\bar{f}(x)\cdot\bar{g}(x)$ mod. $p^{\delta+1}$ there corresponds a factorization $F(x)=f(x)\cdot g(x)$ (p), where $\bar{f}(x)$ and $\bar{g}(x)$ are convergents of $f(x)$ and $g(x)$.

III. If[10] $F(x)\equiv f_0(x)\cdot g_0(x)$ mod. p^{r+1}, and $r>2\rho$, where ρ is the order of the resultant of $f_0(x)$ and $g_0(x)$, then $F(x)=f(x)\cdot g(x)$ (p), where $f(x)$ and $g(x)$ are of the same degrees as $f_0(x)$ and $g_0(x)$ and these are the r-ρth convergents of $f(x)$ and $g(x)$.

As a special case of this we have:

IV. If a positive number ξ_0 exists such that $F(\xi_0)/F'(\xi_0)^2$ has a positive order, then $F(x)=0$ (p) has a root in $k(p)$.

V. If a primitive polynomial is irreducible in $R(p)$ and one of the extreme coefficients is a multiple of p then all intermediate coefficients are multiples of p.

VI. The factors of an Eisenstein polynomial are Eisenstein polynomials.

VII. An Eisenstein polynomial whose constant term is divisible by p^κ and by no higher power of p can have at most κ factors in $k(p)$.

For $\kappa=1$ we have Eisenstein's theorem that an Eisenstein polynomial whose constant term contains only the first power of p is irreducible. See Schönemann[5] and Eisenstein[6] of §13.

24. The Ring $R(p, \alpha)$

Consider an irreducible algebraic equation

$$F(x)=0 \tag{1}$$

of degree n. Let α be one of its roots and $k(\alpha)$ the field determined by α. Let $\omega_1, \omega_2, \cdots, \omega_n$ be a fundamental system of $k(\alpha)$. Then every integer ω of $k(\alpha)$ can be written in the form

$$\omega=x_1\omega_1+x_2\omega_2+\cdots+x_n\omega_n, \tag{2}$$

where the x_i are rational integers, and by giving to the x_i all possible rational values we get all the numbers of $k(\alpha)$. Since the representation of a number by the fundamental system is unique, an integer of $k(\alpha)$

[10] Dickson, *Bull. Amer. Math. Soc.*, 17, 1910, 19–23.

is divisible by p when and only when all x_i in its representation by a fundamental system are multiples of p.

If we next consider the system obtained by letting the x_i in (2) take all values of $k(p)$ and then collecting, in the element of this system, the coefficients of the same powers of p, we have[11] $\alpha_\rho p^\rho+\alpha_{\rho+1}p^{\rho+1}+\cdots$, where the coefficients of the powers of p are now numbers of $k(\alpha)$.

Let us next consider the system of all such series whose coefficients are integers of $k(\alpha)$. With addition, subtraction, and multiplication defined as before it is clear that this new set of elements forms a ring, which we denote by $R(p, \alpha)$. Every number of the ring $R(p, \alpha)$ is a root of an equation of degree n whose coefficients belong to $k(p)$.

The norm of a number of $R(p, \alpha)$ is the product of the number and its conjugates and by a consideration of the convergents it may be shown that this is $(-1)^n$ times the constant term of the equation of which the number is a root. The norm of the product or quotient of two numbers is the product or quotient of the norms.

If α is a root of an equation of degree n which is irreducible in the ordinary sense, then,[12] in $k(p)$, α cannot satisfy an equation of a degree lower than n.

25. Ring $R(p, \alpha)$ When $F(x)$ is Irreducible in $k(p)$

We have assumed that $F(x)$ is irreducible in the ordinary sense, i. e., in the field of the ordinary rational numbers. This does not, however, prevent reducibility in $k(p)$; but we shall first consider the case when $F(x)$ is irreducible also in $k(p)$.

Since in a field division by any element excepting zero is always possible we can apply[13] Euclid's algorithm to polynomials whose coefficients belong to $k(p)$. Every element of $R(p, \alpha)$ is a polynomial in α with coefficients belonging to $k(p)$ and every such polynomial is an element of $R(p, \alpha)$. Hence let $\varphi(\alpha)\neq 0$ be any element of $R(p, \alpha)$. Since $F(x)$ is irreducible, $\varphi(x)$ and $F(x)$ have no common factor and hence $M(x)$ and $N(x)$ exist, such that

$$M(x)\cdot F(x)+N(x)\cdot\varphi(x)=1\,(p).$$

Since $F(\alpha)=0$, we have

$$N(\alpha)\cdot\varphi(\alpha)=1\ \ (p).$$

Hence $\varphi(\alpha)$, and in fact any element of $R(p, \alpha)$ excepting zero, has a reciprocal in the ring and in this case therefore the ring is a field and shall be denoted by $k(p, \alpha)$.

[11] Hensel, *Theorie der Alg. Zahlen.*, Chap. VI, §§2 and 3.

[12] Wahlin, *Trans. Amer. Math. Soc.*, 16, 1915, 502–08.

[13] Fraenkel, Über gewisse Teilbereiche u. Erweiterungen von Ringen. Teubner, 1916.

26. The Field[14] $k(p, \alpha)$

We have stated above that every number of $R(p, \alpha)$ is a root of an equation of degree n. In the case when $F(x)$ is irreducible in $k(p)$ the equation for any number of $k(p, \alpha)$ is either irreducible or it is the power of an irreducible equation.

An integer of $k(p, \alpha)$ is a number which satisfies an equation whose coefficients are all integers of $k(p)$ and in which the coefficient of the highest power of x is a unit of $k(p)$. From this definition and theorem V of §23 regarding polynomials in $k(p)$ it follows that a number of $k(p, \alpha)$ is an integer when and only when its norm is an integer of $k(p)$. Hence of a number and its reciprocal at least one must be an integer.

An integer whose reciprocal is also an integer is a unit. Two integers whose quotient is a unit are equivalent. All integers of $k(p, \alpha)$ which are not units have a norm whose order is a positive rational integer. There must therefore exist some whose norms have the lowest possible order. All such numbers are equivalent. Let Π be any one of them and let f be the order of the norm $n(\Pi)$ of Π.

Every integer of $k(p, \alpha)$ is either a unit or it is divisible by Π, i. e., if β is any integer of $R(p, \alpha)$ either β is a unit or β/Π is an integer. Since p is not a unit it must be divisible by Π and hence p is equivalent to a power of Π. Let this be Π^e. Then $n = e \cdot f$.

The number Π bears the same relation to the numbers of $k(p, \alpha)$ as does p to the numbers of $k(p)$. The number of integers in a complete residual system mod Π is p^f.

We shall associate with the prime numbers of $k(p, \alpha)$ a prime divisor $\mathbf{p}$ and shall say that an integer β of $k(p, \alpha)$ is divisible by $\mathbf{p}^\kappa$ when β/Π^κ is an integer. Since all prime numbers of $k(p, \alpha)$ are equivalent $\mathbf{p}$ is independent of any particular choice of prime number. The integer f is called the degree of $\mathbf{p}$.

Every number of $k(p, \alpha)$ can now be written in the form $\alpha = \alpha_\rho \Pi^\rho + \alpha_{\rho+1}\Pi^{\rho+1} + \cdots$, and the coefficients α_ρ, $\alpha_{\rho+1} \cdots$ belong to a residual system mod. Π, which is obviously also the residual system mod $\mathbf{p}$.

Every number except zero of the residual system mod $\mathbf{p}$ satisfies the congruence

$$x^{p^f-1} \equiv 1 \text{ mod. } \mathbf{p}$$

and hence by theorem IV regarding polynomials in $k(p)$, which is easily extended to $k(p, \alpha)$, we see that in $k(p, \alpha)$ the equation

$$x^{p^f-1} - 1 = 0 \ (p)$$

has $p^f - 1$ solutions, i. e., $k(p, \alpha)$ contains the $p^f - 1$th roots of unity

[14] Hensel, *Theorie d. Alg. Zahlen.*, Chap. 6.

These are all incongruent mod $\mathbf{p}$ and hence together with zero form a complete residual system mod $\mathbf{p}$ and can be used as the coefficient in the expansion in powers of Π.

If η is a primitive p^f-1th root of unity this is in $k(p)$ a root of an irreducible equation of degree f. Hence η defines a sub-field of $k(p, \alpha)$ whose degree is f. This is known[15] as the coefficient field.

The prime number Π can be any one of an infinite number of equivalent prime numbers. The equation relative to the coefficient field of which Π is a root is an Eisenstein equation. When e is not divisible by p, a prime number Π exists whose equation has the form

$$x^e = p\eta_0 \quad (p),$$

where η_0 is a p^f-1th root of unity. If, however, $e = p^s e_0$, then a Π exists[16] which satisfies an equation of the form

$$x^{p^s} + \pi_0 e_{p^s-1} x^{p^s-1-} + \cdots + \pi_0 e_0 \equiv 0 \quad (p),$$

where π_0 is a root of

$$x^{e_0} - p\eta_0 = 0 \quad (p).$$

27. Ring $R(p, \alpha)$ When $F(x)$ is Reducible in $k(p)$

We have already said that the irreducibility of $F(x)$ in the ordinary sense does not prevent its reducibility in $R(p)$ and we shall next suppose that

$$F(x) = F_1(x) \cdot F_2(x) \cdots F_s(x) \quad (p),$$

where $F_i(x)$ is of degree n_i and $n = n_1 + \cdots + n_s$.

But in $R(p)$, α cannot satisfy an equation of degree less than n and hence we have $F_1(\alpha) \cdot F_2(\alpha) \cdots F_s(\alpha) = 0 \ (p)$. No single factor of this product or no product of fewer than all the factors can vanish and hence we see that $R(p, \alpha)$ contains divisors of zero which are not zero, and is therefore not a field.

In order to study the numbers of the ring, we introduce a new definition[17] of equality between the numbers of the ring. We associate with each irreducible factor $F_i(x)$ of $F(x)$ a prime divisor $\mathbf{p}_i$ and shall say that two number $\varphi_1(\alpha)$ and $\varphi_2(\alpha)$ of $R(p, \alpha)$ are equal with respect to $\mathbf{p}_i$, i. e.,

$$\varphi_1(\alpha) = \varphi_2(\alpha) \quad (\mathbf{p}_i),$$

when[18] $\varphi_1(x) - \varphi_2(x)$ is divisible by $F_2(x)$.

---

[15] Hensel, *Theorie d. Alg. Zahlen.*, Chap. 8, §4.
[16] Hensel, *ibid.*, §6.
[17] Mesazo Sano, *Mem. Coll. of Sc.*, Kyoto, 2, 1917, 203–26.
[18] Wahlin, *Trans. Amer. Math. Soc.*, 16, 1915, 502–08; Hensel, *Math. Zeitschrift*, 2, 1918, 433–52.

Since $F_i(x)$ is a polynomial with coefficients in $k(p)$, and according to the new definition of equality $F_i(\alpha)=0$, in the same way as when $F(x)$ was irreducible, it may be shown that every number which is not zero has a reciprocal and hence under the new equality the numbers constitute a field which may be denoted by $k(\mathbf{P}_i, \alpha)$.

The theorems regarding the factorization of polynomials are easily extended to an algebraic field and hence if r is sufficiently large and $F_i^{(r)}(x)$ is the rth convergent of $F_i(x)$, and if $\alpha_i^{(r)}$ is a root of $F_i^{(r)}(x)=0$, then in $k(p, \alpha_i^{(r)})$ $F_i(x)=0$ (p) has a solution. Let this root be α_i. Then $F_i(\alpha_i)=0$ (p) and $F_i(\alpha)=0$ $(\mathbf{p})$. If we now establish a correspondence between $k(\mathbf{p}_i, \alpha)$ and $k(p, \alpha_i)$ such that $\varphi(\alpha)$ and $\varphi(\alpha_i)$ are corresponding number of the two fields, we see that any rational relation existing between numbers of $k(p, \alpha_i^{(r)})$ relative to p is also true for the corresponding numbers of $k(\mathbf{p}_i, \alpha)$ relative to $\mathbf{p}_i$. This isomorphism between the two fields makes it possible to extend to $k(\mathbf{p}_i, \alpha)$ the result for the case when $F(x)$ is irreducible in $k(p)$.

The separation of $R(p, \alpha)$ into simple rings, which in this case as for $R(g)$ are fields is easily effected.[19]

In the preceding work we have seen how by taking r sufficiently large a field can be constructed in which any given equation will have a root. Hensel[20] calls such fields *auflösungs körper* for the given equation.

If two fields both of the lowest possible degree are such that in each of them a given equation has a solution, then there is a (1, 1) correspondence between the numbers of the two fields such that any rational relation existing between the elements of one field is true for the corresponding elements of the other field. The two fields are said to be equivalent. Two fields are equivalent when and only when they are auflösungs fields for the same irreducible equation.[20]

The field in which an equation has as many roots as its degree is called the field of decomposition of the equation. (Hensel *zerlegungs Körper*.)

Application of the foregoing theory to the study of the binomial equation in an algebraic field has been made by Wahlin.[21] He determined the simplest equations whose roots are necessary to solve the binomial equation and from this was able to draw conclusions regarding the factorization of a prime divisor $\mathbf{p}$ in the field formed by the adjunction of a root of the binomial equation.

Cameron[22] has made application to the problem of determining the factorization of a rational prime in the field formed by the composition of two fields.

---

[19] Wahlin, *Trans. Amer. Math. Soc.*, 16, 1915, 502–8.
[20] Hensel, *Jour. für Math.*, 136, 1909, 183–209.
[21] Wahlin, *Jour. für Math.*, 145, 1914, 15, 114–38.
[22] Cameron, *Diss. Marburg*, 1912.

28. The Fundamental Equation

Let $\omega_1, \omega_2, \cdots, \omega_n$ be a fundamental system. The form $u_1\omega_1 + u_2\omega_2 + \cdots + u_n\omega_n$ is called the fundamental form of the field. If we denote the norm of $x - u_1\omega_1 - u_2\omega_2 - \cdots - u_n\omega_n$ by $\psi(x; u_1, u_2, \cdots u_n)$, $\Psi = 0$ is called the fundamental equation of the field.

If $\Psi \equiv \varphi_1^{e_1}\varphi_2^{e_2}\cdots\varphi_s^{e_s}$, mod p, where φ_i are irreducible polynomials modulo p with coefficients which are polynomials in $u_1, \cdots, u_n$, then[23], in $k(\alpha)$, $p = \mathbf{p}_1^{e_1}\cdots\mathbf{p}_s^{e_s}$ where $\mathbf{p}_i (i = 1, \cdots s)$ is a prime divisor.

If we consider Ψ with respect to a modulus which is a power p^a of p, $a > 1$, then

$$\Psi \equiv Q_{1a}Q_{2a}\cdots Q_{sa} \text{ mod } p^a,$$

where $Q_{ia} \equiv Q_{i1} = \varphi_i^{e_i}$ mod p, and if we put $\Phi_i = Q_{i1} + (Q_{i2} - Q_{i1}) + (Q_{i3} - Q_{i2}) + \cdots$, we have

$$\Psi = \Phi_1 \cdot \Phi_2 \cdots \Phi_2(p),$$

which is the factorization[24] of Ψ in $k(p)$.

29. Discriminants and their Divisors

The discriminant D of a field is the square of the determinant formed by the fundamental system and its conjugates. If β is any integer of the field and $D(\beta)$ is the discriminant of this integer, then $D(\beta) = C^2 \cdot D$, where C is a rational integer The divisors of D are called the essential discriminantal divisors and those of C the unessential discriminantal divisors. C is called the index of the integer β.

The discriminant of the fundamental equation is a form in $u_1, u_2, \cdots, u_n$ and D is the greatest common divisor of the coefficents of the form.[25], This, however, is not true if we consider a functional field formed by the adjunction of a variable and consider the algebraic functions of this variable.[26]

The discriminant for a p-adic field $k(p, \alpha)$ can be defined as above when α is a root of an equation which is irreducible in $k(p)$, and when $F(x)$ is reducible in $k(p)$ we can define the discriminant of $k(\mathbf{p}_i, \alpha)$ as being the same as that of the isomorphic field $k(p, \alpha_i)$.

The question of the actual determination of the discriminant of a field resolves itself into the determination of the power of p dividing the discriminant. If we denote by Dp the power of p dividing the discrim-

[23] Hensel, *Jour. für Math.*, 113, 1894, 61–83.
Mertens, *Sitzungsber. Akad. Wien*, 103, IIa, 1894, 5–40.
[24] Bauer, *Jour. für Math.*, 149, 1919, 89–96.
[25] Hensel, *Jour. für Math.*, 113, 1894, 61–83.
[26] Ostrowski, *Göttingen Nachr.*, 1919, 279–98.

inant of $k(\alpha)$, and by $D\mathfrak{p}_i$ the power of p in the discriminant of $k(\mathfrak{p}_i, \alpha_i^{(r)})$, we have [27] the equation

$$Dp = D\mathfrak{p}_1 \cdot D\mathfrak{p}_2 \cdots D\mathfrak{p}_s.$$

Hence we must determine[28] $D\mathfrak{p}_i$. If $\mathfrak{p}_i$ is of degree f_i and its power in p is e_i, then $D\mathfrak{p}_i = p^{f_i(\bar{e}_i - 1)}$, where $\bar{e}_i = e_i$ if $e_i \neq 0$ mod. p;* but if $e_i = p^{r_i} e_i^0$ where e_i^0 is relatively prime to p, then $\bar{e}_i$ lies between the limits $e_i + 1$ and $(r_i + 1)e_i$.

The rational prime p is an essential[29] discriminant divisor when and only when at least one $e_i > 1$.

The relation of the discriminant of a field formed by the composition of two fields to the discriminants of the two fields has been studied by Hensel and Wahlin,[30] the latter with restriction as to the degree of the compounded field.

The discriminants of fields defined by binomial equations have been determined by Landsberg[31] and Westlund[31] and for general fields of algebraic functions by Hensel.[32] See Netto[18] of §20, Rados[13] of §17.

All fields have essential discriminantal divisors, i.e., the discriminant of any field is numerically greater[33] than 1, and in fact[34], when n is the degree of the field, $D > 2^{n-1}$.

If p is a prime which in $k(\alpha)$ is the product of s distinct prime divisors and n the degree of the field, then[35] $(D/p) = (-1)^{n-s}$, when (D/p) is the ordinary Legendrian symbol for quadratic residues.

Though the discriminant of a field is a divisor of the discriminant of all the integers of a field, it is not their greatest common divisor. The indices of all integers of a field may have a common divisor. A necessary condition[36] that a prime p be a common unessential discriminantal divisor is that p be less than the degree of $k(\alpha)$.

---

[27] Hensel, *Theorie der Alg. Zahlen.*, Chap. 9, §4.
[28] Hensel, *ibid.*, p. 219; *Gött. Nachr.*, 1897, 247–53.
Stickelberger, *Verhandlungen der Ersten. Int. Math.Congr. Zürich*, 1897, 182–93.
[29] Dedekind, *Göttingen Abhandlungen*, 29, 1882.
[30] Hensel, *Jour. für Math.*, 120, 1899, 99–108.
Wahlin, *Trans. Amer. Math. Soc.*, 11, 1910, 487–93.
[31] Landsberg, *Jour. für Math.*, 117, 1896–97, 140–47.
Westlund, *Trans. Amer. Math. Soc.*, 11, 1910, 388–92.
[32] Hensel, *Jour. für Math.*, 117, 1896,–7 333–45, 346–55; 118, 1897, 173–85.
[33] Minkowski, *Verhandlungen der Naturforscher und Aertze zu Bremen*, 63, 1890–13; Geometrie der Zahlen, 1896, 130.
Weber u. Wellstein, *Math. Ann.*, 73, 1912–13, 275–85.
Hurwitz, *Math. Zeitschift*, 3, 1919, 123–26.
C. Siegel, *Göttingen Nachr.*, 1922, 17–24.
E. Landau, *ibid.*, 1922.
Chatelet, Leçons sur la Théorie des Nombres, Paris, 1913, Chap. III.
[34] Schur, *Math. Zeitschrift*, 1, 1918, 377–402.
[35] Stickelberger, Verhandlungen der 1 sten Int. Math. Congr. zu Zurich, 1897, 182–93.
Voronoi, Verhandlungen der 3 ter Int. Math. Congr., Heidelberg, 186–89.
Hensel, *Jour. für Math.*, 129, 1905–06, 68–85.
[36] E. Von Zylinski, *Math. Annalen*, 73, 1912, 273–4.
* See last foot-note, p. 50.

If λ is the number of distinct prime divisors of p whose degrees are f, then in order that p be a common unessential discriminantal divisor it is necessary and sufficient[37] that

$$\lambda > \frac{1}{f}\left[p^f - \sum_q p^{f/q} + p^{f/qq'} \cdots\right]$$

where $q, q' \cdots$ are the distinct prime factors of f.

Examples have been given of fields which have common unessential discriminantal divisors. For fields of degree $n \geqq 4$, there are an infinite number whose unessential discriminantal divisors satisfy one of the following conditions:[38]

I. None are essential discriminantal divisors;
II. Some but not all are essential discriminantal divisors;
III. All are essential discriminantal divisors.

See the paper by Rella and those by Speiser, Ch. I, §3.

On discriminants of cubic fields, see Furtwängler and Braun of §2.

30. The Roots of Unity in $k(\mathbf{p}, \alpha)$

In the study of the numbers of the field $k(\mathbf{p}, \alpha)$ the roots of unity[39] which occur play a very important part. We have already seen that when p is the rational prime which is divisible by $\mathbf{p}$ and f is the degree of $\mathbf{p}$, then the p^f-1 th roots of unity are always present and determine the coefficient field. Besides those the only roots of unity which may occur are p^mth roots of unity, i.e., the roots of an equation of the form

$$x^{p^m} - 1 = 0 \ (\mathbf{p}).$$

A necessary and sufficient condition that $k(\mathbf{p}, \alpha)$ shall contain the pth roots of unity is that in the field $-p$ be a $p-1$th power.

31. The Exponental Representation of the Numbers of $k(\mathbf{p}, \alpha)$

By a principal unit of $k(\mathbf{p}, \alpha)$ we understand a unit whose first term is 1. Every number of the field can be written in the form $\pi^\alpha \omega^\beta E$, where π is a prime number, ω a primitive p^f-1th root of unity, and E a principal unit.

An infinite series in $k(\mathbf{p}, \alpha)$ is said to be convergent when it represents a number in the field. In order that a series be convergent it is necessary and sufficient[40] that the order of the various terms shall become infinite with n.

---

[37] Hensel, *Göttingen Nachr.*, 1897, 254–60.
[38] Bauer, *Math. Annalen*, 64, 1907, 573–76.
[39] Wahlin, *Jour. für Math.*, 145, 1914–15, 114–38.
Hensel, *Jour. für Math.*, 146, 1916, 189–215.
[40] Hensel, *Zahlen theorie*, Chap. 6, §4.

The functional equation $f(x+y)=f(x)\cdot f(y)$ has[41] a series solution $f(x)$ in $k(\mathbf{p}, \alpha)$ which converges for all x of orders greater then $1/(p-1)$, where p is the rational prime divisible by $\mathbf{p}$, and when such is the case $f(x)$ represents a principal unit E such that $E-1$ has the same order as x. For the simplest form of the solution Hensel[41] chooses the representation e^x.

Obviously all principal units will not have such an exponential representation, and hence they are classified as non-exponential and exponential units. If E is a non-exponential unit, there exists a ν such that E^{p^ν} is an exponential unit and hence, if $E^{p^\nu}=e^\gamma$, we can choose e^{γ/p^ν} as the exponential representation of E. If $k(\mathbf{p},\alpha)$ does not contain any roots of unity besides those of the coefficient field, e^{γ/p^ν} uniquely defines a principal unit. If however, $k(\mathbf{p}, \alpha)$ contains the p^mth root of unity, the unit defined by e^{γ/p^ν} is not unique and hence, from the various units represented by the symbol, one and only one must be chosen as the one to be associated with e^{γ/p^ν}. This assignment must be so made that the ordinary laws of exponents hold. That is, if $E_1=e^{\alpha_1}$ and $E_2=e^{\alpha_2}$, then $E_1\cdot E_2=e^{\alpha_1+\alpha_2}$. In other words, the non-exponential units which are to be associated with this representation must form a group.

By taking r sufficiently large, the abelian group of residues of the principal units mod. p^r has the property[42] that one element in the base of the group is a primitive p^mth root of unity. By choosing the non-exponential units which do not involve this element in their representation by the base as those which are represented by e^{γ/p^ν}, we find that the required condition is satisfied.

Every number of $k(\mathbf{p}, \alpha)$ can now be represented in the form $\pi^\alpha\omega^\beta e^\gamma$, where ω is a primitive $p^m(p^f-1)$th root of unity.[43]

32. The Multiplicative Representation of the Numbers of $k(\mathbf{p}, \alpha)$

Hensel[44] has developed another representation for the numbers of $k(\mathbf{p}, \alpha)$. A principal unit is said to be of degree k when it has the form $1+\alpha_k\pi^k+\cdots$. If we consider the system of p^f-1 units of degree k when α_k takes the values of the residual system mod. $\mathbf{p}$ (0 excluded), we see that every unit of degree k can be written in the form $\eta=\eta_k\eta^{(k+1)}$, where η_k is a unit of the system defined and $\eta^{(k+1)}$ is a unit of degree $k+1$.

---

[41] Hensel, *Math. Abh.* H. A. Schwarz, 1914, 61–75; *Jour. für Math.*, 145, 1914–15, 92–113.
[42] Wahlin, *Bull. Amer. Math. Soc.*, 23, 1917, 450–55.
[43] Hensel, *Jour. für Math.*, 145, 1914–15, 92–113.
[44] Hensel, *Jour. für Math.*, 146, 1916, 189–215; 151, 1921, 210–12.

If $\omega_1^{(\mathbf{P})}, \omega_2^{(\mathbf{P})} \cdots, \omega_f^{(\mathbf{P})}$ is a fundamental system[45] mod. $\mathbf{p}$, and $\eta_{ik} = 1+\omega_i^{(\mathbf{P})}\pi^k$, then every unit of the system defined above can be written in the form

$$\eta_{1k}^{c_1}\, \eta_{2k}^{c_2} \cdots \eta_{fk}^{c_f}\, \eta^{(k+1)}, \; 0 \leq c_1 < p,$$

where the c_i are not all zero and $\eta^{(k+1)}$ is of degree $k+1$. The units $\eta_{i\kappa}$ are said to form a base for the degree k.

If $\eta_{1k}, \eta_{2k}, \cdots, \eta_{fk}$ is a base for the degree k, then $\eta_{1k}^p, \eta_{2k}^p, \cdots, \eta_{fk}^p$ is a base for the degree $m = \min. (pk, e+k)$, where $p \sim \mathbf{p}^e$, with the exception of the case when $pk = e+k$ and $-p \equiv (\pi^{eo}\gamma g^{(o)})^{p-1}$ mod. $\mathbf{p}^{e+1}$. But also in this exceptional case a base can be found for the degree kp by replacing one properly chosen η_i^p by a new element.

When the exceptional case does not occur we have for all principal units a representation in the form

$$\eta_1^{c_1^{(1)}} \cdot \eta_2^{c_2^{(1)}} \cdots \eta_\lambda^{c_\lambda^{(1)}} \cdot \eta_1^{c_1^{(2)}p} \cdot \eta_2^{c_2^{(2)}p} \cdots \eta_\lambda^{c_\lambda^{(2)}p} \cdots\cdots = \eta_1^{c_1}\, \eta_2^{c_2} \cdots \eta_\lambda^{c_\lambda},$$

when $\lambda = ef$ and the $c_1, c_2, \cdots, c_\lambda$ are rational p-adic numbers.

In the exceptional case the same representation holds for the regular units and for the powers of irregular units beyond the point of irregularity, and by using a new unit to take care of those up to the point of irregularity we have a representation in the form $\eta_0^{c_o}\eta_1^{c_1} \cdots \eta_\lambda^{c_\lambda}$, where $c_0 = 0, 1, 2, \cdots p^v - 1$, where p^v is the highest power of p dividing e, and the c_i $(i \neq 0)$ are rational p-adic numbers.

If $k(\mathbf{p}, \alpha)$ contains the p^mth root of unity, the representation can be still further modified and we obtain a representation which for all units of $k(\mathbf{p}, \alpha)$, and not merely the principal units, has the form

$$\omega^b \eta_0^{c_0} \eta_1^{c_1} \cdots \eta_\lambda^{c_\lambda},$$

where ω is a primitive $p^m(p^f-1)$th root of unity, $b = 0, 1, 2, \cdots p^m(p^f-1)-1$, $c_0 = 0, 1, 2, \cdots p^{-m-1}$, and $c_0, c_1 \cdots, c_\lambda$ are rational p-adic numbers.

33. The Abelian Group of Residues in $k(\mathbf{p}, \alpha)$

The preceding multiplicative representation of the numbers of $k(\mathbf{p}, \alpha)$ furnish a means for the study of the Abelian group of residues mod. $\mathbf{p}^r$ in an algebraic number field. Hensel[46] has made a study of these groups and determined their bases and invariants. Cf. Hensel[17] of §6.

Since the irregular units occur when the pth roots of unity are present in $k(\mathbf{p}, \alpha)$ and they are principal units, if we let $\eta_0, \eta_1, \cdots, \eta_\lambda$ be the base for the principal units, a fundamental relation $\eta_0^{p^{\nu_0}}\, \eta_1^{p^{\nu_1}} \cdots$

[45] Hensel, *Theorie der Alg. Zahlen.*, Chap. 9, §2.
[46] Hensel, *Jour. für Math.*, 146, 1916, 216–228; 147, 1916–17, 1–15.

$\eta_\lambda^{p^{\nu_\lambda}}=1$ exists. By a transformation of the base this may be transformed into the reduced fundamental relation $\eta_0^{p^{\nu_0}}\eta_1^{p^{\nu_1}}\cdots\eta_e^{p^{\nu_e}}=1$ containing the smallest possible number of terms in the product. If we assume that the base is such and put $\bar\eta_i=\eta_0^{p^{\nu_0-\nu_i}}\eta_1^{p^{\nu_1-\nu_i}}\cdots\eta_i$ for $i=0, 1, 2,\cdots, e$, then $\bar\eta_0, \bar\eta_1\cdots, \bar\eta_e$ form a base for the irregular units of $k(\mathbf{p}, \alpha)$.

If η is a unit of degree k and the degrees of $\eta, \eta^p, \eta^{p^2},\cdots, \eta^{p^k}, \eta^{p^{k+1}},\cdots$ are $k, pk, p^2k,\cdots, p_\kappa k, s, s+e,\cdots$ then s is called the degree of irregularity of the unit η and is ∞ if η is regular.

If the degrees of irregularity for the units of $k(\mathbf{p}, \alpha)$ are $s_1, s_2,\cdots,\infty$, and $s_k<s+1\leqq s_{k+1}$ then $\bar\eta_0, \bar\eta_1,\cdots, \bar\eta_k, \eta_{k+1},\cdots, \eta_\lambda$ is a base for the principal units mod. $\mathbf{p}^{s+1}$, and the invariants are $p^{\mu_0}, p^{\mu_1},\cdots, p^{\mu_\lambda}$, where p^{μ_i} is the smallest power of p such that $\eta_i^{p^{\mu_i}}$ is of a degree greater than s. For the irregular units η_i this is easily seen to be $p^{\nu_i+t_i}$, where t_i is the smallest integer such that $s_i+t_ie\geqq s+1$, s_i being the degree of irregularity of η_i.

34. The Generalized Legendre Symbol

If $A=\pi^a\omega^b\eta_0^{c_0}\cdot\eta_1^{c_1}\cdots\eta_\lambda^{c_\lambda}$ is the multiplicative representative of a member of $k(\mathbf{p},\alpha)$, the mth power character of A with respect to $\mathbf{p}$ is denoted[47] by

$$\left\{\frac{A}{\mathbf{p}}\right\}_m=(\xi^a, \xi_0^b, \zeta_0^{c_0}, \zeta_1^{c_1}\cdots\zeta_\lambda^{c_\lambda})$$

where ξ is a primitive mth root of unity, ξ_0 a primitive βth root of unity, $\beta=(m, p^n(p^f-1))$, and $\zeta_0, \zeta_1,\cdots\zeta_\lambda$, are primitive p^rth roots of unity, p^r being the highest power of p dividing m.

This symbol may be used to determine the conditions under which an equation $x^m-A=0$ $(\mathbf{p})$ has a solution in $k(\mathbf{p}, \alpha)$, and since it is first of all necessary that a be a mulitple of m we need only consider further the case when A is a unit in $k(\mathbf{p}, \alpha)$. The given equation then naturally resolves itself into a chain of equations of prime degree l and we consider therefore $x^l-A=0$ $(\mathbf{p})$. The conditions that this have a solution are then the following: (1) If l is prime to $p(p^f-1)$, a solution always exists. (2) If l is a factor of p^f-1, b must be divisible by l. (3) If $l=p$, $p\beta\equiv b$ mod. p^f-1 must have solutions and $c_i\equiv 0$ mod. p, $i=0, 1,\cdots\lambda$.

The reduced Legendre symbol[48] $R\{A/\mathbf{p}\}_m$ is equal to a single root of unity and is the first one in the sequence $\xi^a, \xi_0^b, \zeta_0^{c_0},\cdots, \zeta_\lambda^{c_\lambda}$ which is different from 1 if such a one exists; otherwise it is equal to 1.

[47] Hensel, *Jour. für Math.*, 147, 1916–17, 233–48.
[48] Hensel, *Jour. für Math.*, 151, 1921, 119, 209.

35. Galois Fields

If $F(x)=0$ is an equation defining a Galois field (§3) and if, in $k(p)$,

$$F(x)=F_1(x)\cdot F_2(x)\cdots F_s(x)\ (p),$$

then the group of $F_i(x)=0$ ($\mathbf{p}_i$) is the zerlegungs group of $\mathbf{p}_i$. We have seen that the prime number Π is in the case when $e=p^r e_0$ defined by a pair of equations one of which is binomial of degree e_0 relative to the coefficient field. The group of this equation is the coefficient group. The other equation is an Eisenstein equation of degree p^r relative to the field defined by the binomial equation and its group is the verzwiegungs group.[49]

36. Kummer Fields

In a Kummer field defined by the equation $x^l-s=0$, the prime divisor $\mathbf{p}$ is the product of l distinct prime divisors, l equal prime divisors, or remains a prime according[50] as $R\left\{\frac{A}{\mathbf{p}}\right\}_e$ is 1, or a power of ξ, or a power of ζ.

The same theorem is true also for general relative abelian fields defined by a binomial equation.[51]

37. Norm Residues

If $k(\mathbf{p}, \alpha)$ contains the lth root of unity, the equation $x^l-A=0$ ($\mathbf{p}$), where A is a number of $k(\mathbf{p}, \alpha)$ defines a relative Abelian field $k(\mathbf{p}, \sqrt[l]{A})$. The number B of $k(\mathbf{p}, \alpha)$ is said to be a norm residue when and only when $B=N(B_0)$ ($\mathbf{p}$), where B_0 is a number of $k(P, \sqrt[l]{A})$ and $N(B_0)$ its relative norm. If $k(\mathbf{p}, \alpha)$ contains the l^nth root of unity, but not the primitive l^{n+1}th roots of unity, and if we write A and B in the multiplicative representation[52] $A=\pi^a\omega^b\omega_1^{c_1}\eta_1^{c_2}\cdots\eta_\lambda^{c_\lambda}$, $B=\pi^e\omega^d\omega_1^{d_1}\eta_1^{e_1}\cdots\eta_\lambda c_\lambda$, where ω is a primitive l^nth root of unity and ω_1 the highest root of unity in $R(\mathbf{p}, \alpha)$ whose degree is prime to l, then B is a norm residue when and only when $t\equiv 0$ mod. l, where $t=ad-bc$ when $l>2$, and $t=ad-bc+2^{n-1}ac$ when $l=2$. The norm residue character of B with respect to A is then defined as $\left\{\frac{B, A}{\mathbf{p}}\right\}=\zeta^t$, when ζ is a primitive lth root of unity. For this symbol we have the relations[53]

$$\left\{\frac{B, A}{\mathbf{p}}\right\}\left\{\frac{A, B}{\mathbf{p}}\right\}=1, \quad \left\{\frac{B_1, B}{\mathbf{p}}\right\}\left\{\frac{B_2, A}{\mathbf{p}}\right\}=\left\{\frac{B_1\cdot B_2, A}{\mathbf{p}}\right\}$$

[49] F. Huttig, *Diss. Marburg*, 1907.
[50] Hensel, *Jour. für Math.*, 151, 1921, 112.
[51] Hensel, *Jour. für Math.*, 151, 1921, 200–09.
[52] Hensel, *Jour. für Math.*, 151, 1921, 200–09.
[53] Hensel, *Math. Ann.*, 85, 1922, 1–10.

38. Ring Ideals

The ring as first introduced by Dedekind[54] consists of a set of integers of a field, the set being closed under the operations addition, subtraction and multiplication. Let us denote by G the ring of all integers of a field $k(\alpha)$ and by R any sub-ring. A set of elements I of R is called an ideal when the sum and difference of any two elements of the set belongs to the set, and the product of any element of the set by an element of R belongs to the set.

There exists in G a set of integers k such that the product of any integer of G by one of k is an integer of R. This set is an ideal which is the greatest common divisor of all ideals of G which belong to R. This ideal is called the conductor (Führer) of R.

If $\mathbf{r}$ is an ideal of G and $\mathbf{r}_1 \cdot \mathbf{r}_2 \cdots \mathbf{r}_\sigma$ is its factorization such that $N(\mathbf{r}_1)$, $N(\mathbf{r}_2), \cdots$, $N(\mathbf{r}_\sigma)$ are powers of distinct primes, then a necessary and sufficient condition that $\mathbf{r}$ be a conductor is that each $\mathbf{r}_i$ be a conductor.[55]

The classification of ideals in a ring such as discussed above is made in the same way as in G. Furtwängler[56] has proved the existence of class fields for the rings of an imaginary quadratic field.

The study of the ideals of a more general ring has been made by Masazo Sono.[57] He found that unique factorization of ideals in such a ring does not hold. A maximal ideal of a ring is one which is not contained in any other ideal of the ring excepting the ring itself.

In order that every ideal of the ring shall have a unique representation as a product of power of prime ideals it is necessary and sufficient that, for every maximal ideal P, (a) an ideal of R which contains P is either P or R, and (b) $P^{e+1} \neq P^e$ for all e.

With the additional condition that every ideal of a ring shall have a finite base, E. Noether[58] has studied the factorization of ideals in a general ring.

We observe that in this case it becomes necessary to make a distinction between relatively prime and teilerprime.

An ideal I is said to be relatively prime to an ideal S when if $T \cdot I$ is divisible by S, it follows that T is divisible by S. If S is relatively prime to I, and I to S, they are said to be mutually relatively prime.

An ideal is said to be relatively prime irreducible when it is not the least common multiple of relatively prime proper divisors.[59]

Every ideal can be uniquely represented as the l. c. m. of a finite

---

[54] *Göttingen Abhandlungen*, 1882.
[55] Furtwängler, *Sitzungs. Akad. Wiss. Wien.*, 128, IIa, 1919, 239–46.
[56] *Sitzungs. Akad. Wiss. Wein.*, 128, IIa, 1919, 247; 129, 1920, 161.
[57] *Mem. College of Sci. Kyoto*, 2, 1917, 203–226; 3, 1918, 113–49, 189–97.
[58] *Math. Ann.*, 83, 1921, 24–66.
[59] R is a proper divisor of B if B is divisible by R but R is not divisible by B.

number of ideals which are mutually relatively prime and relatively prime irreducible.

Two ideals are called teilerprime when their greatest common factor is the unit ideal. An ideal is said to be teilerprime-irreducible when it is not the l. c. m. of ideals which are teilerprime each to each.

Every ideal can be represented uniquely as the product of a finite number of ideals, teilerprime each to each, and teilerprime irreducible.

CHAPTER IV

FIELDS OF FUNCTIONS

39. GENERAL FIELDS

L. E. Dickson[1] gave definitions of a field by independent postulates and employed both finite and infinite fields for which there exists a prime p such that $pe=0$ for every element e of the field.

M. Bauer[2] considered a rational prime quantity P of a holoidal[3] domain composed of the polynomials in the independent variables $x_1, \cdots, x_m$ with coefficients in a number field. A root w if an equation $z^n+\cdots+c_n=0$, whose coefficients are integral quantities of the domain, determines a field Γ. Consider the decompositions

$$P=\pi_1^{e_1}\cdots\pi_r^{e_r}, \quad w=\pi_1^{a_1}\cdots\pi_r^{a_r}Q,$$

in Γ, where Q is prime to P, and π_i is a prime ideal. The ratios a_i/e_i are called the characteristic numbers of w with respect to P. All notationally possible characteristic numbers exist. When the coefficients c_i are given, the characteristic numbers of the roots w are found in terms of the numbers connected with a Puiseaux polygon arising in the theory of algebraic functions. When the c_i satisfy certain conditions involving the Puiseaux numbers, there is found the degree of the irreducible factors of $x^n+\cdots+c_n$.

E. Steinitz[4] discussed the extension (by adjunction of new elements) of a general abstract field K, called K algebraically closed if it contains the roots of all algebraic equations with coefficients in K, called K perfect if there exists no polynomial $f(x)$ with coefficients in K which is irreducible in K and has multiple zeros in some extension of K, and proved various theorems involving these concepts.

E. Cahen[5] employed series in x with integral coefficients. By the modulus of $\Sigma a_n x^n$ is meant the absolute value of a_0. A series is said to be divisible by another if the quotient series has all its coefficients integers; this is the case if the modulus of the divisor series is 1, which is then called a unit series. Among all the associated series (i. e., differing only by unit factors) there is one and only one whose coefficients are all $\geqq 0$ and less than the modulus; it is called a reduced series. Given $A\equiv\Sigma a_n x^n$ and $B\equiv\Sigma b_n x^n$, we can find a unique series $Q\equiv q_n x^n$

[1] *Trans. Amer. Math. Soc.*, 4, 1903, 13–20; 6, 1905, 198–204; 8, 1907, 389.

[2] *Jour. für Math.*, 132, 1907, 21–32, 33–35; 134, 1908, 29.

[3] J. König, *Algebraischen Gröszen*, 1903. Cf. review by Dickson, *Bull. Amer. Math. Soc.*, 13, 1907, 358–362.

[4] *Jour. für Math.*, 137, 1910, 167–309. Full report in Encyclopédie des sc. math., t. I, v. 2, 366–385.

[5] *Comptes Rendus*, Paris, 152, 1911, 124–7.

such that all coefficients of $A-BQ$ are $\geqq 0$ and less than the modulus of B. Hence we can find the greatest common divisor D of A and B. Then $x^{\alpha}D \equiv UA+VB$ for a suitable integer $\alpha \geqq 0$, and suitable series U, V. There is unique decomposition into prime series.

J. Nagy[6] gave twenty theorems including: (1) An irreducible algebraic function which takes only integral values for integral arguments is a polynomial. (3) An irreducible algebraic function of m variables, which takes a rational value at every point in m-dimensional space with positive integral coordinates, is a rational function of the m variables, and is a polynomial if the mentioned values are fractions with a finite denominator.

J. Kürschák[7] considered a (*Kürschák*) field K such that every element a of K has a (generalized) *absolute value* (*Bewertung*) which is a real number, denoted by $||a||$, and for which four properties are postulated:

(I) For every $a \neq 0$, $||a|| > 0$, while $||0|| = 0$.

(II) For every a, $||1+a|| \leqq 1+||a||$.

(III) For every two elements, $||ab|| = ||a|| \cdot ||b||$.

(IV) There exists at least one element a of K for which $||a|| \neq 0, 1$.

When K is the field of rational numbers there exists (in additon to ordinary absolute value) for every prime p an absolute value $||a|| = e^{-\alpha}$ of every rational number $a = p^{\alpha}u/v$, other than 0, where u and v are integers not divisible by p ($p^{\alpha}u/v$ being Hensel's p-adic form of a and α the *order* of a with respect to p), and e is the base of natural logarithms.

A sequence $a_1, a_2, \cdots, a_i, \cdots$ of elements of K is called fundamental if

$$\lim_{n=\infty} ||a_{n+p} - a_n|| = 0$$

for p an arbitrary positive integer. If every fundamental sequence of K possesses a limit in K, then K is called *perfect*. By the adjunction of suitably chosen new elements, any Kürschák field can be extended to an algebraically closed perfect Kürschák field. For the above $||a|| = e^{-\alpha}$, the extended field is Hensel's field of p-adic numbers.

A. Ostrowski[8] called an extension K' of a field K *finite* with respect to K if K' contains a finite number of quantities $\omega_1, \cdots, \omega_n$ such that every quantity of K' is expressible in the form $\Sigma\alpha_i\omega_i$ with α_i in K. He proved the following theorems:

(I) Every finite Kürschák extension R of a perfect field K is perfect.

(II) Every algebraic Kürschák extension R of a perfect field K, which contains quantities of arbitrarily high degree in respect to K, is not perfect.

---

[6] *Math. Naturwiss. Berichte aus Ungarn*, 30, 1912 (1915), 324–340.

[7] *Jour. für Math.*, 142, 1913, 211–253; *Math. és termés. ért.*, 30, 1912, 699–745; *Proc. Fifth Internat. Math. Congress*, 1, 1913, 285–9.

[8] *Jour. für Math.*, 143, 1913, 255–284.

(III) The least algebraically closed Kürschák extension of a perfec field K is perfect if and only if it is finite with respect to K.

Theorems I and II were proved here under the assumption that th extension R of K is of the first art, i.e., that every quantity in R satisfie an equation irreducible in K with all roots distinct, but without thi assumption in his[16] later paper.

A special case of (III) gives Kürschák's conjecture that the leas algebraically closed extension of the field of rational p-adic number is not perfect, whence transcendental p-adic numbers exist.

G. Guareschi[9] employed the field Ω of all rational functions of x_1, x with coefficients in an algebraically closed field A. Let K be an alge braic field of order n over Ω. Generalizing a theorem of Hensel,[1] it is shown that there exists in K a fundamental system $\lambda_1, \cdots, \lambda$ such that every integral quantity of K is expressible in the form $\Sigma u_i\lambda_i$ where the u_i are integral quantities of Ω.

T. Kojima[11] proved that if a branch of an algebraic function o $x_1, \cdots, x_k$ (i. e., a root of an irreducible equation whose coefficients ar polynomials in $x_1, \cdots, x_k$) is an integer for all integral values of $x_1, \cdots$ x_k it is a polynomial in $x_1, \cdots, x_k$ with rational coefficients. Hence if for n rational, an algebraic function $f(x_1, \cdots, x_k)$ is equal to the nth power of an integer for all integral values of $x_1, \cdots, x_k$, then f is identica with the nth power of a polynomial in $x_1, \cdots, x_k$ with rational coefficients

If, for n a positive integer, a polynomial $f(x_1, \cdots, x_k)$ with integra coefficients is equal to an nth power of an integer for all integral value of $x_1, \cdots, x_k$, then f is identical with the nth power of a polynomial ir $x_1, \cdots, x_k$ with integral coefficients.

E. Noether[12] showed by examples that there exist domains of integra transcendental numbers not of the type noted by E. Zermelo,[13] and studied the most general domain of integral transcendental numbers, in particular one with an algebraic basis or with a rational basis.

L. E. Dickson[14] put each number a of a field R into correspondence with a unique number $F(a)$ of R. If two operations $\oplus$ and $\odot$ are such that

$$F(a)\oplus F(b)=F(a+b),\ F(a)\odot F(b)=F(ab),$$

for every two equal or distinct numbers a, b of R, they obey the com- mutative, associative, and distributive laws of ordinary addition and

[9] *Atti Reale Istituto Veneto di Sc. Let. Arti*, 72, 1913, 817–822.

[10] *Jahresber. d. Deutschen Math.—Vereinigung* 8, 1900, 221–231; *Acta Math.*, 23, 1900, 339–416. For a report on the arithmetical theory of algebraic functions of two variables, see Encyklopädie der Math. Wiss., Band II_3, Heft. 5, pp. 651–674 (1921).

[11] *Tôhoku Math. Jour.*, 8, 1915, 24–37.

[12] *Math. Annalen*, 77, 1916, 103–128.

[13] *Ibid.*, 75, 1914, 434–442.

[14] *Bull. Amer. Math. Soc.*, 23, 1916, 109–111.

multiplication. When R is the field of rational numbers and a, b, c are integers such that $ab=c$, whence $F(a)\odot F(b)=F(c)$, $F(c)$ is said to be divisible by $F(a)$, and to be a prime if its only divisors are $F(\pm c)$, $F(\pm 1)$. If $a\equiv b \pmod m$ we say that $F(a)\equiv F(b)$ modulo $F(m)$. The analogue of Wilson's theorem is

$$F(1)\odot F(2)\odot\cdots\odot F(p-1)\equiv F(-1) \pmod{F(p)},$$

where p is a prime. This and the analogues of Fermat's and other theorems of the theory of numbers follow by correspondence. Independent proofs by computation were given at great length by L. Schrutka[15] for the case in which $F(a)$ is a special linear function of a.

A. Ostrowski[16] gave more elementary proofs of his[8] three theorems and without his earlier restriction on the first two theorems.

Let R be the least algebraically closed extension of Hensel's field $K(p)$ of the rational p-adic numbers. Let $e_1, e_2, \cdots$ be any roots of unity (belonging to R) whose degrees are not divisible by p. Let $n_1, n_2, \cdots$ be any rational numbers increasing monotonically to infinity. The series $e_1p^{n_1}+e_2p^{n_2}+\cdots$ converges and its limit is algebraic with respect to $K(p)$ if and only if $e_1, e_2, \cdots$ all lie in a finite extension of $K(p)$, i.e., are all powers of a certain root of unity, and if the denominators of $n_1, n_2, \cdots$ are bounded.

A. Ostrowski[17] investigated the solutions ϕ of $\phi(xy)=\phi(x)\cdot\phi(y)$ such that $\phi(x+y)\leqq\phi(x)+\phi(y)$, the variables being rational and the values of ϕ being real. Besides the trivial cases of the function being constantly 0 or 1, or 0 for $x=0$ and 1 for $x\neq 0$, the only other solutions are $\phi(x)=|x|^\rho$, $0<\rho\leqq 1$, and $\phi(x)=c^\xi$, where ξ is the order[7] x of with respect to a prime p, while $0<c<1$. A modulus is called Archimedian if there exists a positive integer n such that $\| n\cdot \text{unit} \| > 1$. Every Kürschák field having an Archimedian modulus is contained in the field of complex numbers, the modulus being the ρth power of its absolute value.

K. Ryghlík[18] gave a new proof of the theorem of Kürschák on the possibility of assigning an absolute value $||a||$ to each element a of an algebraic extension of a Kürschák field K such that $||b||$ is the absolute value of an arbitrary element b of K.

Auric[19] employed a complete holoidal[3] domain A (i.e., with unique decomposition into primes), the domain $\Omega_j\equiv A(\omega_j)$ obtained by adjoining to A a root ω_j of an irreducible equation of degree n with coefficients in A, and the normal or Galois domain L derived by the composition of

[15] *Monatshefte Math. Phys.*, 16, 1905, 167–192; 23, 1912, 92–105.
[16] *Jour. für Math.*, 147, 1917, 191–204.
[17] *Acta Math.*, 41, 1918, 271–284.
[18] *Casopis*, Prague, 48, 1919, 145–165.
[19] *Comptes Rendus*, Paris, 172, 1921, 1400–2.

$\Omega_1, \cdots, \Omega_n$. Two elements of Ω_1 may have a common divisor belonging to L but not to Ω_1. However, L is not in general a complete holoidal domain, but is extended to one by the invention of real or ideal integral numbers ϵ_i, π_i whose norms are the various fundamental units e_i or primes p_i of A. The theory of these ideals is said to be developed as the theory of ordinary ideals except that the new ones are more numerous, and has the same advantage in computation that complex numbers have over real numbers.

V. Gokhale[20] defined compactness of a general Kürschák field as a generalization of the property that in a plane every infinite set of points in a bounded domain has at least one point of condensation. This property under algebraic extensions yields results parallel to these by Ostrowski[8,16] on perfect fields. He gave a complete existential theory of the four properties: compactness, perfection, algebraic closure, having a characteristic (Steinitz[4], i.e., existence of a prime p such that $pe=0$ for every element e).

40. Field of all Algebraic Numbers

G. Kantor[1] proved that all real algebraic numbers can be put into one-to-one correspondence with the natural numbers 1, 2, 3, $\cdots$.

R. Dedekind[2] extended his theory (*Zahlentheorie*, ed. 4, §§161-5) of permutations of algebraic fields of finite order to the field H of all algebraic numbers. If ϕ is a permutation of a field A contained in H, then H possesses at least one permutation ω which is a multiple of ϕ (i.e., ϕ and ω replace each number of A by the same number). This theorem remains true when H is replaced by any sub-field. Finally, he considered both finite and infinite groups of permutations. A conjecture was later disproved by A. Ostrowski.[3]

V. Zemplén[4] aimed to explain Hurwitz's derivation of Dedekind's theory of ideals and to show how it is possible to carry over to the totality of algebraic numbers the laws holding for ordinary integers.

E. Jacobsthal[5] discussed diophantine equations in the domain of all integral algebraic numbers. If α, β, γ are integral algebraic numbers relatively prime in pairs, there exist units ξ and η such that $\beta=\alpha\xi+\gamma\eta$. As a generalization, if γ is relatively prime to each α_i and β_i, and α_i to each β_i and α_k, and β_i to β_k $(i\neq k)$, the system of equations $\beta_i=\alpha_i\xi+\gamma\eta_i$ $(i=1, \cdots, m)$ is satisfied by units $\xi, \eta_1, \cdots, \eta_m$. If a_i and b_i are rela-

[20] University of Chicago Dissertation (in Press).
[1] *Jour. für Math.*, 77, 1874, 258–262.
[2] Festschrift 150. Bestehens K. Gesell. Wiss. Göttingen (Abh. Math. Kl.), 1901, 17 pp.
[3] *Jour. für Math.*, 143, 1913, 258.
[4] *Math. és Phys. Lapok*, 10, 1902, 1–6, 7–27 (Hungarian).
[5] *Math. Annalen*, 74, 1913, 31–65; correction, 312.

tively prime integral algebraic numbers, and if every pair of the numbers $b_k a_i - b_i a_k$ are relatively prime, then

$$(a_0x+b_0y)\ (a_1x+b_1y)\cdots(a_mx+b_my)=\gamma$$

is solvable in integral algebraic numbers when γ is any such number. Two primitive binary quadratic forms are equivalent if and only if their discriminants are associated numbers. It is shown how to find all integral algebraic solutions ξ_i of $\Sigma\gamma_i\xi_i=\beta$.

41. Fields of Rational Functions

A. Kneser[1] gave an elementary arithmetical theory of fields of rational functions and a greatest common divisor process for polynomials in x, y modulo $F(x)$.

D. Mirimanoff[2] gave a method of reducing integral functions of several variables to canonical forms different from the method of L. Kronecker[3] (§12), and supplemented remarks of Kronecker (§§6, 7).

H. Weber[4] defined functionals in a function field and discussed genera, Klassenkorper, class number, and the division of elliptic functions.

L. Kronecker[5] proved by induction on n that every integral quantity of a domain $(R, R', \cdots, R^{(n)})$ can be expressed in one and but one way as a product of prime factors of the domain.

K. Hensel[6] considered the totality of rational functions with constant coefficients of a square matrix A. Let $f(r)=0$ be the equation satisfied by A and write

$$f(r)=(r-r_1)^{d_1}\cdots(r-r_h)^{d_h},\ f_i(r)=f(r)/(r-r_i)^{d_i}.$$

Since the $f_i(r)$ have no common factor, there exist functions $g_i(r)$ such that $\Sigma f_i g_i=1$. Write $f_i(r)g_i(r)\equiv E_i(r)$ modulo $f(r)$, $A_i(r)=E_i(r)\times(x-r_i)$, $A^0_i=E_i$. Then $A_i^{x_i}$ $(i=1, \cdots, h;\ x_i=0, 1, \cdots, d_i-1)$ form a fundamental system for the domain $K(r)$ of residues modulo $f(r)$ of the rational functions of r with constant coefficients. Replacing r by A, and writing 1 for the identity matrix, we obtain a normal fundamental system $A_i^{x_i}$ in terms of which every matrix of the domain $K(1, A)$ can be expressed linearly with constant coefficients, while $A_i^{d_i}=0$. Two domains $K(1, A)$ and K $(1, B)$ are equivalent if there exists a matrix P such that $PAP^{-1}=B$. There is found a complete system of linearly independent matrices commutative with a given matrix. Applications are made to bilinear and quadratic forms.

---

[1] *Jour. für Math.*, 102, 1888, 20–55, Part II.

[2] *Math. Soc. Moscow*, 19, 1897, 850–868; *Fortchritte Math.*, 28, 1897, 88.

[3] *Jour. für Math.*, 92, 1882; Werke, II, 263–294.

[4] *Math. Annalen*, 48, 1897, 433–73; 49, 1897, 83; 50, 1898, 1–26; Verhand. Intern. Math.—Kongresses, 1898, I, 113–22.

[5] Vorlesungen . . . Determinanten . . . von K. Hensel, 1, 1903, 248–262.

[6] *Jour. für Math.*, 127, 1904, 116–166.

J. Kürschák[7] proved that two forms $F(x_1, \cdots, x_m)$ and $G(x_1, \cdots, x_m)$ with coefficients in a complete orthoid domain have another such form as their greatest common divisor if and only if the resultant of $F(x_1+\lambda y_1, \cdots, x_m+\lambda y_m)$ and $G(x_1+\lambda y_1, \cdots, x_m+\lambda y_m)$ with respect to λ vanishes. When F and G are regular in x_i, J. König[8] had given the condition that their resultant with respect to x_i shall vanish.

L. Autonne[9] recalled that the totality of polynomials in n independent variables form a complete and well-defined holoidal domain, in the terminology of J. König,[8] pp. 7, 13, 70. A set of elements form a holoidal domain if they possess the ordinary laws of addition and multiplication, contains the unit 1, and is not modular (so that no sum of elements 1 is zero). It is complete, if every pair of its quantities has a greatest common divisor belonging to the domain. It is well-defined when a method is given to decide whether or not any number of the domain is divisible by any other number and, if divisible, to find the quotient.

Autonne proved that these properties continue to hold when the variables are subject to the relation $x_1^2+\cdots+x_n^2=0$, $n\neq 3$, $n\neq 4$.

E. Jacobsthal[10] gave another proof of the theorem of Weber (Algebra, II) that, if the ω_i are functionals not containing t, the functional $\omega_0 t^r+\cdots+\omega_r$ is integral if and only if all the ω_i are integral. (VII) If $\beta_1, \cdots, \beta_r$ are any integral or fractional functionals not containing y, the reciprocal of $y^r+\beta_1 y^{r-1}+\cdots+\beta_r$ is an integral functional. (VIII) If $\alpha_0, \cdots, \alpha_r$ are integral functionals, Θ is any functional, and u a variable not in $\Theta, \alpha_0, \cdots, \alpha_r$, and if we divide $G(u)\equiv\alpha_0 u^r+\cdots+\alpha_r$ by $u-\Theta$, we obtain a quotient with integral functional coefficients if $G(\Theta)$ is an integral functional. (IX) If $\alpha_0, \cdots, \alpha_r$ are integral, and $\beta_1, \cdots, \beta_m$ any functionals, no one containing u, and if $G(u)$ is exactly divisible by $g(u)=u^m+\beta_1 u^{m-1}+ \cdots +\beta_m$, then $G(u)/g(u)$ has integral functional coefficients. Conversely, (IX) implies (VII).

R. Konig[11] discussed the parallel between algebraic number theory and function theory.

E. Jacobsthal[12] stated that in applying algebraic integral functionals to algebraic number theory it is less convenient to use Weber's definition than the following. A functional ω is called integral if there exists a primitive function P such that ωP is an integral function with integral algebraic coefficients. We deduce their elementary properties direct from the corresponding properties of integral algebraic numbers. There

[7] *Math. Annalen*, 60, 1905, 317–8.
[8] Einleitung in die allgemeine Theorie der algebraischen Gröszen, 1903, 99.
[9] *Nouv. Ann. Math.*, (4), 7, 1907, 49–77.
[10] *Jour. für Math.*, 140, 1911, 266–276.
[11] *Jahresber. d. Deutschen Math.—Vereinigung*, 23, 1914, 181–192.
[12] Math. Abh. H. A. Schwartz 50 Doktorjubiläum, Berlin, 1914, 142–156.

is no need of integral rational functionals. The development of the theory of functionals is sketched up to the uniqueness of decomposition into primes.

E. Noether[13] employed a domain Ω containing at most a finite number of parameters, a field $K_{n,\,\rho}$, and any system $S_{n,\,\rho}$ of rational functions of $x_1, \cdots, x_n$ with coefficients in Ω, both of algebraic rank ρ (i.e., containing ρ algebraically independent functions, but not $\rho+1$). A finite number of functions of $S_{n,\,\rho}$ form a rational basis if every function of $S_{n,\,\rho}$ is a rational function of them with coefficients in Ω. It is proved that every field $K_{n,\,\rho}$ has a rational basis of at most $\rho+1$ functions. It was known that it has a rational basis of ρ functions if $\rho=1$ or 2, but not in general if $\rho>2$. Hence any system $S_{n,\,\rho}$ of rational functions has a rational basis.

A linear system is one which contains $cf(x)+dg(x)$ when it contains f and g, where c and d are arbitrary numbers of Ω. If also $f\cdot g$ belongs to the system, we have a domain of integrity. It is proved that any linear system $L_{n,\rho}$ (and hence any domain of integrity $I_{n,\,\rho}$) has a rational basis of at most $\rho+1$ functions.

A finite number of polynomials of a domain of integrity $G_{n,\,\rho}$ of polynomials constitutes an integrity basis if every polynomial of $G_{n,\,\rho}$ can be expressed as a polynomial in them with coefficients in Ω. Certain general types of domains $G_{n,\,\rho}$ are shown to have an integrity basis; but this important part of the memoir does not admit of brief report. Her criterion for the existence of a basis does not permit of wide application since it requires certain eliminations. For the case of a single variable, her theory shows that every system of polynomials has a finite basis.

A. Ostrowski[14] recalled the remark of Hilbert[15] that the system of functions $x^\alpha y^{\alpha^2}$ $(\alpha=1, 2, \cdots)$ does not have a finite basis, and proved that the system $x^{\alpha_i}y^{\beta_i}$ $(i=1, 2, \cdots)$, where α_i, β_i are integers $\gtreqless 0$, has a finite basis if and only if both the lower limit and the upper limit of the set $(\cdots, \alpha_i/\beta_i, \cdots)$ belong to that set. There is given an extension to monomial functions of n variables. From the existence of a basis when $n=1$ follows at once E. Noether's[13] theorem that every system of polynomials in one variable has a basis.

Let K be the least field which contains a system F of forms

$$f_i=x^{\alpha_i}y^{\beta_i}\cdots t^{\delta_i} \quad (i=1, 2, \cdots),$$

so that K consists of the totality of rational functions of the f_i with rational coefficients. Let J denote the domain of integrity of K, so

[13] *Math. Annalen*, 76, 1915, 161–196; prelim., *Jahresber. Deutschen Math.—Vereinigung*, 22, 1913, 316–9.

[14] *Math. Annalen*, 78, 1917, 94–119.

[15] *Göttingen Nachrichten*, 1891, 232–242.

that J consists of those polynomials in $x, \cdots, t$ with integral coefficients which belong to K. It is proved that J has a finite basis.

G. Pólya[16] called a polynomial $P(x)$, whose coefficients belong to an algebraic field K, integral-valued (*ganzwertig*) in K if for every integral (algebraic) number ξ of K the value $P(\xi)$ is an integral number of K. For example, $\frac{1}{2}x(x-1)$ is integral-valued in the field of all rational numbers.

There is said to exist in a field K a regular basis $F_0(x), F_1(x), \cdots$ of the integral-valued polynomials in K if $F_m(x)$ is of degree m and if every integral-valued polynomial of degree m of K is expressible in the form

$$\beta_0 F_m(x)+\beta_1 F_{m-1}(x)+\cdots+\beta_m F_0(x),$$

where $\beta_0, \cdots, \beta_m$ are integral numbers of K. It is shown that, if K is the field of all rational numbers, we may take

$$F_m(x)=x(x-1)(x-2)\cdots(x-m+1)/m!.$$

Express each integral-valued polynomial of degree m of K in the form $(a/m!)x^m+\cdots$. Then zero and the various integral numbers a form an ideal α_m of K. There exists in K a regular basis of its integral-valued polynomials if and only if $\alpha_0, \alpha_1, \alpha_2, \cdots$ are all principal ideals.

If $[x]$ denotes the greatest integer $\leqq x$, and $N(\pi)$ the norm of π, and if π_i ranges over all prime ideals of K, then for each ideal divisor λ of

$$I_m=\prod_{i=1}^{\infty} \pi_i^{\psi_i(m)}, \qquad \psi_i(m)=\sum_{\nu=1}^{\infty}\left[\frac{m}{N(\pi_i)^\nu}\right],$$

and only for such divisors λ, there exist polynomials of degree m in x, whose coefficients are integral numbers of K with no common ideal divisor other than 1, whose values for all integral x are divisible by λ. For $\lambda=I_m$, one such polynomial $H_m(x)=x^m+\cdots$ has unity as its highest coefficient.

For a quadratic field K there exists a regular basis if and only if every ideal divisor of the discriminant of K is a principal ideal.

A. Ostrowski[17] proved by means of Pólya's[16] results that $I_m=m!/\alpha_m$ and then that the integral-valued polynomials in K possess a regular basis if and only if, for each rational prime p, all products of distinct prime ideal factors of p of the same degree (i.e., have the same power of p as norm) are principal ideals. If we assume also that K is a normal (Galois) field, all prime ideal factors of p have the same degree, and their product is p if p has no multiple factor. Then the above condition is satisfied if p is not a divisor of the discriminant of K. But if p divides the discriminant and if $p=(\pi_1 \cdots \pi_i)^e$ is its decomposition into prime

[16] *Jour. für Math.*, 149, 1919, 97–116.
[17] *Jour. für Math.*, 149, 1919, 117–124.

ideals, the condition for a regular basis is that the product $\pi_1 \cdots \pi_i$ be a principal ideal.

A polynomial in $x_1, \cdots, x_n$ is called integral-valued in K if it takes integral values in K for all integral numbers $x_1, \cdots, x_n$. If at least one such polynomial F_p corresponds to each product P of powers of $x_1, \cdots, x_n$, and if every integral-valued polynomial in K is expressible as a linear function of the F_p with integral coefficients in K, the F's are said to form a regular basis of the totality G of all integral-valued polynomials in K. Then those polynomials in G which involve only x_n possess a regular basis in the sense of Pólya. Thus the above are necessary conditions for the existence of a regular basis of G. They are proved to be also sufficient conditions. One such basis is given by the polynomials

$$\frac{\alpha_{m_1}}{m_1!} \cdots \frac{\alpha_{m_n}}{m_n!} H_{n_1}(x_1) \cdots H_{m_n}(x_n).$$

An extension to n variables is given to Pólya's theorem on the I_m, which need not now all be principal ideals.

42. Field of the Algebraic Functions of one Variable

Hensel[1] gave in 1921 a report on the arithmetical theory of algebraic functions of one variable. None of the following papers are cited.

L. Bauer[2] considered the field Ω of all rational functions of z and a root of an irreducible equation of degree n whose coefficients are rational functions of z. There exists a basis $\omega_1, \cdots, \omega_n$ of the integral algebraic functions of z in Ω such that $\omega_1 = 1$. Then every prime ideal whose norm is $z - z_0$ is representable as a modul $[z-z_0, \omega_2 - c_2, \cdots, \omega_n - c_n]$, where $c_2, \cdots, c_n$ are constants, and conversely.

J. C. Fields[3] gave algebraic proofs of the Riemann-Roch theorem under special assumptions.

K. Hensel[4] and G. Landsberg[5] noted contrasts and analogies between algebraic functions of one variable and algebraic numbers.

H. Jung[6] spoke of the genus of the equation $G(y, x) = 0$ defining y as an algebraic function of x as the rank of the field $K(x, y)$.

When the latter is of rank 1 we obtain all algebraic fields over it if we adjoin to $K(x, y)$ any root function of $K(x, y)$ (root of a rational

[1] *Encyklopadie der Math Wiss.*, Band II$_3$, Heft 5, pp. 533–650. The reference on p. 564, note 36, to Mertens should be Wien Sitzber., 1893, 2a, pp. 497–522; that on p. 593 to Hensel should be Jahresber d. D. M. V., 1 (1892), pp. 56–59.

[2] *Math. Annalen*, 32, 1888, 151–6; the error of writing ν for $\mathbf{o}$ is corrected *ibid.*, 41, 1893, 492, note.

[3] *Acta Math.*, 26, 1902, 157–170; *Jour. für Math.*, 124, 1902, 179–201.

[4] *Sitzungsber. Berlin Math. Gesell.*, 1, 1902, 29–32.

[5] *Jahresber. d. Deutschen Math.—Vereinigung*, 14, 1905, 93–101.

[6] *Jour. für Math.*, 127, 1904, 103–115.

function which behaves everywhere as a rational function of x, y), then adjoin any root function of the extended field, etc.

G. Landsberg[7] discussed fundamental systems, the Riemann-Roch theorem and its analogue in the theory of algebraic numbers.

J. Wellstein[8] gave an arithmetic-algebraic theory of algebraic functions differing from that of Weber (Algebra, III, 1908) partly in the employment of (homogeneous) forms in x_1, x_2, instead of polynomials in x $(x=x_1/x_2)$. His integral functionals obey the laws of divisibility of ordinary arithmetic. Any functional Θ has a basis $\Theta_1, \cdots, \Theta_n$ such that all functionals divisible by Θ is a linear function of the Θ_i whose coefficients are integral quantities of a certain domain containing x_1 and x_2. There is a discussion of prime functionals.

43. Modular Systems

Generalizing ordinary congruence of integers, Kronecker regarded two elements $\mathbf{M}$ and $\mathbf{M}^1$ of a given domain of integrity as congruent with respect to a modular system $(\mathbf{M}_1, \cdots, \mathbf{M}_k)$, whose elements $\mathbf{M}_1, \cdots \mathbf{M}_k$ belong to that domain if $\mathbf{M}-\mathbf{M}^1$ is a linear homogeneous function of $\mathbf{M}_1, \cdots, \mathbf{M}_k$ with coefficients in the domain. We here report only on papers not cited in the discussion of modular systems in the Encyclopedie des sciences mathématiques, *I*, 2, 342–366; *I*, 3, 403–6.

E. Netto[1] collected theorems due to Kronecker and applied them to the discriminant of a polynomial in n variable.

H. Laurent[2] employed polynomials $\phi_1, \cdots, \phi_n$ in $x_1, \cdots, x_n$ of degrees $m_1, \cdots, m_n$ such that $\phi_1=0, \cdots, \phi_n=0$ have exactly $\mu=m_1\cdots m_n$ distinct sets of finite common solutions and such that a certain determinant Δ of order μ formed of these solutions is not zero. He studied the solution of $AX\equiv B$, and more generally any congruence $F(X)\equiv 0$ with respect to the modular system $(\phi_1, \cdots, \phi_n)$. There is an application to elimination.

L. Kronecker[3] determined a prime modular system with respect to which a given polynomial in one variable can be represented as a product of linear factors. The application is to Galois resolvents.

H. Laurent,[4] in a study of elimination between n equations, gave results chiefly in Kronecker's Festschrift (Jour. für Math., 92, 1882).

E. Netto[5] applied modular systems to the law of inertia of quadratic forms in n variables.

---

[7] *Göttingen Nach.*, 1897, 91–101; *Math. Annalen*, 50, 1898, 577–582.
[8] *Festschrift H. Weber*, 1912, 457–479.
[1] *Acta Math.*, 1, 1882, 382–3.
[2] *Nouv. Ann. Math.*, (3), 5, 1886, 432–7, 456–60.
[3] *Jour. für Math.*, 100, 1887, 490–510; Werke, III$_1$, 209.
[4] *Jour. école polyt.*, 60, 1890, 107–136.
[5] *Jour. für Math.*, 110, 1892, 184–7.

G. Landsberg[6] considered briefly modular systems in their fundamental form.

K. Hensel[7] gave elementary properties of pure modular systems of rank 2, viz., $(\mathbf{M})=(F_1, \cdots, F_\nu)$, where the $F_i(x)$ are polynomials with integral coefficients having no common factor. He found the number of all polynomials in x with integral coefficients which are incongruent modulo $(\mathbf{M})$, and the number of them which are prime to $(\mathbf{M})$. These problems had been solved previously only for the simplest case of the prime modular system (p, P), where p is a prime integer and $P(x)$ is irreducible modulo p.

O. Pund[8] wrote $S^m(a_1, \cdots, a_n)$ for the modular system with the elements $a_1^m, \cdots, a_n^m$, and proved by induction that

$$S^m(a_1, \cdots, a_n)\cdot S^{(m-1)(n-1)}(a_1, \cdots, a_n)=S^{n(m-1)+1}(a_1,\cdots, a_n).$$

Let S_k denote the modular system whose elements are the $\binom{n}{k}$ products of $a_1, \cdots, a_n$ taken k at a time, and write $S_0=1$. Then

$$(S_{i+1}S_k,\ S_{k+1}S_i)=S_{k+1}S_i \quad (i\geqq k).$$

Write P_k for $\Pi(a_{i_1}, \ldots, a_{i_k})$, the product extending over all combinations $i_1, \cdots, i_k$ of $1, \cdots, n$ taken k at a time. There is proved the formula[9] which expresses P_i as a product of the systems S_k^t. Conversely, S_k is a quotient of products of the P_i^t. This is used to exhibit the least common multiple of several moduli.

Pund[10] proved that to every finite commutative group of order $n+1$ corresponds a modular system whose elements are linear functions of n variables.

Pund[11] noted that a modular system whose elements are all linear functions of x with integral coefficients can be reduced to $(ax+b, c)$. For x integral, the latter is equivalent to $d(x+r, m)$, where d is the g.c.d. of a, b, c, while $m=d^{n-1}c/\delta$, δ being the *g.c.d.* $(a^n, d^{n-1}c)$ of the two arguments written, and n is the least integer for which $(a^{n+1}/d^{n+1}, c/d)=(a^n/d^n, c/d)$.

H. Kühne[12] proved by induction that

$$(1)\qquad P=(p, f_1(x_1), f_2(x_2;x_1), \cdots, f_n(x_n;x_1, \cdots, x_{n-1}))$$

is a prime modular system of the domain of the polynomials in $x_1, \cdots, x_n$ with integral coefficients, if p is an odd prime integer; $f_1(x_1)$ of degree k_1 and is irreducible modulo p; $f_2(x_2;\, x_1)$, regarded as a function of x_2,

[6] *Jahresber. d. Deutschen Math.—Vereinigung*, 4, 1894–5, 111–2.
[7] *Jour. für Math.*, 119, 1898, 175–185.
[8] *Mitt. Math. Gesell. Hamburg*, 3, 1898, 325–332.
[9] Dirichlet Dedekind, Zahlentheorie, ed. 4, 1894, Suppl. XI.
[10] *Mitt. Math. Gesell. Hamburg*, 3, 1899, 371–6.
[11] *Ibid.*, 3, 1900, 423–6.
[12] *Jour. für Math.*, 124, 1902, 121–133.

is of degree m_2 and irreducible modulis $p, f_1(x_1)$; etc. Fermat's theorem is generalized to modulus P. The application is to higher residues and reciprocity laws.

Kühne[13] discussed the approximate solution of congruences with respect to the prime modular system (1). Let **B** denote the domain of the $p^{m_1 \cdots m_n}$ residues modulo P of the polynomials in $x_1, \cdots, x_n$ with integral coefficients. Let B denote the domain of the rational functions of a new variable x with coefficients in **B**. The degree of the quotient $a=\phi/\psi$ of two polynomials is the degree of ϕ minus the degree of ψ. If ψ is not a power of x, the formal division of ϕ by ψ yields a remainder of degree $<-\omega$ and a quotient involving the powers $x^{\alpha}, \cdots, x^{-\omega}$ and called a decimal approximating to a. Let

$$F(y)=y^{\mu}+a_1 y^{\mu-1}+ \cdots + a_{\mu}$$

have coefficients in B and be irreducible in B. Let α_k be the degree of a_k and choose an integer η such that $j\eta \gtreqless \alpha_j$ $(j=1, \cdots, \mu)$, with at least one equality sign. Then $y=x^{\eta}z$ transforms $F(y)$ into

$$x^{\mu\eta}\mathbf{G}(z)+x^{\mu\eta-1}\mathbf{G}'(z)+x^{\mu\eta-2}\mathbf{G}''(z)+\cdots$$

Decompose $\mathbf{G}(z)$, whose coefficients belong to **B**, into $\mathbf{G}_1(z)\cdots\mathbf{G}_m(z)$ modulo P, where each $\mathbf{G}_i(z)$ is a power of a function irreducible in **B**. Then $F(y)$ is a product of factors $F_1, \cdots, F_m$, relatively prime in pairs, with decimal coefficients belonging to **B**.

With $F(y)$ as an additional modulus, the residues of polynomials in y with coefficients in B form a field Y having a basis $B_1, \cdots, B_{\mu}$ whence every integral quantity of Y has the form $C(y)\equiv\Sigma k_i B_i$, each k_i being an integral quantity of B. The resultant of $C(y)$ and the approximate divisor $F_{\rho}(y)$ of $F(y)$ is called the ρth partial norm of C. There exist only a finite number of quantities C the degrees of whose partial norms do not exceed a certain limit.

A quantity of Y the degree of whose norm is zero is called a unit. As a generalization of Dirichlet's theorem on units, it is shown that every unit of Y is expressible as $W\Pi E_i^{k_i}$, where $E_1, \cdots, E_{m-1}$ are independent units, k_i is an integer, W is one of the finite number of roots of unity in Y, and m is the above number of distinct irreducible factors modulo P of $\mathbf{G}(z)$.

F. Severi[14] proved theorems of Lasker[15] on moduli of algebraic forms.

E. Fischer[16] defined a linear family of forms to be one which contains every $c_1\phi_1+c_2\phi_2$, where c_1, c_2 are constants, if it contains ϕ_1 and ϕ_2. In case a set of residues with respect to a modul $M=(f_1(x), \cdots, f_k(x))$

---

13 *Jour. für Math.*, 126, 1903, 102–115.
14 *Atti R. Accad. Torino*, 41, 1906, 205–223.
15 *Math. Annalen*, 60, 1905, 20–115, 607–8.
16 *Jour. für Math.*, 140, 1911, 48–82.

s a linear family of forms, it is called a residue family with respect to M. linear family L of forms $\phi(x)$ is called a fundamental system with espect to M if every form is expressible as $\Sigma_{i=1}^{i=v} g_i(x)\phi_i(x)$, where the $_i(x)$ are forms which are polynomials in $f_1, \cdots, f_k$ with integral coeffiients, while the ϕ_i are forms in L, and if there exists no other linear amily which is a part of L and has the preceding property. If no one f $f_1, \cdots, f_k$ is of dimension zero, the concept of a fundamental system ith respect to M is shown to coincide with the concept of a residue amily with respect to M. A set of forms is called a *Staat* if the sum of ny two of its forms of like dimension belongs to the set, and if when (x) and $h(x)$ belong to the set so do also the product $k \cdot h$ and

$$\bar{k}\left(\frac{\partial}{\partial x}\right) \cdot h(x)$$

here the coefficients of $\bar{k}(x)$ are conjugate imaginary to those of $k(x)$), nd when, for example, $f(x_1, x_2) = 3x_1^2 + 5x_1x_2$,

$$f\left(\frac{\partial}{\partial x_1}, \frac{\partial}{\partial x_2}\right) u \equiv 3\frac{\partial^2 u}{\partial x_1^2} + 5\frac{\partial^2 u}{\partial x_1 \partial x_2}.$$

H. S. Vandiver[17] considered a finite algebra composed of a finite umber of elements combined under addition, subtraction, and multiication, subject to the commutative, associative, and distributive laws, d such that the sum, difference, or product of any two elements is a niquely determined element of the set, and having an element playing e rôle of unity under multiplication. Division may not be possible. mong several examples of such an algebra is that of the classes of sidues with respect to a certain modular system. Cf. Kircher.[23]

A. Hurwitz[18] called a form T a *Trägheitsform* of the modul $M =$ $_1, \cdots, f_r)$, where the f_i are forms with coefficients in a given domain, every form of $(f_1, \cdots, f_r, T)$, whose degree exceeds a certain limit, longs to M. A modul M is called closed if it has no Trägheitsform other than forms in M.

H. Fuss[19] proved that the groups of the classes of residues modulo M reducible in the field P of the coefficients of M if and only if the modul is representable as the least common multiple of two relatively ime moduls whose coefficients belong to P.

F. S. Macaulay[20] discussed the resolution of a modular system into imary systems.

E. Kircher[21] employed a modular system $M = (m_n, \cdots, m_1, m)$,

[17] *Trans. Amer. Math. Soc.*, 13, 1912, 293–304.

[18] *Annali di Mat.*, (3), 20, 1913, 113–152.

[19] Modulsysteme und höhere komplexe Kommutative Zahlsysteme, Diss., 1913 l, 70 pp. Cf. Schmeidler [24].

[20] *Math. Annalen*, 74, 1913, 66–121.

[21] *Trans. Amer. Math. Soc.*, 16, 1915, 413–434.

where m is an ideal of an algebraic field Ω, while, for $i=1, \cdots, n$, m_i is a polynomial in $x_1, \cdots, x_i$ with coefficients in Ω. After establishing the unique factorization of M into relatively prime simple modular systems he considered the classes of residues of polynomials in $x_1, \cdots, x_n$ whose coefficients are integers in Ω, with respect to M as modulus, and found the conditions that these classes form a group. Finally there are obtained generalizations of Fermat's and Wilson's theorems.

F. S. Macaulay[22] published a book on this subject.

E. Kircher[23] carried out a suggestion by Vandiver and proved that any finite algebra of Vandiver's[17] type can be represented by the classes of residues of a modular system of Kircher's preceding paper.

W. Schmeidler[24] proved Fuss'[19] theorem in general form and discussed groups of hypercomplex numbers with a denumerable basis.

Schmeidler[25] investigated a modul the group of the classes of residues with respect to which is irreducible.

A. J. Kempner[26] showed that a certain type of modular system related to the residues of polynomials in x with respect to a composite integral modulus, is in canonical form.

44. Modul

A system of numbers such that the (sum or) difference of any two numbers of the system belongs to the system is called a *modul*.

F. Mertens[1] gave a detailed proof of the following theorem due to Dedekind.[2] Given any system of linear forms $f_1, \cdots, f_m$ in $x_1, \cdots, x_n$ with integral coefficients of rank n, we can find a reduced system of forms

$$\omega_i = c_{i1}x_1 + \cdots + c_{ii}x_i \quad (i=1, \cdots, n)$$

with integral coefficients such that $0 \leq c_{ik} < |c_{kk}|$ for each $i>k$, while the ω's are linear functions of the f's with integral coefficients and vice versa. The sign of each c_{kk} may be chosen at pleasure, but in other respects the ω's are uniquely determined by the f's.

E. Steinitz[3] employed a "finite" modul $\mathbf{d} = M(\delta_1, \cdots, \delta_n)$ composed of

$$c_1\delta_1 + \cdots + c_n\delta_n, \tag{1}$$

where $c_1, \cdots, c_n$ are ordinary integers. It is assumed that (1) vanishes

[22] The Algebraic Theory of Modular Systems, Cambridge University Tract No. 19, 1916. Review in *Bull. des. sc. math.*, (2), 41, 1917, 141.
[23] *Amer. Jour. Math.*, 39, 1917, 272–280.
[24] *Math. Zeitschrift*, 3, 1919, 29–42.
[25] *Ibid.*, 5, 1919, 224–66; extension of his Göttingen Diss., 1917; *Math. Ann.* 79, 1918, 56-75.
[26] *Trans. Amer Math. Soc.*, 22, 1921, 240 seq.
[1] *Sitzungsber. Akad. Wiss. Wien.* (*Math.*), 104, IIa, 1895, 103–121.
[2] *Zahlentheorie*, ed. 3, 1879, §165, pp. 486–93; ed. 4, 1894, §172, 518–20.
[3] *Math. Annalen*, 52, 1899, 1–57.

nly when each $c_i=0$. Consider the modul $\mathbf{a}=M(\alpha_1, \cdots, \alpha_a)$ deter-
nined by

$$\alpha_i=c_{i1}\delta_1+\cdots+c_{in}\delta_n \quad (i=1, \cdots, a),$$

where we may evidently assume that $a\leqq n$. The matrix

$$A=\begin{pmatrix} c_{11}\cdots c_{1n} \\ \cdots\cdots \\ c_{a1}\cdots c_{an} \end{pmatrix}$$

s called the basis of **a**. Let **b** be another such modul whose basal natrix B has b rows. Then **b** is divisible by **a** (i.e., every number of b belongs to **a**) if and only if there exists a matrix P such that $B=PA$. Put into the same *class* with A all matrices having the same determinantal divisors as A, the kth determinantal divisor of A being the g.c.d. f all its k-rowed minors. In particular, a new basis of the modul **a** elongs to the same class as A.

By annexing rows of zero elements when $a<n$, we obtain from A square matrix which is a basis of **a**.

Let A be any n-rowed square matrix which is a basis of **a**. Let E be an n-rowed square matrix whose n^2 elements are integers whose eterminant is ± 1. Then AE is the basis of a modul which is said to be erived from **a** by the unimodular transformation [E]. From a modul **a** an be derived by unimodular transformation every modul of the same lass as **a** and no further moduls.

An investigation is made of the number $\psi(A)$ of moduls which belong o the same class as A. The following concepts are employed in this echnical study. Two systems (rows)of numbers $a_1, \cdots, a_n$ and $b_1, \cdots b_n$ re called congruent with respect to **a** if $a_1-b_1, \cdots, a_n-b_n$ are equal o the coefficients $c_1, \cdots, c_n$ of a number (1) belonging to **a**. Any row s said to be a residue of all the rows congruent to it. Two matrices ach having r rows and n columns are called congruent with respect o **a** if their corresponding rows are congruent, and then each is said to e an r-rowed residue of the other. Let $\phi_r(\mathbf{a})$ denote the number of r-rowed residues such that, if the r rows are annexed to the rows of a natrix which is a basis of **a**, there results the initial modul $M(\delta_1, \cdots, \delta_n)$. This $\phi_r(\mathbf{a})$ is expressed in terms of Jordan's generalization of Euler's -function. Two moduls **a** and **a**′ are called isomorphic if there exists a 1, 1) correspondence between the residues ρ_i of **a** and the residues ρ_i' of **a**′ uch that $\rho_i+\rho_k$ corresponds to $\rho_i'+\rho_k'$. The number of isomorphisms f **a** with itself is designated by $\chi(\mathbf{a})$. The functions ψ, ϕ, χ are studied n relation to each other and to analogous functions.

R. Dedekind[4] developed his remarks (Zahlentheorie, ed. 4, 499,

[4] *Math. Annalen*, 53, 1900. 371–403.

510, 556) that the dual group generated by three arbitrary modul **a**, **b**, **c** by the continued formation of g.c.d. (sum) of two and l.c.m (difference) consists of 28 moduls which are distinct in general.

A. Châtelet[5] employed an n-rowed square matrix $A=(a_{ij})$ whose determinant is not zero and a point $(p_1, \cdots, p_n)$ such that $p_i=\Sigma a_{ij}x$ The unique solutions $x_1, \cdots, x_n$ are called the coordinates of the point relative to A. By a modul of points is meant an aggregate of points $(p_1, \cdots, p_n), (q_1, \cdots, q_n), \cdots$ such that $(p_1 \pm q_1, \cdots, p_n \pm q_n)$ is a point of the aggregate. It is of dimension $n-k$ if there exist exactly k independent relations $\lambda_{1i}p_1+\cdots+\lambda_{ni}p_n=0$ $(i=1, \cdots, k)$ between the coordinates of each of its points. All points whose coordinates relative to A are integers form a modul of dimension n.

Let T be an n-rowed square matrix with integral elements, and the identity matrix. Let $|T-\lambda I|=0$ be an irreducible equation with the roots $\lambda_1, \cdots, \lambda_n$. The matrix having the latter as its diagonal elements and zeros elsewhere is denoted by $E=[\lambda_1, \cdots, \lambda_n]$ and called an elementary matrix. There exists a matrix A such that $T=AEA^{-1}$, $|A|\neq 0$ If also $T=BEB^{-1}$, then $A^{-1}B$ is commutative with E and hence is an elementary matrix E', whence $B=AE'$, so that B is said to be derived from A by a dilitation. Let S be any matrix of determinant $\neq 0$ which is commutative with T and write $B=SA$. Then $BEB^{-1}=STS^{-1}=T$ whence $B=AE'$, $S=AE'A^{-1}$. Hence all matrices with integral elements which are commutative with T form a group G composed of AEA^{-1}, $AE'A^{-1}, \cdots$, whose elementary matrices $E, E', \cdots$ evidently form a group. To the latter correspond points $(\lambda_1, \cdots, \lambda_n), (\lambda_1', \cdots, \lambda_n'), \cdots$ of a modul **G** simply isomorphic with G. Also **G** is simply isomorphic with the modul **M** formed of $\lambda_1, \lambda_1', \cdots$. Conversely, given any ring **M** of algbraic integers, make correspond to each number λ_1 of it the point whose coordinates are λ_1 and its conjugates $\lambda_2, \cdots, \lambda_n$. We obtain a simply isomorphic modul **G** of points $(\lambda_1, \cdots, \lambda_n)$. The latter determines a matrix $E=[\lambda_1, \cdots, \lambda_n]$ and hence also AEA^{-1}, where A is any fixed matrix. Then all the AEA^{-1} have integral elements if and only if A, apart from a dilitation, is a base of an ideal of the modul **G**. These notions are applied to prove the existence of a fundamental system of units in a ring of degree 2 or 3.

Châtelet[6] employed his preceding correspondence between each integer of a field and a matrix with integral elements to conclude that every ideal can be represented by the g.c.d. of the matrices corresponding to the numbers of the ideal.

E. Steinitz[7] considered rectangular matrices $A=(a_{ik})$, $B=(b_{ik})$

[5] *Annales sc. école norm. sup.*, (3), 28, 1911, 105–202. Cf. Châtalet, Leçons sur la théorie des nombres, Paris, 1913.

[6] *Comptes Rendus*, Paris, 154, 1912, 502–4 (159, 1913, 1386–9).

[7] *Math. Annalen*, 71, 1912, 328–354.

whose elements are integral numbers of an algebraic field R. If the number of columns of A is equal to the number of rows of B, we obtain by multiplication a matrix $C=(\sum_l a_{il}\, b_{lk})$ having as many rows as A and as many columns as B. If $B=PAQ$, B is said to be divisible by A. If also A is divisible by B, A and B are called equivalent. By the g.c.d. of several algebraic numbers is meant the ideal g.c.d. of the principal ideals defined by those numbers. The g.c.d. δ_k of the k-rowed minors of A is called the kth determinantal divisor of A. Set $\delta_k=0$ when k exceeds the number of rows or columns of A. If δ_{r+1} is the first vanishing determinantal divisor, r is called the rank of A. By Laplace's development of a determinant, δ_k divides δ_{k+1}. The ideals

$$\epsilon_1=\delta_1\ ,\ \epsilon_2=\frac{\delta_2}{\delta_1}\cdots,\ \epsilon_r=\frac{\delta_r}{\delta_{r-1}},\ \epsilon_{r+1}=0,\ \epsilon_{r+2}=0,\cdots$$

are called the elementary divisors of A. It follows at once that equivalent matrices have the same determinantal divisors and hence the same elementary divisors.

If A has m rows, n columns, and rank $r>0$, its r-rowed minors form a matrix A', the elements in each row (column) of which are formed from r fixed rows (columns) of A. Since the rows of A' are proportional, the g.c.d. of the elements of the separate rows of A' belong to a certain class κ of ideals, called the row-class of A. Similarly for the column-class of A. The main theorem is that two rectangular matrices are equivalent if and only if they have the same elementary divisors and the same row-class and the same column-class. There are auxiliary theorems on the solution of a system of linear congruences with respect to an ideal modulus.

A modul $\mathbf{A}_n$ of degree n is a system of rows each with n integral numbers of the field R such that (*i*) if σ is a row in $\mathbf{A}_n$, also the row $a\sigma$, formed of the products of the numbers of σ by an arbitrary integral number of R, is a row of $\mathbf{A}_n$; and (*ii*) the row $\sigma+\tau$ formed of the sums of corresponding numbers of two rows in $\mathbf{A}_n$ is a row of $\mathbf{A}_n$. A basis of $\mathbf{A}_n$ is a matrix A or system of m rows $\sigma_1, \cdots, \sigma_m$ of $\mathbf{A}_n$ such that every row of $\mathbf{A}_n$ is of the form $a_1\sigma_1+\cdots+a_m\sigma_m$, where the a's are integral numbers of R. This basis is called irreducible if there exists no basis of fewer than m rows. An irreducible basis of a modul $\mathbf{A}_n$ of rank r has r rows if $\mathbf{A}_n$ belongs to the principal class, otherwise $r+1$ rows.

Steinitz[8] continued his investigation on matrices. By means of further results on moduls, he proved (p. 312) that a necessary condition that matrix B be divisible by matrix A is that every elementary divisor of B be divisible by the corresponding elementary divisor of A; this condition is also sufficient if the ranks of A and B are distinct; but when

[8] *Math. Annalen*, 72, 1912, 297–345.

their ranks are both r, an additional necessary and sufficient condition is that, when δ_r and δ_r' denote the rth determinantal divisors of A and B, the (integral) ideal δ'_r/δ_r must have at least one divisor which belongs to the class (Column-class of B)/(Column-class of A). There is a long discussion of an ideal system belonging to a field R, i.e., a system of rows closed under addition and multiplication by an arbitrary integral number of R. Finally if A and B are left-equivalent m-rowed matrices of rank r, if $m>r$, and if g is an arbitrary integral number of R, there exists a matrix G of determinant g for which $B=GA$.

E. Stiemke[9] proved that a modul composed of a denumerable set of numbers has a basis if and only if each of its divisors is a modul with a finite basis.

45. Arithmetic of Hypercomplex Numbers

All numbers of any algebraic field $F(\theta)$ of degree n are linear functions of $1, \theta, \theta^2, \cdots, \theta^{n-1}$ with rational coefficients. As a generalization, we consider the linear functions (elements) with rational coefficients of the units $e_1, \cdots, e_n$ of any closed system of hypercomplex numbers (linear algebra) and study the elements called integral.

R. Lipschitz[1] called a quaternion integral if its four coordinates are rational integers. He gave a complicated theory leading to the factorization of integral quaternions into primes, but with an essential difference when the norm is a multiple of 4.

A. Hurwitz[2] made the following assumptions for a system of integral quaternions: (i) It contains only quaternions with rational coordinates. (ii) The system is closed under addition, subtraction, and multiplication. (iii) The system has a finite basis $q_1, \cdots, q_n$ such that every number of the system is expressible as $\Sigma a_i q_i$ where the a_i are rational integers. (iv) The system contains the quaternion units $1, i, j, k$. (v) The system is a maximal one, i.e., is not contained in a larger system having properties (i)-(iv). The only systems satisfying (i)-(iv) are the system of all quaternions whose four coordinates are integers and the system whose four coordinates are either all integers or all halves of odd integers. Hence the latter two types give the Hurwitz integral quaternions. All quaternion ideals are principal (so that their introduction is superfluous). Any two integral quaternions have a right-hand g.c.d. which is unique apart from one of the 24 units. Making allowance for noncommutativity, we find that the laws of factorization in arithmetic hold also here.

---

[9] *Comptes Rendus*, Paris, 157, 1913, 273–4.

[1] Untersuchungen über die Summen von Quadraten, Bonn, 1886. French transl., *Jour. de Math.*, (4), 2, 1886, 393–439.

[2] *Göttingen Nachrichten*, 1896, 311–340. Amplified in his Vorlesungen über die Zahlentheorie der Quaternionen, Berlin, 1919, 74 pp.

L. G. du Pasquier[3] called a square matrix integral if its μ^2 elements are all rational integers. Two such integral matrices have a right-hand g.c.d. if the determinant of one is not zero. Every right-hand ideal is a principal ideal.

Du Pasquier[4] extended Hurwitz's definition of integral to any system of hypercomplex numbers, requiring instead of (iv) merely that the system shall contain the principal unit 1. It is proved at length that every maximal system of integral two-rowed square matrices, not having a basis of fewer than four matrices, has a basis of the form

$$t_1=\begin{pmatrix} g_3-\dfrac{g_1g_2}{g} & \dfrac{c\epsilon}{dg} \\ \dfrac{\epsilon' dg_2}{cg} & \dfrac{g_1g_2}{g}\end{pmatrix},\ t_2=\begin{pmatrix} 0 & 0 \\ \dfrac{\epsilon' d}{c} & g_1\end{pmatrix},\ t_3=\begin{pmatrix}1 & 0\\ 0 & 1\end{pmatrix},\ t_4=\begin{pmatrix} g & 0\\ 0 & 0\end{pmatrix},$$

where $\epsilon'^2=\epsilon^2=1$, while c, d, g, g_1, g_2, g_3 are rational integers such that $cdg\neq 0$ and $(gg_1g_3-g_1^2g_2-\epsilon\epsilon')/g^2$ is an integer k (whence the determinant of t_1 is g_2k). The integral matrices need not include all having rational integral elements.

If $e_1^2=e_1$, $e_1e_2=e_2e_1=e_2$, $e_3^2=e_3$, while all further products e_ie_j are zero, every system of integral numbers $x_1e_1+x_2e_2+x_3e_3$ has a basis

$$g^2g_1e_1,\quad e_1+e_3=1,\quad gg_1g_2e_1+\gamma e_2,$$

where g, g_1, g_2 are rational integers, $g\ g_1\neq 0$, and γ is rational $\neq 0$. No one of these is maximal. A detailed study is made for the case $g=g_1=1$, $g_2=0$, $\lambda=1/p$, whence e_1, e_2/p, e_3 is a basis; there does not always exist a g.c.d.

He[5] noted that there is no maximal system of integral numbers $x+ye$, with $e^2=0$, and pointed out the failure of the laws of factorization, but did not show how they could be restored.

He[6] listed for each associative system of hypercomplex numbers in 2 or 3 units the systems of integral numbers and the maximal systems if such exist; and later[7] those in 4 units. When there exist one or more maximal systems, factorization of integral numbers into primes is always possible, though not unique, but becomes unique by introducing ideals. In the contrary case, whatever definition be taken for integral numbers, the laws of arithmetic are not restored by the introduction of ideals.

L. E. Dickson[8] gave a new theory of the arithmetic of quaternions

[3] *Vierteljahrsschrift Naturf. Gesell. Zurich*, 51, 1906, 55–129 (thesis); 52, 1907, 243–8.
[4] *Ibid.*, 54, 1909, 116–148; *l'enseignement math.*, 17, 1915, 340–3; 18, 1916, 201–260.
[5] *Nouv. Ann. Math.*, (4), 18, 1918, 448–461.
[6] *Bull. Soc. Math. France*, 48, 1920, 109–132.
[7] Comptes Rendus du Congrès International des Mathématiciens, Strasbourg, 1920 (Toulouse, 1921), 164–175.
[8] *Proc. London Math. Soc.*, (2), 20, 1921, 225–232.

in which, following Lipschitz, the integral quaternions are those whose coordinates are rational integers exclusively. Call such a quaternion odd if its norm is odd. If at least one of two integral quaterions is odd, they have a g.c.d. which is expressible as a linear combination of them. The theory of factorization into primes follows readily. For applications[9] to Diophantine equations, we readily remove the factors $1+i$, $1+j$, $1+k$, to obtain an odd quaternion and then proceed as in elementary arithmetic.

Dickson[10] proved that the integers of any system of hypercomplex numbers obtained by the definition given by either Hurwitz[2] or Du Pasquier[4] do not in general have unique factorization into primes even after the introduction of ideals of any kind. He gave a new definition which overcomes this difficulty by using the assumptions (*i*), (*ii*), (*v*) of Hurwitz, replacing (*iii*) by the assumption that the equation satisfied by the general number of the system shall have rational integral coefficients, and requiring instead of (*iv*) the presence of 1 only.

M. Kiseljak[11] obtained unimportant results for

$$(e_0=1,\ e_1,\ e_2):\ e_1^2=e_1e_2=e_2e_1=e_2^2=0.$$

He called Σa_ie_i integral if and only if a_i is a rational integer, and noted cases when decomposition into primes is not unique.

[9] Comptes Rendus du Congrès International des Mathématiciens, Strasbourg, 1920 (Toulouse, 1921), 50–52.

[10] Grundlagen einer Zahlentheorie eines speziellen Systems von komplexen Grössen mit drei Einheiten, Bonn, 1905.

[11] *Jour. de Math.*, 1923.

ALGEBRAIC NUMBERS—II

Report of the Committee on Algebraic Numbers [1]

H. S. Vandiver, *Chairman;* G. E. Wahlin

PREFACE

The National Research Council Committee on Algebraic Numbers published in February, 1923 a report [1] on algebraic numbers which aimed to cover all the literature on the theory of algebraic numbers after 1895. The committee now plans to publish from time to time reports on various topics in this subject designed to cover all the literature on those topics which has appeared since the beginning of their history. The present volume is the first of these reports. It is hoped that, ultimately, all the published chapters will be combined, after revision, into two or three volumes.

The present work is not intended as an introduction to the subjects treated. It was planned primarily for investigators who have had considerable familiarity with the theory of algebraic numbers. Naturally, much use has been made of the previously mentioned bulletin on Algebraic Numbers as well as of Dickson's History of the Theory of Numbers.

The notations of the authors quoted herein are employed in every case except when they are confusing or very cumbrous.

The committee is indebted to Professor L. J. Mordell, who has read critically all the proof sheets and through whose suggestions many obscurities have been removed.

H. S. Vandiver.

October, 1927

[1] Algebraic Numbers, National Research Council Bulletin No. 28.

CONTENTS

CHAPTER I

THE CLASS NUMBER IN AN ALGEBRAIC NUMBER FIELD

Introduction

In attempting to discover a proof of Fermat's last theorem Kummer enlarged the domain of rationality by the adjunction of roots of unity to the domain of rational numbers. In the field formed by the adjunction of a primitive cube root of unity to the rational numbers, an arithmetic similar to that of the rational numbers is possible and, due to this fact, by this method it is possible to show that the equation

$$x^3+y^3=z^3$$

has no solution in rational integers x, y, z. It therefore seems reasonable to expect that, by the adjunction of $e^{\frac{2\pi i}{l}}$, it should be possible to prove that

$$x^l+y^l=z^l$$

has no solution in rational integers. The problem is, however, much more complex in the general case and has not been settled except under certain restrictions on the exponent l.

Most of the results found by Kummer are considered in the report by Hilbert [1] and the rest will be considered later in this report in connection with the more recent discoveries.

A brief exposition of the main points in the connection between the theory of algebraic numbers and Fermat's theorem is given by Mordell.[2]

The fundamental theorem in the theory of rational numbers states that any rational integer can be resolved into the product of prime factors in one and only one way. Kummer discovered that this theorem is, in general, not true in the cyclotomic number fields. (Cf. Hensel [40] of Chapter II.) This led him to the introduction of ideal numbers and by means of prime ideal numbers he was able to establish unique factorization in the enlarged number fields.

These ideas of Kummer were later extended by Kronecker and by Dedekind who defined ideals and by means of them established unique factorization in any algebraic number field.

[1] Jahresber. Deut. Math. Ver., 4: 175-546 (1897). French translation by Levy and Got.

[2] Three Lectures on Fermat's Last Theorem. Cambridge Univ. Press, 1921.

After having defined an algebraic integer as a root of an algebraic equation with rational integral coefficients and that of the highest power of the unknown unity, let us consider the integers of a number field $K(\alpha)$. It may happen that the greatest common divisor of two integers β and γ of the field is an integer of the field or it may be an algebraic integer which does not belong to the field. In either case the totality of all integers of the field which are divisible by this greatest common divisor is an ideal of the field according to the Dedekind definition of an ideal. In the case when the greatest common divisor is an integer of the field under consideration, the ideal is called a principal ideal of the field.

When all the ideals of a field are principal ideals it is possible to develop the arithmetic of the field in a manner similar to that of the rational numbers. An example of such a field is the field of the cube roots of unity mentioned above.

In the general case many problems reduce to the consideration of the question whether or not certain ideals are principal ideals.

1. The Equivalence and Classification of Ideals

For any given ideal $\mathfrak{i}$ in an algebraic number field $K(\alpha)$ there exist in the field ideals $\mathfrak{j}$ such that each product $\mathfrak{i} \cdot \mathfrak{j}$ is a principal ideal. Two ideals $\mathfrak{i}_1$ and $\mathfrak{i}_2$ are equivalent when for the same ideal $\mathfrak{j}$ the products $\mathfrak{i}_1 \cdot \mathfrak{j}$ and $\mathfrak{i}_2 \cdot \mathfrak{j}$ are principal ideals. This equivalence shall be expressed by

$$\mathfrak{i}_1 \sim \mathfrak{i}_2.$$

The equivalence of ideals has the following properties:

(1) $\mathfrak{i} \sim \mathfrak{i}$,

(2) From $\mathfrak{i}_1 \sim \mathfrak{i}_2$ follows $\mathfrak{i}_2 \sim \mathfrak{i}_1$,

(3) From $\mathfrak{i}_1 \sim \mathfrak{i}_2$ and $\mathfrak{i}_2 \sim \mathfrak{i}_3$ follows $\mathfrak{i}_1 \sim \mathfrak{i}_3$,

(4) From $\mathfrak{i}_1 \sim \mathfrak{i}_2$ and $\mathfrak{i}_3 \sim \mathfrak{i}_4$ follows $\mathfrak{i}_1\mathfrak{i}_3 \sim \mathfrak{i}_2\mathfrak{i}_4$.

The ideals are then separated into classes as follows. All ideals equivalent to a given ideal $\mathfrak{i}$ are put in the same class and constitute the class. If $\mathfrak{i}_1$ belongs to a class C_1 and $\mathfrak{i}_2$ belongs to a class C_2 then $\mathfrak{i}_1 \cdot \mathfrak{i}_2$ belongs to a class C_3 which contains all the products of an ideal of C_1 and an ideal of C_2. We then define the multiplication of classes by saying that the class C_3 is the product of the classes C_1 and C_2.

With multiplication so defined, the classes of ideals constitute an abelian group with the class containing the principal ideals, known as the principal class, as the unit element of the group.

The totality of all ideals of a field do not constitute a group. If, however, we consider fractional ideals[3] the ideals do constitute an abelian group with the principal ideals as a sub-group. In this case the group of classes is the quotient group, and the class number, which in all cases is the number of classes, is the index of the group of principal ideals under the group of all ideals.

In each class of ideals there exists an integral ideal whose norm does not exceed $|\sqrt{d}|$, where d is the discriminant of the field. From this fact it follows that the class number is finite in any algebraic number field. This class number will be denoted by h.

The above theorem together with other theorems due to Minkowski furnish a method for the computation of the number of classes in any given field.

The determination of the general expression for the class number of an algebraic number field is one of the most interesting and also one of the most difficult problems in the theory of algebraic numbers. The following pages contain a report of the work which has been done on this problem.

Sometimes variations of the problem are considered. One such variation is that in which restricted equivalence is considered. Two ideals i_1 and i_2 are equivalent in the restricted sense when and only when an ideal j exists such that $i_1 j = (\beta)$ and $i_2 j = (\gamma)$ are principal ideals and $N(\beta)$ and $N(\gamma)$ have the same sign.

Other variations of the problem are the considerations of the classification of the ideals of a ring in an algebraic number field and such problems of equivalence as are considered by Weber and by Landau in articles mentioned in a later part of this report.

2. On the Density of Ideals in a Class and in a Field

The investigations of Dirichlet,[4] which were extended to a general algebraic number field by Dedekind, show that we can speak of the density of the ideals of a certain class and that this density is the same for all classes of a given field. This fact is expressed by the following well-known theorem:

Let $K(\alpha)$ be any algebraic number field and C any class of ideals in $K(\alpha)$. Furthermore, denote by T the number of ideals in C whose norms do not exceed t, then

$$\lim_{t\to\infty} \frac{T}{t} = \kappa$$

[3] Hecke; Vorlesungen über die Theorie der algebraischen Zahlen. Leipzig, Akad. Verlagsges., 1923.

[4] J. reine angew. Math., 19: 324-369 (1839); Werke, I, 411-461.

where κ is independent of the class C and only dependent on the field $K(a)$. The actual expression for κ is

$$\kappa = \frac{2^{r_1+r_2}\pi^{r_2}R}{w|\sqrt{d}|}$$

where r_1 is the number of real, and r_2 the number of pairs of conjugate imaginary fields among $K(a)$ and its conjugates, R is the regulator, d the discriminant and w the number of roots of unity in $K(a)$. From the form of κ it is easy to see that it is independent of the class C and only dependent on the field under consideration.

If we next let T denote the number of ideals of the field whose norms do not exceed t, we see that the last stated theorem yields the following:

$$\operatorname*{Lim}_{t \to \infty} \frac{T}{t} = h \cdot \kappa.$$

The general problem of the determination of the class number for any field has thus been reduced to the evaluation of

$$\operatorname*{Lim}_{t \to \infty} \frac{T}{t}$$

for all ideals of the field.

The evaluation of this limit leads to the well-known Dedekind zeta function which is defined by the following equation

$$\zeta_K(s) = \sum_{\mathfrak{a}} \frac{1}{N(\mathfrak{a})^s}$$

where the summation extends over all ideals $\mathfrak{a} \neq 0$ of the field. The function $\zeta_K(s)$ is a continuous function of s for all values of the real part of s greater than 1 and its relation to the class number problem is expressed by the equation

$$\operatorname*{Lim}_{s \to 1} (s-1)\zeta_K(s) = h \cdot \kappa.$$

By a ring in an algebraic number field we understand a system of integers of the field which includes the unit element and has the further property that the sum, difference, and product of any two integers in the system is an integer in the system. The classification of ideals in a ring is effected in a manner similar to that used for the field, and similar expressions for the class number relations may be developed. A treatment of this problem and the development of the relations existing between the class number of a field and that of a ring in the field is given by BACHMANN.[5]

[5] Allgemeine Arithmetik der Zahlenkörper. Leipzig, Teubner, 1905. Chap. 9.

The details of the development of the expression for the class number in a general algebraic number field in terms of the zeta function are given by DEDEKIND,[6] WEBER,[7] Hilbert,[1] Bachmann,[5] LANDAU,[8] Hecke,[3] and FUETER.[9]

In this connection may also be mentioned the theorems on the finiteness of the class number due to Minkowski.

MINKOWSKI[10] shows that in a general algebraic number field having the discriminant d, each class of ideals contains at least one ideal whose norm is less than $|\sqrt{d}|$. The proof of this theorem is included in several of the treatises on the theory of algebraic numbers.

MINKOWSKI[11] has proved the theorem that each class of ideals in a general algebraic number field contains at least one ideal whose norm is less than

$$\frac{\Gamma\left(1+\frac{n}{2}\right)}{\Gamma(\frac{1}{2})^n}\cdot\frac{2^n}{n^n}|\sqrt{d}|,$$

where n is the degree and d the discriminant of the field.

Minkowski[11] has also proved that if in an algebraic number field of degree n and discriminant d, the irreducible equation which one of its generating numbers satisfies has s pairs of imaginary roots, then in each class of ideals there is at least one ideal whose norm is less than

$$\left(\frac{4}{\pi}\right)^s\frac{n!}{n^n}|\sqrt{d}|.$$

3. THE GENERAL ZETA FUNCTION

The reduction of the expression for the class number to a finite form is dependent on the specific laws governing the factorization of the rational primes in the field considered and hence has been accomplished only in certain special cases. LANDAU[12] has studied the zeta function for a general algebraic number field and obtained a reduction in the expression for the class number, which, though it is not in finite form, is of interest in that it appears as a generalization of the corresponding expressions in the cases of the more special fields in which the problem has been studied.

[6] DIRICHLET; Vorlesungen über Zahlentheorie, Braunschweig, 1874.
[7] Algebra, 2nd Ed. Bd. 2. 1899.
[8] Algebraische Zahlen und der Ideale; Leipzig, Teubner, 1918.
[9] Synthetische Zahlentheorie; Leipzig, Teubner, 1925.
[10] J. reine angew. Math., 107: 295 (1891); Werke.
[11] Diophantische Approximationen, Leipzig, 1907.
[12] J. reine angew. Math., 127: 162-174 (1904).

Let $\zeta(s)$ be the Riemann zeta function. Then from the fact that

$$\lim_{s \to 1} (s-1)\zeta(s) = 1$$

and the relation

$$\lim_{s \to 1} (s-1)\zeta_k(s) = h \cdot \kappa$$

it follows that

$$\lim_{s \to 1} \frac{\zeta_k(s)}{\zeta(s)} = h \cdot \kappa.$$

The quotient $\zeta_k(s)/\zeta(s)$ for $s > 1$ can be developed in a Dirichlet series

$$\sum_{n=1}^{\infty} \frac{c_n}{n^s}$$

corresponding to the series

$$\sum_{n=1}^{\infty} \frac{\left(\frac{d}{n}\right)}{n^s}$$

in the theory of the quadratic number-fields. This series $\sum \frac{c_n}{n^s}$ is unique.

The possibility of such a representation follows from the relation

$$\zeta_k(s) = \sum_{n=1}^{\infty} \frac{F(n)}{n^s}$$

where $F(n)$ is the number of distinct ideals in $K(a)$ whose norms are n; and from

$$\frac{1}{\zeta(s)} = \sum_{v=1}^{\infty} \frac{\mu(v)}{v^s}$$

where $\mu(v)$ is the Möbius function. By multiplication this gives

$$\frac{\zeta_k(s)}{\zeta(s)} = \sum_{n=1}^{\infty} \sum_{v=1}^{\infty} \frac{F(n)\mu(v)}{(nv)^s}$$

$$= \sum_{n=1}^{\infty} \frac{\sum_{v/n} \mu(v) F\left(\frac{n}{v}\right)}{n^s}$$

where $\sum_{v/n}$ denotes a summation extending over all divisors v of n. Hence we have a Dirichlet series $\sum \frac{c_n}{n^s}$ in which

$$c_n = \sum_{v/n} \mu(v) F\left(\frac{n}{v}\right).$$

Since a Dirichlet series converging for $s=s_0$ is continuous for $s>s_0$ it follows that if the series

$$\sum_{n=1}^{\infty} \frac{\sum_{v/n} \mu(v) F\left(\frac{n}{v}\right)}{n^s}$$

converges for $s \to 1$ then

$$h \cdot \kappa = \sum_{n=1}^{\infty} \frac{\sum_{v/n} \mu(v) F\left(\frac{n}{v}\right)}{n}. \tag{1}$$

Landau[12] shows that this convergence condition is fulfilled and hence the equation (1) gives an expression for the class number in terms of an infinite series.

4. Quadratic Fields

Dedekind[6] uses the quadratic number field as an example for the illustration of his general theory and develops an expression for the class number of such fields. A finite expression for the class number for quadratic fields is given by Hilbert.[1]

Sommer[13] gives a proof of the theorem: If the discriminant of a quadratic field contains only one prime factor, the class number is odd.

If we consider an imaginary quadratic field $k(\sqrt{-m})$ having the discriminant d and the class number $h(d)$, Landau[14] has shown that if the inequality

$$h(d) < d^{\frac{1}{2}-\delta}$$

has an infinite number of solutions for some positive δ, then, for each positive w, after a certain number of fields, the discriminants d_1 and d_2 of any two successive fields satisfy the inequality

$$|d_2| > |d_1|^w.$$

In the proof of this fact he uses, besides the series

$$L_1(s) = \sum_{n=1}^{\infty} \frac{X_1(n)}{n^s}; \qquad X_1(n) = \left(\frac{d_1}{n}\right);$$

and

$$L_2(s) = \sum_{n=1}^{\infty} \frac{X_2(n)}{n^s}; \qquad X_2(n) = \left(\frac{d_2}{n}\right);$$

also

$$L_3(s) = \sum_{n=1}^{\infty} \frac{X_1(n) X_2(n)}{n^s}.$$

[13] Vorlesungen über Zahlentheorie, Leipzig u. Berlin, 1907.
[14] Göttingen Nachr., Math. Phys. Kl., 1918: 277-284.

LANDAU[15] has also shown that when for an imaginary quadratic field $k(\sqrt{-m})$ the function $\zeta_k(s)$ has no zeros in the region $\frac{1}{2}<s<1$ then the class number for the field is at least $|\sqrt{d}|/\log|d|$, and from this he deduces the fact that for each positive w there exists a c such that, from a certain point on, any two successive solutions d_1 and d_2 of

$$h(d)<c\frac{|\sqrt{d}|}{\log|d|}$$

will also satisfy the inequality

$$|d_2|>|d_1|^w.$$

LANDAU[16] has also developed expressions for the upper and lowe bounds for the class number of an imaginary quadratic field. Let $s=\sigma+\tau$ be the variable in $\zeta(s)$.

I. If $\zeta(s)\neq 0$ for $\sigma>\frac{1}{2}$ or also only for $|s-1|\leqq\theta$ where θ is free fron m, then for $m>e^e$ there exist positive constants b_3 and b_4, dependent onl on θ, such that

$$b_3\frac{\sqrt{m}}{\log\log m\cdot\log\log\log m}<h<b_4\sqrt{m}\log\log m\cdot\log\log\log m.$$

II. If $L(s)\neq 0$ for $\frac{1}{2}\leqq\sigma<1$, $|\tau|<3$ then

$$h<e^{a_2\log^{a_3}m}$$

where a_2 and a_3 are positive absolute constants and $a_3<1$.

For a method of determining the class number of a quadratic fiel without the use of the zeta function, see Hecke.[3]

5. CUBIC FIELDS

DEDEKIND[17] has made an exhaustive study of the cubic fields define by a binomial equation. He determines the laws of factorization of th rational primes in such a field and applies them in making the necessar reductions in the zeta function.

Any cubic field defined by a binomial equation can be considered defined by an equation of the form

$$x^3-ab^2=0$$

where a and b are relatively prime and neither is divisible by the squa of a rational prime. Two types of fields present themselves for consider tion. I, in which $a^2-b^2\not\equiv 0$ mod 9; and II, in which $a^2-b^2\equiv 0$ mod

[15] Göttingen Nachr., Math.-Physik. Kl., 1918: 285-295.

[16] Math. Annalen, 79: 388-401 (1918).

[17] J. reine angew. Math., 121: 40-121 (1900).

If k be used to denote $3ab$ for fields of type I and ab for fields of type II, then the field discriminant is $3k^2$ and the class invariant

$$\kappa = \frac{2\pi \log \epsilon}{k\sqrt{3}}$$

where ϵ is the fundamental unit. For the study of the zeta function for these fields Dedekind uses the expression of the function as an infinite product

$$\zeta(s) = \prod_{\mathfrak{p}} \frac{1}{1 - \frac{1}{N(\mathfrak{p})^s}}$$

the product extending over all prime ideals of the field.

For the determination of the laws of factorization and their application, a consideration of the quadratic fields defined by a primitive cube root of unity becomes necessary. This leads to the definition of the character of the prime ideals $\psi(\mathfrak{p})$ as follows:

(a) $\psi(\mathfrak{p}) = 0$ if $\mathfrak{p}$ is a factor of k,
(b) $\psi(\mathfrak{p}) = 1$ if $\mathfrak{p}$ is a factor of 3 but not of k,

and for all other prime ideals

(c) $$\psi(\mathfrak{p}) = \left(\frac{ab^2}{\mathfrak{p}}\right)_3$$

where $\left(\frac{ab^2}{\mathfrak{p}}\right)_3$ is a cube root of unity and is the cubic residue character of ab^2 with respect to the modulus $\mathfrak{p}$.

Let $F(p)$ denote that part of the infinite product for which the prime ideals are factors of the rational prime p. We may then write

$$\zeta(s) = \prod_p F(p),$$

the product extending over all rational primes. Moreover, using the character $\psi(\mathfrak{p})$ defined, it may be shown that

$$F(p) = \frac{1}{1 - \frac{1}{p^s}} \cdot \prod_{\mathfrak{p}} \frac{1}{1 - \frac{\psi(\mathfrak{p})}{N(\mathfrak{p})^s}}$$

the product now extending over all ideal prime factors of p.

If v is an algebraic integer of the field of the cube roots of unity and x any rational integer, then all algebraic integers of this field which for some x are congruent to xv with respect to the modulus k constitute a modul k_v. These moduls are of three types according as in $\psi(v) = \rho^i$, the exponent i, is 0, 1, or 2. We can speak of these as types 0, 1, and 2. For each modul select a base (α_j, β_j), the subscript being used to denote the type, and put $w_j = \frac{\alpha_j}{\beta_j}$ and denote its conjugate by w'_j.

Further

$$\eta(w_j) = e^{\frac{\pi i w_j}{12}} \prod_{n=1}^{\infty} (1 - e^{2\pi i w_j n})$$

and

$$H(w_j) = \eta(w_j)\eta(-w'_j)\sqrt{i(w'_j - w_j)};$$

and then

$$\epsilon^h = \frac{\Pi H(w_1)}{\Pi H(w_0)}$$

where the two products extend over all moduls of the types indicated by the subscripts.

By using Minkowski's [11] theorem that in every class of ideals there exists an ideal j satisfying the condition

$$(2) \qquad N(j) < \left(\frac{4}{\pi}\right)^r \frac{n!}{n^n} |\sqrt{d}|$$

where n is the degree of the field and r the number of imaginaries among the n conjugate fields, REID [18] discusses the computation of the class number for a general cubic field. He determines the least exponent t such that j^t is a principal ideal. If C is the class containing j, he forms the classes $C, C^2, C^3, \ldots C^t$ and determines whether or not all ideals satisfying the condition (2) belong to the classes thus found. If such is not the case, he forms new classes in the same way until all have been determined. The article concludes with two tables. Table I lists 172 cubic fields defined by equations of the form $x^3 + ax + b = 0$ and Table II, all fields defined by equations of the form $A_0x^3 + A_1x^2 + A_2x + A_3 = 0$, all coefficients having absolute values less than 3. For each field listed he gives the discriminant of the equation, the discriminant of the field, the class number, a base, units and the factors of some rational primes.

WESTLUND [19] considers the cubic sub-fields of the cyclotomic fields $K(e^{\frac{2\pi i}{p}})$ defined by the $\frac{p-1}{3}$ term periods, where p is a prime congruent to 1 mod. 3. The equation for the three periods is of the form [20]

$$x^3 + x^2 - \frac{p-1}{3}x - \frac{3p-1+pA}{27} = 0$$

$$A^2 + 27B^2 = 4p.$$

[18] Am. J. Math., 23: 68-83 (1909). Göttingen Dissertation.
[19] Jahresber. Deut. Math. Ver., 22: 135-140 (1913).
[20] WEBER's Algebra, 2nd Ed., Bd. 1: 629.

1 is defined by

$$\sum_{t=1}^{p-2} \rho^{\operatorname{ind}(t^2+t)} = \frac{A+b\sqrt{-3}}{2}, \qquad \rho = \frac{-1+\sqrt{-3}}{2}.$$

He gives the laws of factorization for these fields and at the end gives a table of all primes which enter into the determination of the class number for all p from 7 to 97.

Reid [18] and Westlund [19] do not make use of the general formula or the zeta function.

6. Cyclotomic Fields

A large part of the work connected with the class number has been devoted to the cyclotomic fields. Hilbert's report [1] contains an account of the work up to 1895. Attention may here be called to an error noted by Mitchell [28] in the finite expression for the class number as given by Hilbert.[1]

The class number problem arose in the early investigations of the arithmetic theory of the cyclotomic fields. Kummer,[21, 22] following suggestions taken from the methods of Dirichlet in his investigation of quadratic forms, develops the general expression for the class number of the cyclotomic fields generated by the lth root of unity, l being a prime. The same problem is also solved in Hilbert,[1] Dedekind,[6] Weber,[7] Fueter,[9] and Got.[23]

The general expression for the class number of the field of the primitive nth roots of unity (n composite) was found by Kummer.[24]

If ξ is a primitive nth root of unity, and $f(\xi)$ a polynomial such that $f(\xi^\kappa) = f(\xi)$ for some κ prime to n, then $f(\xi)$ generates a subfield of $K(\xi)$. Fuchs [25] has made a study of these subfields and computed an expression for their class number.

The class number of subfields of the fields of the roots of unity has also been studied by Weber.[7] Weber [7, 26] contains the investigation of the 2^mth roots of unity and shows that in this case the class number is odd.

The works of Kummer on the class number are reported in H. J. S. Smith.[27]

[21] J. reine angew. Math., 40: 93-116 (1850).
[22] J. de Math., 16: 377-488 (1850).
[23] Annales de la Faculté de Toulouse, Sec. 3, 3: 17-20 (1911).
[24] Monatsberichte, Berlin, 1863: 21-28.
[25] J. reine angew. Math., 65: 74-111 (1866).
[26] Acta Math., 8: 193-263 (1886).
[27] Report on the Theory of Numbers, part II, § 50. Collected Mathematical Papers. 1: 112-114. Report of the British Ass'n, Part II, 1860: 134-136.
[28] Bull. Nat. Research Council, No. 28: 17 (1923).

The following theorem is due to Kummer.[21] If K_1 and K_2 are two subfields of the field of the primitive lth roots of unity, l a prime, and K_1 is a subfield of K_2 then the class number of K_1 is a factor of the class number of K_2. Hilbert[1] has called attention to the fact that there is an error in Kummer's proof of this theorem.

Furtwängler[29] gives a proof of the following theorem which is easily seen to include that of Kummer[21] as a special case.

If K_1 and K_2 are two subfields of the field of the nth roots of unity where n is a power of a single prime, and if K_1 is a subfield of K_2 then the class number of K_1 is a divisor of the class number of K_2.

In the proof two cases are considered. First, let p be a rational prime which is not a factor of the relative degree of K_2 with respect to K_1. It is then seen that p must occur in the class number of K_2 with an exponent at least as great as its exponent in the class number of K_1.

Next, if p is a divisor of the relative degree it is seen that a reduction in the power of p in the class number in passing from K_1 to K_2 is possible only when between K_1 and K_2 there are two fields K'_1 and K'_2 such that K'_2 is relative cyclic with respect to K'_1 and has the relative discriminant ± 1. This is seen to be impossible since, by a known theorem regarding the factorization of prime ideals in cyclotomic fields, the relative discriminant contains at least one prime.

By an example it is shown that the theorem is not in general true when m is not the power of a single prime.

Westlund[30] has investigated the relation between the class number of $K(r)$, $(r = e^{\frac{2\pi i}{p^n}})$, and $K(r')$, $(r' = e^{\frac{2\pi i}{p^{n-1}}})$, p being an odd rational prime. The method used is similar to that of Weber[7] for $p=2$. Denote by h and h' the class numbers of $K(r)$ and $K(r')$ respectively and let h_2 be the class number of $K(r+r^{-1})$ and h'_2 that of $K(r'+r'^{-1})$. We may then write $h=h_1h_2$ and $h'=h'_1h'_2$, $h_1=h'_1A$, $h_2=h'_2B$ and $h=h'E$. The numbers h_1 and h_2 are known as the first and second factors of the class number of $K(r)$ and h'_1 and h'_2 as the first and second factors of the class number of $K(r')$.

Westlund (*l. c.*) develops expressions for A and B following the method used by Weber and shows that A is an integer and that B has the form $p^{-\sigma}I$ where I is an integer dependent on the regulator of a fundamental system of normal units. A unit in $K(r+r^{-1})$ which is not ± 1 and whose norm relative to $K(r'+r'^{-1})$ is ± 1 is a normal unit.

[29] J. reine angew. Math., 134: 91-94 (1908).
[30] Trans. Am. Math. Soc., 4: 201-212 (1903).

Whether or not A and I are divisible by p and what is the value of σ remains unsettled. Cf. Vandiver.[41]

Weber[7, 26] as already noted, has proved that the class number of the field of the 2^mth roots of unity is odd. This has been generalized by Furtwängler[31] who proves that if l is an arbitrary prime number, then the class number of the field of the l^nth roots of unity is divisible by l when and only when l is a factor of the class number of the field of the lth roots of unity. Cf. Furtwängler[49] of Chapter II.

If the class number of the field of the lth roots of unity is divisible by l then the first factor h_1 of the class number is divisible by l, but the second factor h_2 is not necessarily divisible by l. The only cases of $l<100$ for which h is divisible by l are $l=37$, 59, and 67 and in none of these cases is the second factor divisible by l. Cf. Kummer.[32]

Kummer[21, 22] shows that in the fields of the lth roots of unity, l being a prime, the first and second factors of the class number are integers. Kummer[22] contains a table of values of the first factor for all primes less than 100. Without proof Kummer[22] also gives the following asymptotic value for the first factor of the class number

$$\frac{l^{\frac{l+3}{4}}}{2^{\frac{l-3}{2}}\pi^{\frac{l-1}{2}}}.$$

The latter part of Kummer[22] is devoted to a consideration of the class number for $l=37$, 59, 67. These are the only primes less than 100 whose class number is divisible by l.

Kummer[21] also has shown that the first factor of the class number is divisible by l when l is a factor of the numerator of one of the first $\dfrac{l-3}{2}$ Bernoulli numbers.

Kummer[33] gives a table of values of the first factor of the class number for all n from 2 to 100. In this it appears that the first factor is not necessarily integral when n is composite. Kronecker[34] shows that 2 is the only number which can occur as a denominator of the first factor.

Let g be a primitive number with respect to the modulus l and denote by g_σ the least positive residue of g^σ. The cyclotomic units $e_\sigma(r)$, $\sigma=0, 1, 2\ldots, \mu-1$, $\mu=\dfrac{l-1}{2}$; $r=e^{\frac{2\pi i}{l}}$, are defined by the equation

$$e_\sigma(r)=\frac{r^{g_{\sigma+1}}-r^{-g_{\sigma+1}}}{r^{g_\sigma}-r^{-g_\sigma}}.$$

[31] J. reine angew. Math., 140: 29-32 (1911).
[32] J. reine angew. Math., 40: 117 (1850).
[33] Monatsberichte, Berlin, 1861: 1051-1053.
[34] Werke, Bd. 1: 125.

Put $c_\sigma = 0$ when e_σ is positive, and $c_\sigma = 1$ when e_σ is negative, and let w be a primitive μth root of unity. Put

$$\psi(w) = c_0 + c_1 w + c_2 w^2 + \ldots + c_{\mu-1} w^{\mu-1}$$

and

$$\Psi(w) = w^{\rho} \sum_{i=1}^{\frac{q-1}{2}} \frac{1}{i} \left(w^{\mathrm{ind}(v_i-1)} + w^{\mathrm{ind}(v_i-3)} + \ldots\right).$$

Here q is a prime and $\rho = \mathrm{ind}\; q$.

$$v_i = \left|\frac{q-2i}{q}\right|$$

where the symbol $\left|\frac{a}{b}\right|$ is used to denote the least positive solution of the congruence

$$bx \equiv a \bmod l.$$

KUMMER[35] proves the following theorems:

I. For all those primes l for which the first factor of the class number of $k(e^{\frac{2\pi i}{l}})$ is not divisible by 2 all real units which, with their conjugates, are positive are the squares of units.

II. The second factor of the class number is not divisible by 2 when the first factor is prime to 2.

III. If the second factor of the class number is divisible by 2 then $\psi(w)$ and $\psi(w^{-1})$ are divisible by the same factors of 2.

IV. The odd prime q is not a factor of the class number if $\Psi(w)$ is relatively prime to q.

Using the method of KRONECKER,[36] MIRIMANOFF[37] develops a new criterion for the divisibility of the second factor of the class number of $K(e^{\frac{2\pi i}{l}})$ by l.

If we suppose that $h_1 = q_1 l^{t_1}$ and $h_2 = q_2 l^{t_2}$ and that C is any class of ideals in the field $K(r + r^{-1})$, $(r = e^{\frac{2\pi i}{l}})$ and consider the q_2th power of C expressed by means of the base of the abelian group of all q_2th powers of the classes in $K(r + r^{-1})$ then

$$C^{q_2} \sim C_1^{x_1} C_2^{x_2} \ldots C_e^{x_0} \qquad 0 \leqq x_i < l^{b_i}.$$

The classes of $K(r)$ whose ideals have relative norms with respect to $K(r + r^{-1})$ which belong to the principal class of this field constitute a group of order h_1 and if $\overline{C}$ is any class of this group

$$\overline{C}^{q_2} \backsim \overline{C}_1^{y_1} \overline{C}_2^{y_2} \cdot \ldots \cdot \overline{C}_{e_1}^{y_{e_1}} \qquad 0 \leqq y_i < l^{\overline{b}_i}.$$

[35] Monatsbericht Kgl. Preuss. Akad., 1870: 855-880.

[36] J. reine angew. Math., 93: 1-52 (1882).

[37] J. reine angew. Math., 109: 82-88 (1892).

HECKE[38] has studied these class groups. By means of FURTWÄNGLER'S[39] general existence proof for class fields, he shows that there are at least e independent classes $A_1, A_2, \ldots, A_e$ such that their l^{th} powers and their relative norms are in the principal class of $K(r+r^{-1})$ and no equivalence

$$A_1^{m_1}A_2^{m_2}\ldots A_e^{m_e}\sim C$$

exists where C is a class in $K(r+r^{-1})$ if $m_1, m_2, \ldots, m_e$ are not divisible by l. The group with the base $\overline{C}_1, \overline{C}_2 \ldots, \overline{C}_e$ is the largest such group and hence $e_1 \geqq e$. If $e_1=0$, $e=0$ and from this is obtained another proof of Kummer's theorem that the second factor of the class number is divisible by l only when the first factor is divisible by l.

VANDIVER[40] has determined the residue of the first factor of the class number of $K(e^{\frac{2\pi i}{l}})$ with respect to the modulus l^b.

$$h_1 \equiv \frac{\prod_{s=1}^{l-2} l(-1)^{(sl^b-1)/2}B_{(sl^b+1)/2}}{2^{\frac{1}{2}(l-3)}} \mod l^b$$

where B_i is the ith Bernoulli number.

If h_1 is the first factor of the class number of $K(e^{\frac{2\pi i}{l^m}})$ and h'_1 that of $K(e^{\frac{2\pi i}{l^{m-1}}})$ and if $a=\frac{h}{h'_1}$ VANDIVER[41] shows that

$$a \equiv [\prod_{i=1}^{\frac{l-3}{2}} B_i]^{l^{m-2}(l-1)} \mod l$$

and makes application to Fermat's last theorem.

WOLFSKEHL[42] shows that if ξ is a primitive l^{th} root of unity and $\eta_0, \eta_1, \ldots, \eta_{e-1}$ the e periods of f terms and if i_1 is any ideal of $k(\eta)$ then there exists an ideal i_2 such that $i_1 \cdot i_2$ is a principal ideal and $N(i_2) \leqq l^{\frac{l}{2}}$. From this it is then shown that in the fields of the 11th and 13th roots of unity the first factor of the class number is 1.

Minkowski[10] has shown that in the fields of the 17th and 19th roots of unity the second factor of the class number is equal to one.

[38] Göttingen Nachr., Math. Phys. Kl., 1910: 420-424.
[39] Math. Ann., 63: 1-37 (1906).
[40] Bull. Am. Math. Soc., 25: 458-461 (1919).
[41] Proc. Natl. Acad. Sci., 6: 416-421 (1920).
[42] J. reine angew. Math., 99: 173-178 (1886).

Let p and l be two primes such that $p-1$ is divisible by l. Then the field $K(e^{\frac{2\pi i}{p}})$ contains a cyclic subfield of degree l, and its discriminant contains only one prime p. The class invariant κ for this cyclic field is

$$\frac{2^{l-1}}{p^{\frac{l-1}{2}}}\cdot R,$$

where R is the regulator.

This field is the only cyclic field of degree l having p as the only divisor of its discriminant. FUETER[43] has determined the laws of factorization of the rational primes in this field and the finite expression for the class number.

Since the field is cyclic and p is the only prime in its discriminant, p is the lth power of a prime ideal and every other prime is either prime or the product of l distinct primes in the field.

Let ξ be a primitive l^{th} root of unity and g a primitive root of p. Then every integer n which is not divisible by p is congruent to $g^{\text{ind } n}$. If we now set

$$\left(\frac{n}{p}\right)_l=\xi^{\text{ind } n} \qquad \text{if } n\not\equiv 0 \bmod p,$$

$$\left(\frac{n}{p}\right)_l=0 \qquad \text{if } n\equiv 0 \bmod p,$$

then every rational prime q is, in the cyclic subfield, the product of l distinct primes or is itself a prime according as $\left(\frac{q}{p}\right)_l$ is or is not equal to 1.

The following theorem is a generalization of one due to Kummer.

If $f(x)=\sum_{m=1}^{\infty} a_m \cos mx \qquad 0<x<2\pi$

is an absolutely convergent series, then for $n=1, 2, 3, \ldots, l-1$

$$\sum_{\sigma=1}^{p-1}\left(\frac{\sigma}{p}\right)_l^n f\left(\frac{2\pi\sigma}{p}\right)=\Lambda_n\sum_{m=1}^{\infty} a_m\left(\frac{m}{p}\right)_l^{l-n}$$

where

$$\Lambda_n=\sum_{\nu=0}^{p-2}\xi^{\nu n}Z^{g^\nu}$$

$Z=e^{\frac{2\pi i}{p}}$.

By this theorem it is found possible to evaluate

$$\lim_{s\to 1}(s-1)\zeta(s)$$

[43] J. reine angew. Math., 147: 174-183 (1917).

and hence determine the class number for this field. The final form of the result is

$$h=\frac{\Delta}{R}$$

where R is the regulator and

$$\Delta=(-1)^{\frac{l-1}{2}}\begin{vmatrix} lg\, e_1, & lg\, e_2, \ldots & lg\, e_{l-1} \\ lg\, e_2, & lg\, e_3, \ldots & lg\, e_l \\ \cdots & \cdots & \cdots \\ lg\, e_{l-1}, & \ldots\ldots & lg\, e_{l-3} \end{vmatrix}$$

e_i being the relative norm in the cyclic subfield of the unit

$$\frac{(Z^{g^i}-1)(Z^{-g^i}-1)}{(Z^{g^{i-1}}-1)(Z^{-g^{i-1}}-1)},$$

and $lg\, e_i=\log|e_i|$.

Hilbert[1] calls attention to the fact that KRONECKER[44] made an error in his attempt to establish some of Kummer's results by arithmetic means.

7. RELATIVE ABELIAN FIELDS

Every relative abelian field which forms an absolute Galois field with respect to an imaginary quadratic field $K(\sqrt{m})$ is obtained by the adjunction of $e^{2\pi i z}$ and $j(w)$ where z is a rational number, w a number of the imaginary quadratic field and $j(w)$ the complete invariant of the modular function.

FUETER[45] [46] has made a study of the class number for such fields.

$K(\sqrt{m})$ is an imaginary quadratic field. Let f be a rational integer whose separation into rational prime factors is given by the equation

$$f=l_1^{r_1}l_2^{r_2}\ldots l_n^{r_n}.$$

All numbers of $K(\sqrt{m})$ which satisfy the condition

$$a\equiv 1 \bmod f$$

constitute a number ray whose conductor is f. A ray ideal consists of all those numbers of a field ideal, prime to f, which belong to the ray. Two ray ideals i_1 and i_2 are said to be equivalent in the restricted sense when $i_1=ai_2$ where a is a number of the ray. Two ray ideals i_1 and i_2 are said to be equivalent in the wider sense if $i_1=ai_2$ and for each power l^r of a prime factor of f there exists in $K(\sqrt{m})$ a unit e such that $ea\equiv 1 \bmod l^r$. Ray ideals which are equivalent belong to the same class.

[44] Werke, Bd. 1: 276.
[45] Göttingen Nachr. Math. Phys. Kl., 1907: 288-298.
[46] Rendiconti Circolo Matematico di Palermo, 29: 380-395 (1910).

Equivalence as above defined is spoken of as equivalence with respect to the modulus f.

All numbers of $K(\sqrt{m})$ which, with respect to the modulus f, are congruent to rational numbers constitute a ring with the conductor f.

As above, by a ring ideal is meant all the numbers of a field ideal, relatively prime to f, which belong to the ring. Two ring ideals i_1 and i_2 are equivalent or belong to the same class when $i_1 = \alpha i_2$ and α is a number of the ring.

The norms of all field ideals belonging to the same class can be represented by a quadratic form

$$F = AX^2 + BXY + CY^2$$

where X and Y vary over all rational integers.

Fueter's first problem is that of the determination of the restrictions which must be imposed on X and Y in order that the numbers represented by the quadratic form shall be the norms of the ideals of a ray class or a ring class. This problem is solved and is expressed by the theorem: Let d be the negative discriminant of $K(\sqrt{m})$ and let us consider all ideals i_1 such that $i_1 = \alpha i$,

$$\alpha \equiv \frac{a + b\sqrt{d}}{2} \bmod f, \qquad 0 < a < f, \qquad 0 \leqq b < f$$

then F gives the norms of all ideals i_1, when

$$X = \frac{a + bB}{2} + f \cdot x, \qquad Y = -Ab - f \cdot y$$

and x and y vary over all rational integers.

Each norm is represented once if $f \neq 2$ and twice if $f = 2$.

The evaluation of $\sum \frac{1}{F^s}$ where the summation extends over all values of x and y leads to a generalization of a formula due to Kronecker.

By setting $b = 0$ we obtain an expression for $\sum_i \frac{1}{N(i)}$ where the summation extends over all ideals of a ring class or a ray class.

As has already been noted above, the abelian field relative to an imaginary quadratic field consists of cyclotomic fields and fields of complex multiplication. To each such field there corresponds in $K(\sqrt{m})$ a ring or a ray according as this field is the complex multiplication field or this field together with a cyclotomic field. The conductor is obtained from the primes in the relative discriminant and the relation between the ring or ray with equivalence in the wider sense is expressed by the theorem.

For all prime ideals of the same ring class or ray class we have the same factorization law in the super field.

Having thus determined the laws of factorization the author evaluates

$$\lim_{s \to 1} (s-1)\zeta_k(s)$$

and obtains a finite expression for the number of classes.

HECKE[47] shows that if K_1 is a field which is relative cyclic of degree l with respect to K_2 and has a relative discriminant which is prime to l and if H and h are the class numbers of K_1 and K_2 respectively, then H/h can be expressed by the logarithm of a certain transcendental function. By taking K_2 as the field of rational numbers he obtains the theorem: The class number of each solvable field whose discriminant is relative prime to its degree can be expressed as an integral of the logarithm of a transcendental function similar to the expression obtained by Kummer for cyclotomic fields by means of logarithms of cyclotomic units.

In a later work HECKE[48] states the theorem: If K is a totally real field (by a totally real field is meant one which with all its conjugates is real) and δ is a totally negative number of K then $\sqrt{\delta}$ generates an imaginary relative quadratic field K_1 and if H and h are the class numbers of K_1 and K respectively then H/h can be expressed as an elementary arithmetic function of δ. The proof of the theorem is given for the case when K is a quadratic field.

The case when K is a totally real cubic field has been studied by REIDEMEISTER[49] who obtains an expression similar to that obtained by Hecke.

Let $Q(\mathfrak{p})=0$ when $\mathfrak{p}$ is a divisor of δ, and $Q(\mathfrak{p})=\left(\frac{\delta^*}{\mathfrak{p}}\right)$ where $\mathfrak{p}$ and δ are relatively prime and δ^* is δ times the square of an integer of K, $\left(\frac{\delta^*}{\mathfrak{p}}\right)$ being the quadratic residue symbol. Furthermore, if

$$\mathfrak{a}=\mathfrak{p}_1^{a_1}\cdot\mathfrak{p}_2^{a_2}\cdots\mathfrak{p}_r^{a_r}$$

$$Q(\mathfrak{a})=Q(\mathfrak{p}_1)^{a_1}\cdot Q(\mathfrak{p}_2)^{a_2}\cdots Q(\mathfrak{p}_r)^{a_r}$$

and

$$L(S,Q)=\sum_j \frac{Q(j)}{N(j)^s}$$

[47] Verhandlungen der Naturforschendengesellschaft in Basel, 28: 365-372 (1917).
[48] Göttingen Nachr. Math: Phys. Kl., 1921: 1-23.
[49] Abh. aus d. Math. Sem. Hamburg., 1921: 27-48.

where the summation extends over all ideals of K, then

$$\frac{H}{h}=\frac{\kappa}{\kappa_1}L(1,Q)$$

where

$$\kappa_1=\frac{2^3\pi^3R(K_1)}{W|\sqrt{d^2N(\Delta)}|}$$

and

$$\kappa=\frac{4R(K)}{|\sqrt{d}|}.$$

Here W is the number of roots of unity in K_1, $R(K_1)$ and $R(K)$ the regulators of K_1 and K respectively, $N(\Delta)$ the norm of the relative discriminant of K_1, taken as an ideal in K, and d the discriminant of K.

8. The Distribution of the Prime Ideals in the Classes

One of the interesting problems connected with the classification of ideals is that of the distribution of the prime ideals in the classes. This problem has been investigated by Landau.[50] If an algebraic number field K has the property that the sum $\sum \frac{1}{N(\mathfrak{p})}$ extending over all prime ideals of the principal class (classification in the restricted sense) diverges, and if $P(t)$ is the number of prime ideals of a given class whose norms do not exceed t, and m a certain real number, then

$$\lim_{t\to\infty}\frac{\log^m t}{t}\left(P(t)-\frac{1}{h}\int_2^t\frac{du}{u}\right)=0.$$

From this it follows that asymptotically the number of prime ideals in a given class is independent of the class.

The same problem is considered by Landau[51] in connection with the problem of the primes in an arithmetic progression. The fact expressed by the last theorem may also be expressed by the equation

$$P(t)=\frac{1}{h}\int_2^t\frac{du}{u}+O(te^{-\sqrt[d]{\log t}})$$

where by $O[g(x)]$ is meant a function having the property that for all x greater than some ξ the quotient $|O[g(x)]/g(x)$ is limited. Landau[51] shows that $d>8$. See also Hecke.[52]

[50] Math. Ann., 63: 145-204 (1907).
[51] Sitzungsberichte Wien, 117: IIa, 1095-1107 (1908).
[52] Göttingen Nachr. Math. Phys. Kl., 1917: 299-318.

Another theorem proved by Landau [35] is the following: If K is a field such that the sum $\sum \frac{1}{N(\mathfrak{p})}$ diverges, and $R(t)$ is the number of ideals having an odd number of prime factors, and $S(t)$ the number of ideals having an even number of prime factors, and in each case norms not exceeding t, then

$$\lim_{t \to \infty} \frac{R(t)}{S(t)} = 1.$$

If $H(t, C)$ is the number of ideals in the class C whose norms do not exceed t, then

$$H(t, C) = at + O(t^{\theta})$$

where a is a positive constant dependent only on the field, and $\theta = n/(n+2)$ where n is the degree of the field.

A system S of numbers of an algebraic number field constitutes an ideal if with α and β also $\lambda\alpha + \mu\beta$ belongs to S when λ and μ are integers of the field and when there exists a fixed number $v \neq 0$ such that the product of v by any number of S is an algebraic integer. By this definition α and β are not necessarily integers and if α and β are fractions we have a fractional ideal. Hecke [36] proves the following generalization of Dirichlet's theorem regarding the primes in an arithmetic progression.

If f is an ideal of an algebraic number field, and r an arbitrary ideal prime to f, then in the class to which $\frac{1}{r}$ belongs there is an infinite number of prime ideals $\mathfrak{p}$ such that in the principal ideal $(\xi) = \mathfrak{p} \cdot r$ ξ is congruent to a unit mod f.

A further study of the distribution of the prime ideals in the classes is given by LANDAU [53] in connection with the study of the zeta function.

For further developments see LANDAU.[54]

In a series of three articles WEBER [55] has studied groups of numbers and ideals of a group. Two ideals i_1 and i_2 of a group O are said to be equivalent with respect to a subgroup O', if $i_1 = i' i_2$ where i' is an ideal of O'. (Same definition as "ray," cf. FUETER.[55a]) The class number is the index of O' under O. He shows that under certain assumptions regarding the groups each class must contain an infinite number of prime ideals.

[53] Math. Zeitschrift, 2: 52-154 (1918).

[54] Einführung in die elementare und analytische Theorie der algebraischen Zahlen und der Ideale. Berlin, Teubner, 1918.

[55] Math. Ann., 48: 433-473 (1896); 49: 83-100 (1897); 50: 1-26 (1897).

[55a] Jahresber. Deut. Math. Verein, 20: 1-47 (1911).

Landau [50] has developed other theorems regarding this generalized idea of classification. He shows that if $P(t)$ is the number of prime ideals with norms not exceeding t in each class, then

$$P(t)=\frac{1}{h}\int_2^t \frac{du}{\log u}+O(te^{-\sqrt[4]{\log t}})$$

and further, that if $R(t)$ is the number of ideals with norms not exceeding t and having an odd number of prime factors, and $S(t)$ the number of ideals with norms not exceeding t and having an even number of prime factors, then

$$\lim_{t\to\infty}\frac{R(t)}{S(t)}=1.$$

Landau makes the same assumptions regarding the groups and fields as does Weber.

Based on the general existence proof for class fields and the method of Weber,[55] FURTWÄNGLER [56] arrives at the theorem: If $\mathfrak{p}_i$ varies over all the prime ideals of a class in a field whose class number is h, then

$$\sum_{\mathfrak{p}_i}\frac{1}{N(\mathfrak{p}_i)^s}=\frac{1}{h}\log\frac{1}{s-1}+f(s)$$

where $f(s)$ is a function of the real variable s which remains finite as s approaches 1.

Ideas similar to those of Weber [55] are used by Fueter.[9, 45, 46]

9. Special Problems

Following an article by Reuschle on the factors of rational primes in certain cyclotomic fields, KUMMER [57] discusses the distribution of the factors of rational primes among the 8 classes of the field of the 29th roots of unity. The ideals are not principal ideals and hence do not belong to the principal class. He finds that each of the other seven classes contains four of the 28 conjugate prime ideals and in the same class are found those four whose corresponding roots of $x^{29}-1=0$ have their sum equal to a period of four terms. In this field the square of any ideal is a principal ideal.

For the field of the 31st roots of unity the first factor of the class number is 9. Reuschle has computed the 9th powers of the ideal factors of 2 and found them to be principal ideals. KUMMER [58] has shown that the cubes of the prime factors of 2 are not principal ideals.

[56] Math. Ann., 63: 37 (1907).
[57] Monatsberichte, Berlin, 1860: 744.
[58] Monatsberichte, Berlin, 1870: 755-766.

H. H. MITCHELL[59] shows that if h_1 is the first factor of the class number of $K(e^{\frac{2\pi i}{l}})$ where l is a prime such that $l-1$ is not a power of 2, and if $2e$ is an integer such that $(l-1)/2e$ is odd, and if q is a prime such that $q^{\frac{l-1}{2l}} \equiv 1 \bmod l$, then in the field of the $2e$ periods, q is the product of $2e$ prime ideals which constitute e pairs of conjugate imaginary ideals, and if an ideal be selected from each of the e pairs the h_1th power of their product is a principal ideal.

Mitchell also shows that if two conjugate imaginary prime factors of q be raised to the h_1th power the resulting ideals belong to the same class.

Further references on Chapter I:

BEEGER. K. Akad. van Weten. Verslagen, Amsterdam, 28: 293-311, 427-446, 1021-1023 (1919); 29: 331-360 (1919); K. Akad. van Weten. Proceedings, Amsterdam, 21: 395-414 (1919).

VEREBRUSSOV. Mémoire sur les classes des nombres complexes idéaux conjuges avec l'application à la demonstration du dernier théorème de Fermat, Paris, Gauthier-Villars, 18 p. (1912).

[59] Trans. Am. Math. Soc., 19: 119-126 (1918).

CHAPTER II

IRREGULAR CYCLOTOMIC FIELDS AND FERMAT'S LAST THEOREM

Introduction

The present chapter is concerned with the properties of irregular cyclotomic fields, which are those defined by a primitive p^n-th root of unity in which the class number of the field is divisible by the odd prime p, and the application of both regular and irregular cyclotomic fields to Fermat's last theorem. The latter topic has been reported on in Dickson's History of the Theory of Numbers, Volume 2, Chapter 26, pages 731-776. That chapter contains abstracts of papers which appeared prior to the year 1920. The present report is designed to cover all papers on Fermat's last theorem which employ the theory of cyclotomic fields as well as all papers on the subject which have appeared since January 1920. Also, for easy reference, abstracts of a few other papers on the theorem are included. Since important features of papers so far published are the particular devices employed to obtain criteria for the solution of Fermat's equation (1), considerable space has been devoted to descriptions of these devices provided that algebraic numbers are involved.

Papers treating the divisibility of the class number of the field defined by a primitive p^n-th root of unity by p^k are included here as well as in chapter one.

A number of results in the theory of irregular cyclotomic fields are contained in the papers by Kummer.[17, 20, 23, 39] Furtwängler,[43, 49] in investigations concerning the class fields and laws of reciprocity in a relative cyclic field obtained general results which include as special cases theorems concerning irregular cyclotomic fields. This was pointed out by Pollaczek,[76] who made important additions to the theory.

If

$$(1) \qquad x^p+y^p+z^p=0$$

is satisfied in rational integers x, y and z prime to the odd prime p, this will be referred to as Case I of Fermat's last theorem; and if one of these integers is divisible by p with x, y and z prime to each other, this will be referred to as Case II of the theorem.

In this connection it may be noted that although many contributions have been made to the first case of the theorem no paper has been published on the second case since Kummer's 1857 memoir which is proved to represent an advance over his results of that paper.

LEGENDRE[1] published a proof of the following theorem due to Sophie Germain:

If there exists an odd prime p, such that

$$\xi^n+\eta^n+\zeta^n\equiv 0 \pmod p$$

has no set of integral solutions ξ, η, ζ each not divisible by p, and such that n is not the residue of the nth power of any integer modulo p, then $x^n+y^n+z^n=0$ has no integral solutions each prime to n. Cf. Wendt,[26] Dickson,[35] Vandiver.[84]

LAMÉ[2] essayed to prove Fermat's last theorem but assumed without proof that integers in the field $\Omega(\alpha)$, where α is a primitive n-th root of unity, n being an odd prime, decomposed uniquely into prime factors in the field. This error was pointed out by LIOUVILLE[3] in commenting on Lamé's first article. Lamé recognized this lacuna but showed that this theorem was true for the case $n=5$ and affirmed that it was also true for the cases 7, 11, 13, and he believed it true for n general. He proved that the equation

$$A^5+B^5+C^5=0$$

is impossible for integers A, B, C, in the field $\Omega(\alpha)$, $\alpha^5=1$, $\alpha\neq 1$. KUMMER[4] pointed out in connection with Lamé's work that unique decomposition into prime factors did not hold in all cyclotomic fields defined by an n-th root of unity, n prime.

WANTZEL[5] proved that Euclid's g.c.d. process holds for complex integers $a+b\sqrt{-1}$ (already proved by C. F. GAUSS[6]) and for complex integers formed from an imaginary cube root of unity, and stated that a like result holds for complex integers $a_0+a_1r+a_2r^2+\ldots+a_{n-1}r^{n-1}$, where r is an imaginary n-th root of unity with n arbitrary, since the norm (or modulus) of this number is <1 when $a_0, \ldots, a_{n-1}$ are between 0 and 1 [erroneous, Cauchy[7]].

CAUCHY[7] showed that the final statement by Wantzel[5] is false for $n=7$ and for any prime $n=4m+1\geqq 17$. He pointed out lacunae in the proposed

[1] Mem. Acad. Sci. Inst. France, 6: 1-60 (1823). Thèorie des nombres ed. 2, 1808, second supplement 1825, 1-40.

[2] Compt. Rend., 24: 310-315, 352, 569-572, 888 (1847). Jour. de Math. (1), 12: 137-184 (1847).

[3] Compt. Rend., 24: 315-316 (1847).

[4] Compt. Rend., 24: 899-900 (1847). Jour. de Math., (1), 12: 136 (1847).

[5] Compt. Rend., 24: 430-434 (1847).

[6] Comm. Soc. Sc. Göttingen Recentiores, 7, 1832, § 46; Werke, II, 1863, 117. German transl. by H. Maser, Gauss' Untersuchungen über höhere Arith., 1889, 556.

[7] Compt. Rend., 24: 469-481 (1847); Oeuvres (1), X, 240-254.

proof by Lamé[2] of Fermat's last theorem. He defined the factorial of a complex number in the form used by Wantzel[5] to be the product of itself and the complex numbers obtained from it by replacing r by the remaining primitive n-th roots of unity, and obtained upper limits for such factorials [norms]. He[8] proved that any common factor of $M_h = Ar^h + B$ and M_k divides M_0 if A and B are relatively prime.

Cauchy[9] attempted to prove the false theorem that the norm of the remainder obtained on dividing one complex number by another can always be made less than the norm of the divisor. He concluded (falsely) that a product of complex integers can be decomposed into complex primes in a single manner, and that the other laws of divisibility of integers hold for these complex integers.

Cauchy[10] noted (erroneous) conclusions which follow from the assumption that his preceding theorems hold for a given number n; in particular, errors relating to the factors $A + r^i B$ of $A^n + B^n$. He promised to discuss later the objections which can be raised against proofs in his preceding paper.

Cauchy[11] further developed the subject and admitted at the end of his final paper that his basic theorem is false, failing for $n = 23$.

Cauchy[12] obtained results, most of which are included in Kummer's[13] general theorems on cyclotomic integers and Fermat's last theorem; in the fifth paper, p. 179 (Oeuvres, p. 362) he gives without proof the result that if $a^n + b^n + c^n = 0$ is satisfied in rational integers a, b, c, prime to each other, n a prime > 2, then

$$u_{a_1} u_{a_2} \cdots u_{a_{\frac{n-1}{2}}} = [F(\rho)]^n \omega(\rho),$$

where

$$\left| \begin{array}{lll} u = a + b\rho, & \rho^n = 1, & \rho \neq 1, \\ u_k = a + b\rho^k, & & \\ l \cdot a_l \equiv 1 \pmod{n}, & & \end{array} \right.$$

and $F(\rho)$ is a polynomial in ρ with rational integral coefficients, $\omega(\rho)$ is a power of ρ (cf. Kummer,[20] p. 63, for $r = 1$). Also (p. 181, Oeuvres, p. 364) he stated that $a^n + b^n + c^n = 0$ is impossible in rational integers not divisible by the odd prime n if

$$1 + 2^{n-4} + 3^{n-4} + \ldots + \left(\frac{n-1}{2}\right)^{n-4}$$

[8] Compt. Rend., 24: 347-348 (1847); Oeuvres (1), X, 224-226.

[9] Compt. Rend., 24: 516-528 (1847); Oeuvres (1), X, 254-268.

[10] Compt. Rend., 24: 578-584 (1847); Oeuvres (1), X, 268-275.

[11] Compt. Rend., 24: 633-636, 996-999, 1022-1030 (1847); Oeuvres (1), X, 276-285, 296-308.

[12] Compt. Rend., 25: 37-46, 46-54, 93-99, 132-136, 177-182, 242-243, 285-288 (1847); Oeuvres (1), X, 324-351, 354-371.

is not divisible by n, that is, if the Bernoulli number $B_{(n-3)/2}$ is not divisible by n. (Cf. Kummer,[20] p. 64.)

KUMMER[13] founded a theory of ideal numbers. Let λ be a prime integer and α a primitive λ-th root of unity, $ef=\lambda-1$. (Throughout the remainder of this report we shall use the term "integer in the field $\Omega(\alpha)$" in lieu of Kummer's expression "complex number".)

$$\eta_0=\alpha^{\gamma^0}+\alpha^{\gamma^e}+\alpha^{\gamma^{2e}}+\ldots+\alpha^{\gamma^{(f-1)e}},$$
$$\eta_1=\alpha^{\gamma^1}+\alpha^{\gamma^{e+1}}+\alpha^{\gamma^{2e+1}}+\ldots+\alpha^{\gamma^{(f-1)e+1}},$$
$$\ldots\ldots\ldots\ldots\ldots\ldots\ldots\ldots$$
$$\eta_{e-1}=\alpha^{\gamma^{e-1}}+\alpha^{\gamma^{2e-1}}+\alpha^{\gamma^{3e-1}}+\ldots+\alpha^{\gamma^{fe-1}},$$

(γ denoting a primitive root of λ), are the roots of an irreducible equation of degree e having rational integral coefficients, which we shall symbolize by

$$F(y)=y^e+A_1y^{e-1}+A_2y^{e-2}+\ldots+A_{e-1}y+A_e=0.$$

He then establishes the following theorem:

If q be a rational prime integer satisfying the congruence $q^f\equiv 1$, mod λ, the congruence $F(y)\equiv 0$, mod q, is completely resolvable, i. e., it is possible to establish an indeterminate congruence of the form

$$F(y)\equiv(y-u_0)(y-u_1)\ldots(y-u_{e-1}),\ \text{mod } q,$$

$u_0, u_1, \ldots, u_{e-1}$ denoting rational integers, congruent or incongruent, mod q.

Every equation which subsists between two functions of the periods will subsist as a congruence for the modulus q when we substitute for the periods the roots of the congruence $F(y)\equiv 0$ taken in a certain order.

If we put, the c's being rational integers,

$$\psi(\eta_0)=c_0\eta_0+c_1\eta_1+c_2\eta_2+\ldots+c_{e-1}\eta_{e-1},$$
$$\psi(\eta_1)=c_0\eta_1+c_1\eta_2+c_2\eta_3+\ldots+c_{e-1}\eta_0,$$
$$\psi(\eta_2)=c_0\eta_2+c_1\eta_3+c_2\eta_4+\ldots+c_{e-1}\eta_1,$$
$$\ldots\ldots\ldots\ldots\ldots\ldots\ldots\ldots$$
$$\psi(\eta_{e-1})=c_0\eta_{e-1}+c_1\eta_0+c_2\eta_1+\ldots+c_{e-1}\eta_{e-2},$$

we also have

(I.) The necessary and sufficient condition that $\psi(\eta)$ should be di-

[13] De numeris complexis qui radicibus unitatis et numeris realibus constant, Breslau, 1844. (Jour. de Math., I, 12: 185-212 (1847).) Ueber die Divisoren gewisser Formen der Zahlen, welche aus der Theorie der Kreistheilung entstehen. J. reine angew. Math., 30: 107-116 (1846). Zur Theorie der complexen Zahlen, Berlin Monatsberichte for March, 1845, or J. reine angew. Math., 30: 319-326 (1847). Ueber die Zerlegung der aus Wurzeln der Einheit gebildeten complexen Zahlen in ihre Primfactoren. J. reine angew. Math., 35: 327-367 (1847). Recherches sur les nombres complexes. Jour. de Math., I, 16: 377-498 (1851).

visible by q (i. e., that the coefficients $c_0, c_1, \ldots, c_{e-1}$ should be all separately divisible by q) is that the e congruences

$$\psi(u_0)=c_0u_0+c_1u_1+c_2u_2+\ldots+c_{e-1}u_{e-1}\equiv 0, \text{ mod } q,$$
$$\psi(u_1)=c_0u_1+c_1u_2+c_2u_3+\ldots+c_{e-1}u_0\equiv 0, \text{ mod } q,$$
$$\ldots\ldots\ldots\ldots\ldots\ldots\ldots\ldots\ldots\ldots\ldots\ldots$$
$$\psi(u_{e-1})=c_0u_{e-1}+c_1u_0+c_2u_1+\ldots+c_{e-1}u_{e-2}\equiv 0, \text{ mod } q,$$

should be simultaneously satisfied.

(II.) The necessary and sufficient condition that the norm of $\psi(\eta)$, taken with respect to the periods, i. e., the number $\psi(\eta_0)\psi(\eta_1)\ldots\psi(\eta_{e-1})$, should be divisible by q, is that *one* of the e congruences

$$\psi(u_0)\equiv 0,\ \psi(u_1)\equiv 0,\ \ldots,\ \psi(u_{e-1})\equiv 0, \text{ mod } q,$$

should be satisfied.

If $f(\alpha)$ is any integer in the field $\Omega(\alpha)$, it is possible to find integers in $\Omega(\alpha)$ of the same form as $\psi(\eta_0)$, $\psi_0, \psi_1, \ldots, \psi_{f-1}$, so that

$$f(\alpha)=\psi_0(\eta_0)+\alpha\psi_1(\eta_0)+\alpha^2\psi_2(\eta_0)+\ldots+\alpha^{f-1}\psi_{f-1}(\eta_0),$$

the ψ's being in the field $\Omega(\alpha)$.

Kummer then proves the theorems:

(I.) The necessary and sufficient condition that $f(\alpha)$ should be divisible by q, is that the congruences

$$\psi_0(u_k)\equiv 0,\ \psi_1(u_k)\equiv 0,\ \ldots,\ \psi_{f-1}(u_k)\equiv 0, \text{ mod } q,$$

should be simultaneously satisfied for every value of k.

(II.) And the condition that the norm of $f(\alpha)$ should be divisible by q, is that the same congruences should be satisfied for some one value of k.

When the congruences $\psi_0(u_k)\equiv 0$, $\psi_1(u_k)\equiv 0, \ldots, \psi_{f-1}(u_k)\equiv 0$ (mod q), are simultaneously satisfied, $f(\alpha)$ is said to be *congruent to zero* (*mod q*), *for the substitution* $\eta_0=u_k$.

In order to lead up to Kummer's definition of ideal numbers, let q be a rational integer belonging to the exponent f and suppose first that it is possible to express it as the norm (where this norm is taken with respect to the periods) of an integer $\psi(\eta_0)$, which contains the periods of f terms only, so that

$$q=\psi(\eta_0)\cdot\psi(\eta_1)\ldots\psi(\eta_{e-1}).$$

In view of the above results we may distinguish the e factors of q by means of substitutions which render them congruent to 0, modulo q, so that if $\psi(\eta_{e-k})\equiv 0$ (mod q), if we substitute therein u_k in place of η_0, then $\psi(\eta_{e-k})$ *is said to be the factor appertaining to the substitution* $\eta_0=u_k$.

He then shows that if $f(\alpha)$ is congruent to 0 (mod q) for any substitution $(\eta_0=u_0)$, $f(\alpha)$ is divisible by the factor of q appertaining o that substitution. Further, it is shown that these factors of q in the ield are incapable of resolution into two other factors in the field unless one of them is a unit, and if any one of them divides the product of wo factors, it will divide one of the two factors separately.

In order to make use of these ideals in connection with primes q elonging to the exponent f which cannot be decomposed into the product of e integers in the field, he defines an ideal factor of q as a factor of $f(\alpha)$ where $f(\alpha)$ is congruent to 0 under the substitution $\eta_0 = u_0$; that is, $f(\alpha)$ *is said to contain the ideal factor of q appertaining to the substitution* $\eta_0 = u_0$. Kummer, using this definition, arrives at theorems equivalent to the statement that an integer in the field $\Omega(\alpha)$ may be decomposed into prime ideal factors in but one way; the case of divisors of the ational integer λ is treated separately.

He then defines classes of ideal numbers in a way which is quite analogous to similar definitions in Dedekind's theory of ideals. This being the case, we shall employ the modern terminology in connection with these aspects of Kummer's theory, in particular, if an ideal P is such hat P^h is a principal ideal but no lower power of P has that property, hen P is said to *belong to the exponent* h.

KUMMER[14] obtained results concerning Fermat's last theorem. These esults, together with the methods by which they are derived are entirely ncluded in Kummer.[18]

The second article is entitled "Beweis des Fermatschen Satzes die Unmöglichkeit von $x^\lambda - y^\lambda = z^\lambda$ für eine unendlichen Anzahl Primzahlen λ," and at the beginning of it Kummer states in effect that he proves hat the relation is impossible for an infinity of primes λ but he does not know for just which λ's the assumptions hold. Kummer does not, however, in any of his papers prove that there exists an infinity of regular primes although he apparently believed in its existence. He made similar tatements in letters to Kronecker (cf. Kummer,[39] pp. 75, 84) and in his Vorlesungen über Zahlentheorie, I, 1901, 23, Kronecker stated that Kummer proved the impossibility of $x^\lambda + y^\lambda = z^\lambda$ for an infinity of primes λ and at first believed that his proof applied to nearly all λ's, but later believed the contrary.

Kummer (Hensel,[40] p. 32) is elsewhere quoted as believing it probable hat there are approximately as many regular primes as irregular (excepional) primes. (Cf. Kummer,[23] Jensen.[58])

DIRICHLET[15] commented on the results and methods in Kummer's[14] article.

[14] Berlin Monatsberichte, 1847: 132-139, 305-319.
[15] Berlin Monatsberichte, 1847: 139-141.

KUMMER [16] determined the number of nonequivalent classes of ideal in the field $\Omega(a)$, where a is a primitive λ-th root of unity, λ an odd prime This number H is found to be $H=\frac{P}{(2\lambda)^{\mu-1}}\times\frac{D}{\Delta}$. In this formula P is a quantity defined by the equations

$$P=\phi(\beta)\cdot\phi(\beta^3)\cdot\phi(\beta^5)\ldots\phi(\beta^{\lambda-2}),$$
$$\phi(\beta)=1+\gamma_1\beta+\gamma_2\beta^2+\gamma_3\beta^3+\ldots+\gamma_{\lambda-2}\beta^{\lambda-2},$$

β representing a primitive root of the equation $\beta^{\lambda-1}=1$, γ a primitiv root of the congruence $\gamma^{\lambda-1}\equiv 1, \bmod \lambda$, and $\gamma_1, \gamma_2, \gamma_3, \ldots$, the leas positive residues of $\gamma, \gamma^2, \gamma^3, \ldots$ for the modulus λ; D is the logarithmi determinant of a particular system of independent but not necessaril fundamental units, $e(a), e(a^\gamma), e(a^{\gamma^2}), \ldots, e(a^{\gamma^{\mu-2}})$ defined by th equation

$$e(a)=\sqrt{\frac{(1-a^\gamma)(1-a^{-\gamma})}{(1-a)(1-a^{-1})}}=\pm\frac{a^{\mu(\gamma-1)}(1-a^\gamma)}{1-a}=\pm\frac{\sin\frac{k\gamma\pi}{\lambda}}{\sin\frac{\pi}{\lambda}},$$

so that if

$$a=e^{\frac{2ik\pi}{\lambda}},$$

$$D=\begin{vmatrix} L.e(a), & L.e(a^\gamma), & L.e(a^{\gamma^2}), & \ldots, & L.e(a^{\gamma^{\mu-2}}) \\ L.e(a^\gamma), & L.e(a^{\gamma^2}), & L.e(a^{\gamma^3}), & \ldots, & L.e(a^{\gamma^{\mu-1}}) \\ L.e(a^{\gamma^2}), & L.e(a^{\gamma^3}), & L.e(a^{\gamma^4}), & \ldots, & L.e(a^{\gamma^{\mu}}) \\ \cdots & \cdots & \cdots & \cdots & \cdots \\ L.e(a^{\gamma^{\mu-2}}), & L.e(a^{\gamma^{\mu-1}}), & L.e(a^{\gamma^{\mu}}), & \ldots, & L.e(a^{\gamma^{2\mu-}}) \end{vmatrix}$$

Also,

$$\Delta=\begin{vmatrix} L.c_1(a), & L.c_2(a), & \ldots, & L.c_{\mu-1}(a) \\ L.c_1(a^\gamma), & L.c_2(a^\gamma), & \ldots, & L.c_{\mu-1}(a^\gamma) \\ \cdots & \cdots & \cdots & \cdots \\ L.c_1(a^{\gamma^{\mu-2}}), & L.c_2(a^{\gamma^{\mu-2}}), & \ldots, & L.c_{\mu-1}(a^{\gamma^{\mu-2}}) \end{vmatrix}$$

where $c_1(a), c_2(a), \ldots, c_{\mu-1}(a)$ is any system of $\mu-1$ fundament units and $\mu=(\lambda-1)/2$. Quantities defined by the symbols $L.c_1(a)$ $L.c_2(a)$, etc., are the arithmetical logarithms of the real units $c_1(a)$, etc taken positively.

Each of the two factors $P/(2\lambda)^{\mu-1}$ and D/Δ, of which the value of H is composed, is separately an integral number.

KUMMER [17] proved that the number of distinct classes H of integers i the field $\Omega(a)$, where a is a primitive λ-th root of unity, λ an odd prim

[16] J. reine angew. Math., 40: 93-116 (1850).

[17] J. reine angew. Math., 40: 117-129 (1850). J. de Math., (1), 16: 473-486 (1851 Abstract in Berlin Monatsberichte, 1847: 305-319.

is divisible by λ if, and only if, λ is a divisor of one of the first $(\lambda-3)/2$ Bernoulli numbers.

For the demonstration, Kummer starts with the first factor of the class number which is

$$\frac{P}{(2\lambda)^{\mu-1}},$$

where

$$P=\phi(\beta)\cdot\phi(\beta^3)\cdot\phi(\beta^5)\ldots\phi(\beta^{\lambda-2}),$$
$$\phi(\beta)=1+\gamma_1\beta+\gamma_2\beta^2+\gamma_3\beta^3+\ldots+\gamma_{\lambda-2}\beta^{\lambda-2},$$

and β is a primitive root of $x^{\lambda-1}=1$. If we represent the product

$$(\gamma\beta-1)\phi(\beta)=(\gamma\gamma_{\lambda-2}-1)+(\gamma-\gamma_1)\beta+(\gamma\gamma_1-\gamma_2)\beta^2+\ldots$$
$$+(\gamma\gamma_{\lambda-3}-\gamma_{\lambda-2})\beta^{\lambda-2},$$

by

$$\lambda[b_0+b_1\beta+b_2\beta^2+\ldots+b_{\lambda-2}\beta^{\lambda-2}],\qquad\text{or}\qquad\lambda\psi(\beta),$$

(b_m denoting the quotient $\dfrac{\gamma\gamma_{m-1}-\gamma_m}{\lambda}$ or $I\ \dfrac{\gamma\gamma_{m-1}}{\lambda}$, if I represents the greatest integer contained in the fraction before which it is placed), we obtain by multiplication the equality

$$(\gamma^\mu+1)P=\lambda^\mu\psi(\beta)\cdot\psi(\beta^3)\ldots\psi(\beta^{\lambda-2});$$

or, since $\gamma^\mu+1$ is divisible by λ, and may be, by choice of γ, supposed not divisible by λ^2,

$$2^{\mu-1}G\cdot\frac{P}{(2\lambda)^{\mu-1}}=\psi(\beta)\cdot\psi(\beta^3)\ldots\psi(\beta^{\lambda-2}),$$

G denoting a coefficient prime to λ. The congruence $\dfrac{P}{(2\lambda)^{\mu-1}}\equiv 0$, mod λ, is therefore equivalent to the congruence

$$\psi(\beta)\cdot\psi(\beta^3)\ldots\psi(\beta^{\lambda-2})\equiv 0,\ \text{mod}\ \lambda,$$

which may, in its turn, be replaced by the following,

$$\psi(\gamma)\cdot\psi(\gamma^3)\ldots\psi(\gamma^{\lambda-2})\equiv 0,\ \text{mod}\ \lambda.$$

For, if there be an equation which, considered as a congruence for a given modulus λ, is completely resolvable for that modulus, any symmetric function of the roots of the congruence is congruent for the modulus λ, to the corresponding function of the roots of the equation. The symmetric function

$$\psi(\beta)\cdot\psi(\beta^3)\ldots\psi(\beta^{\lambda-2}),$$

of β, β^3, ..., $\beta^{\lambda-2}$, which are the roots of the equation $x^\mu+1=0$, is therefore congruent to $\psi(\gamma)\cdot\psi(\gamma^3)\ldots\psi(\gamma^{\lambda-2})$ which is the same function of γ, γ^3, γ^5, ..., $\gamma^{\lambda-2}$, the roots of the congruence $x^\mu+1\equiv 0$, mod λ.

Hence the necessary and sufficient condition for the divisibility of $P/(2\lambda)^{\mu-1}$ by λ is that one of the μ congruences included in the formula

$$\psi(\gamma^{2n-1}) \equiv 0, \text{ mod } \lambda, \; n=1, 2, 3, \ldots, \mu,$$

should be satisfied. Now

$$\gamma^{-(2n-1)}\psi(\gamma^{2n-1}) \equiv b_0\gamma_{\lambda-2}^{2n-1} + b_1\gamma_0^{2n-1} + b_2\gamma_1^{2n-1} + \ldots + b_{\lambda-2}\gamma_{\lambda-3}^{2n-1}.$$

The right-hand member of this congruence may be written in the form

$$\begin{aligned}
&1[(t_1+1)^{2n-1}+(t_1+2)^{2n-1}+\ldots+t_2^{2n-1}],\\
&+2[(t_2+1)^{2n-1}+(t_2+2)^{2n-1}+\ldots+t_3^{2n-1}],\\
&\ldots\ldots\ldots\ldots\ldots\ldots\ldots\ldots\ldots\ldots\ldots\ldots\\
&+(\gamma-1)[(t_{\gamma-1}+1)^{2n-1}+(t_{\gamma-1}+2)^{2n-1}+\ldots\\
&\qquad\qquad\qquad\qquad+(\lambda-1)^{2n-1}] \equiv 0 \pmod{\lambda},
\end{aligned}$$

where t_s is the greatest integer contained in $(s\lambda)/\gamma$. Write

$$\chi(x) = \frac{x^{2n}}{\Pi_{2n}} - \frac{x^{2n-1}}{2\Pi_{2n-1}} + \frac{B_1x^{2n-2}}{\Pi_{2n-2}\Pi_2} - \frac{B_2x^{2n-4}}{\Pi_{2n-4}\Pi_4} + \ldots + \frac{(-1)^nB_{n-1}x^2}{\Pi_2\Pi_{2n-2}},$$

where $B_1=1/6$, $B_2=1/30$, etc., are the Bernoulli numbers and $\Pi_r=r!$ Then

$$1^{2n-1}+2^{2n-1}+3^{2n-1}+\ldots+(x-1)^{2n-1}=\Pi_{2n-1}\chi(x),$$

provided x is a positive integer. By means of these, the last congruence becomes

$$\chi(t_1+1)+\chi(t_2+1)+\chi(t_3+1)+\ldots+\chi(t_{\gamma-1}+1) \equiv 0 \pmod{\lambda}.$$

The integer t_s can be written in the form $(s\lambda-r_s)/\gamma$ where r_s is a positive integer less than γ. Using this in the last congruence and neglecting the multiples of λ, we obtain

$$\chi\left(\frac{\gamma-r_1}{\gamma}\right)+\chi\left(\frac{\gamma-r_2}{\gamma}\right)+\ldots+\chi\left(\frac{\gamma-r_{\gamma-1}}{\gamma}\right) \equiv 0 \pmod{\lambda}.$$

Since $r_1, r_2, \ldots, r_{\gamma-1}$ are the numbers $1, 2, 3, \ldots, \gamma-1$, in some order, we then obtain

$$\chi\left(\frac{1}{\gamma}\right)+\chi\left(\frac{2}{\gamma}\right)+\chi\left(\frac{3}{\gamma}\right)+\ldots+\chi\left(\frac{\gamma-1}{\gamma}\right) \equiv 0 \pmod{\lambda}.$$

To transform this congruence we use the following known expansion of $\chi(x)$ in the infinite series

$$\chi(x) = \frac{(-1)^nB_n}{\Pi_{2n}} - \frac{(-1)^n2}{(2\pi)^{2n}}\left(\frac{\cos 2x\pi}{1^{2n}}+\frac{\cos 4x\pi}{2^{2n}}+\frac{\cos 6x\pi}{3^{2n}}+\ldots\right),$$

where x is contained within the limits 0 and 1. Setting in this $x=0$, $1/\gamma$, $2/\gamma$, ..., $(\gamma-1)/\gamma$ in turn, and adding, we obtain

$$\chi\left(\frac{1}{\gamma}\right)+\chi\left(\frac{2}{\gamma}\right)+\chi\left(\frac{3}{\gamma}\right)+\ldots+\chi\left(\frac{\gamma-1}{\gamma}\right)$$
$$=\frac{(-1)^n\gamma B_n}{\Pi_{2n}}-\frac{(-1)^n 2\gamma}{(2\pi)^{2n}}\left[\frac{1}{\gamma^{2n}}+\frac{1}{(2\gamma)^{2n}}+\frac{1}{(3\gamma)^{2n}}+\ldots\right],$$

and using

$$1+\frac{1}{2^{2n}}+\frac{1}{3^{2n}}+\ldots=\frac{(2\pi)^{2n}B_n}{2\Pi_{2n}},$$

we have

$$\chi\left(\frac{1}{\gamma}\right)+\chi\left(\frac{2}{\gamma}\right)+\ldots+\chi\left(\frac{\gamma-1}{\gamma}\right)=\frac{(-1)^n(\gamma^{2n}-1)B_n}{\gamma^{2n-1}\Pi_{2n}}.$$

The condition for the divisibility of H by λ is therefore that one of the μ congruences included in the formula $B_n(\gamma^{2n}-1)\equiv 0$, mod λ, should be satisfied. The last of these congruences, or $B_\mu(\gamma^{2n}-1)\equiv 0$, is never satisfied; for it is easily proved that the denominator of B_μ contains λ as a factor, while

$$\gamma^{2\mu}-1=(\gamma^\mu+1)(\gamma^\mu-1),$$

though divisible by λ, is not divisible by λ^2. Hence, since γ is a primitive root of λ, a necessary and sufficient condition that the first factor of the class number is divisible by λ is that one of the Bernoulli numbers B_s, $s=1, 2, \ldots, \mu-1$, is divisible by λ.

Kummer then examines the divisibility of the second factor of the class number by λ on the basis of certain theorems proved in Section II of his article now being discussed. It is possible to find an independent system of units $e(a)$, $e(a^\gamma)$, ..., $e(a^{\gamma^{\mu-2}})$, in which

$$e(a)=\sqrt{\frac{(1-a^\gamma)(1-a^{-\gamma})}{(1-a)(1-a^{-1})}},$$

such that a certain power of every unit in the field may be expressed as a product of integral powers of the elements of this independent system, and also

$$\epsilon_1(a)^{n_1}=e(a)^{r'_1}\cdot e(a^\gamma)^{r'_2}\ \ldots e(a^{\gamma^{\mu-2}})^{r'_{\mu-1}},$$
$$\epsilon_2(a)^{n_2}=e(a)^{r_1^{(2)}}\cdot e(a^\gamma)^{r_2^{(2)}}\ \ldots e(a^{\gamma^{\mu-2}})^{r_{\mu-1}^{(2)}},$$
$$\cdots\cdots\cdots\cdots\cdots\cdots\cdots\cdots\cdots\cdots\cdots$$
$$\epsilon_{\mu-1}(a)^{n_{\mu-1}}=e(a)^{r_1^{(\mu-1)}}\cdot e(a^\gamma)^{r_2^{(\mu-1)}}\ldots e(a^{\gamma^{\mu-2}})^{r_{\mu-1}^{(\mu-1)}}$$

where $\epsilon_1(a)$, $\epsilon_2(a)$, ..., $\epsilon_{\mu-1}(a)$ designate a fundamental system of units and where the exponent n_h has no factor in common with all of the integral exponents $r_1{}^h$, $r_2{}^h$, ..., $r^h{}_{\mu-1}$; also the parentheses are omitted from the superscripts in the r's.

We obtain from Section II, p. 398, of Kummer's article

$$\frac{D}{\Delta}=\frac{n_1\cdot n_2\ldots n_{\mu-1}}{R}$$

in which R is the determinant,

$$\begin{vmatrix} r_1^{\,1}, & r_2^{\,1}, & \ldots, & r^1_{\mu-1}, \\ r_1^{\,2}, & r_2^{\,2}, & \ldots, & r^2_{\mu-1}, \\ \ldots & \ldots & \ldots & \ldots \\ r_1^{\mu-1}, & r_2^{\mu-1}, & \ldots, & r^{\mu-1}_{\mu-1}. \end{vmatrix}$$

From the expression we have just given for D/Δ, it follows that there exists a unit in $\Omega(a)$ such that

$$\epsilon(a)^n=e(a)^{r_1}\cdot e(a^\gamma)^{r_2}\ldots e(a^{\gamma^{\mu-2}})^{r_{\mu-1}},$$

where n is an integer divisible by λ but $r_1, r_2, \ldots, r_{\mu-1}$ are integers not all divisible by λ. It is easily seen that the λth power of an integer in the field $\Omega(a)$ is congruent to a rational integer (mod λ). Consequently,

$$e(a)^{r_1}\cdot e(a^\gamma)^{r_2}\ldots e(a^{\gamma^{\mu-2}})^{r_{\mu-1}}\equiv c \pmod{\lambda}.$$

It is now noted that if we have two integers in the field $\Omega(a)$, say $f(a)$ and $f_1(a)$ such that $f(a)=f_1(a)$, then we may replace this relation by an equation involving an indeterminate x as follows:

$$f(x)=f_1(x)+(1+x+x^2+\ldots+x^{\lambda-1})\psi(x),$$

where $\psi(x)$ is a polynomial in x with rational integral coefficients. Hence we may write

$$e(x)^{r_1}\cdot e(x^\gamma)^{r_2}\ldots e(x^{\gamma^{\mu-2}})^{r_{\mu-1}}$$
$$=c+\lambda\phi(x)+(1+x+x^2+\ldots+x^{\lambda-1})\psi(x).$$

In this equality take the logarithms of each member, differentiate both members with respect to x, multiply each by x, substitute $x=a$, and we have

$$r_1\frac{ae'(a)}{e(a)}+r_2\gamma\frac{a^\gamma e'(a^\gamma)}{e(a^\gamma)}+\ldots+r_{\mu-1}\gamma^{\mu-2}\frac{a^{\gamma^{\mu-2}}e'(a^{\gamma^{\mu-2}})}{e(a^{\gamma^{\mu-2}})}$$
$$=\frac{\lambda a\phi'(a)+[a+2a^2+3a^3+\ldots+(\lambda-1)a^{\lambda-1}]\psi(a)}{c+\lambda\phi(a)}.$$

From this relation we obtain easily

(2) $$r_1F(a)+r_2\gamma F(a^\gamma)+\ldots+r_{\mu-1}\gamma^{\mu-2}F(a^{\gamma^{\mu-2}})$$
$$\equiv M[a+2a^2+\ldots+(\lambda-1)a^{\lambda-1}],$$

where M is congruent to an integer modulo λ and

$$\frac{2e'(a)}{e(a)}=F(a),$$

giving $e(\alpha)$ its actual value. It is found after some transformations that

(3) $$F(\alpha)=\gamma-1+2b_0\alpha+2b_1\alpha^{\gamma}+2b_3\alpha^{\gamma^2}+\ldots+2b_{\lambda-2}\alpha^{\gamma^{\lambda-2}}$$

n which

$$b_s=\frac{\gamma\gamma_{s-1}-\gamma_s}{\lambda}.$$

Writing

$$M(\alpha+\gamma\alpha^{\gamma}+\gamma^2\alpha^{2\gamma^2}+\ldots+\gamma^{\lambda-2}\alpha^{\gamma^{\lambda-2}})$$

or the second member of (2) and comparing the coefficients of the arious powers of α we obtain from (3), after the new forms of the F's re substituted, the system of congruences

$$\left.\begin{array}{l} r_1b_0\ \ +\gamma r_2b_{\lambda-2}+\gamma^2r_3b_{\lambda-3}+\ldots+\gamma^{\mu-2}r_{\mu-1}b_{\lambda-\mu+1}-K\equiv M \\ r_1b_1\ \ +\gamma r_2b_0\ \ +\gamma^2r_3b_{\lambda-2}+\ldots+\gamma^{\mu-2}r_{\mu-1}b_{\lambda-\mu+2}-K\equiv \gamma M \\ r_1b_2\ \ +\gamma r_2b_1\ \ +\gamma^2r_3b_0\ \ +\ldots+\gamma^{\mu-2}r_{\mu-1}b_{\lambda-\mu+3}-K\equiv \gamma^2 M \\ \ldots\ldots\ldots\ldots\ldots\ldots\ldots\ldots\ldots\ldots\ldots\ldots \\ r_1b_{\lambda-2}+\gamma r_2b_{\lambda-3}+\gamma^2r_3b_{\lambda-4}+\ldots+\gamma^{\mu-2}r_{\mu-1}b_{\lambda-\mu}\ \ -K\equiv \gamma^{\lambda-2}M \end{array}\right\}(\text{mod }\lambda),$$

here

$$r_1+\gamma r_2+\gamma^2r_3+\ldots+\gamma^{\mu-2}r_{\mu-1}=K.$$

hese congruences, multiplied respectively by 1, γ^{2n-1}, $\gamma^{2(2n-1)}$, ..., $^{(\lambda-2)(2n-1)}$, and added, give a sum which may be decomposed into the wo factors

$$\left(\begin{array}{l} r_1+\gamma^{2n}r_2+\gamma^{4n}r_3+\ldots \\ \qquad +\gamma^{2(\mu-2)n}r_{\mu-1}\end{array}\right)\cdot\left(\begin{array}{l} b_0+b_1\gamma^{2n-1}+b_2\gamma^{2(2n-1)}+\ldots \\ \qquad +b_{\lambda-2}\gamma^{(\lambda-2)(2n-1)}\end{array}\right)\equiv 0,$$

odulo λ, for $n=1, 2, 3, \ldots, \mu-1$. If we assume that the second factor not divisible by λ for any of the given values of n, it follows that

$$\left.\begin{array}{l} r_1+\gamma^2r_2\qquad +\gamma^4r_3\qquad +\ldots+\gamma^{2(\mu-2)}r_{\mu-1}\qquad \equiv 0, \\ r_1+\gamma^4r_2\qquad +\gamma^8r_3\qquad +\ldots+\gamma^{4(\mu-2)}r_{\mu-1}\qquad \equiv 0, \\ \ldots\ldots\ldots\ldots\ldots\ldots\ldots\ldots\ldots\ldots \\ r_1+\gamma^{2(\mu-1)}r_2+\gamma^{4(\mu-1)}r_3+\ldots+\gamma^{(\mu-2)(\mu-1)}r_{\mu-1}\equiv 0, \end{array}\right\}(\text{mod }\lambda).$$

he determinant

$$\left|\begin{array}{lllll} 1 & \gamma^2 & \gamma^4 & \ldots & \gamma^{2(\mu-2)} \\ 1 & \gamma^4 & \gamma^8 & \ldots & \gamma^{4(\mu-2)} \\ \ldots & \ldots & \ldots & \ldots & \ldots \\ \ldots & \ldots & \ldots & \ldots & \ldots \\ 1 & \gamma^{2(\mu-1)} & \gamma^{4(\mu-1)} & \ldots & \gamma^{(\mu-2)(\mu-1)} \end{array}\right|$$

not divisible by λ since it is the product of factors of the form $\gamma^{2k}-\gamma^{2h}$, nere k and h are distinct and each less than μ, hence

$$r_1\equiv 0,\quad r_2\equiv 0,\quad r_3\equiv 0,\quad \ldots,\quad r_{\mu-1}\equiv 0\ (\text{mod }\lambda),$$

and this is contrary to the supposition that these exponents are not al divisible by λ, consequently

$$b_0+b_1\gamma^{2n-1}+b_2\gamma^{2(2n-1)}+\ldots+b_{\lambda-2}\gamma^{(\lambda-2)(2n-1)}$$

must be divisible by λ for some value of n if D/Δ is divisible by λ. Bu this condition is precisely a necessary and sufficient condition that th first factor of the class number be divisible by λ.

KUMMER[18] applied his methods to Fermat's last theorem. He consider the equation

$$u^\lambda+v^\lambda+w^\lambda=0 \tag{4}$$

where u, v and w are integers in the field $\Omega(\alpha)$ prime each to each, an proved that the relation did not hold for λ an odd prime greater than and not dividing any of the first $(\lambda-3)/2$ Bernoulli numbers.

Kummer makes use of two theorems established by him on p. 447 an 487 of the second article cited, namely, under the assumption that does not divide any of the first $(\lambda-3)/2$ Bernoulli numbers, then i the λ-th power of the ideal equals an integer in the field, the ideal itsel is an integer in the field. The second theorem states that under the sam assumption every unit in the field which is congruent to a rational intege modulo λ equals the λ-th power of another unit.

In (4) we note that in place of integers u, v, w, we may write th same integers multiplied by α^k. Hence we can determine k so that α^k has the form $a+(1-\alpha)^2P$ where a is a rational integer and P is a integer in the field $\Omega(\alpha)$, as may be easily shown. Hence we write

$$u=a+(1-\alpha)^2P,$$
$$v=b+(1-\alpha)^2Q,$$
$$w=c+(1-\alpha)^2R,$$

where a, b, c are rational integers, and we shall assume that none of the is divisible by λ, which is equivalent to the assumption that none of th integers u, v, w is divisible by $1-\alpha$. Factoring $u^\lambda+v^\lambda$, we obtain th equation

$$(u+v)\cdot(u+\alpha v)\cdot(u+\alpha^2 v)\ldots(u+\alpha^{\lambda-1}v)=-w^\lambda.$$

It is then shown that since $1-\alpha$ is prime to u, v, w, then all of th foregoing factors are prime to each other. Hence, using the theore established in Article V, Kummer concludes that

$$u+\alpha^r v=\alpha^\rho E_r(\alpha)t_r^\lambda, \tag{5}$$

[18] J. reine angew. Math., 40: 130-138 (1850). J. de Math., (1), 16: 488-498 (1851

where t_r is an integer in the field $\Omega(a)$, $a^\rho E_r(a)$ is a unit in the field such that $E_r(a) = E_r(a^{-1})$, and obtains the congruence

$$u + a^r v \equiv a^\rho E_r(a) \cdot m \pmod{\lambda},$$

where m is a rational integer. In (5) set a^{-1} in lieu of a, and we obtain a result which gives, as before, if $u' = u(a^{-1})$ and $u = u(a)$, etc.,

$$u' + a^{-r} v' \equiv a^{-\rho} E_r(a) \cdot m \pmod{\lambda},$$

and comparison with the last congruence mentioned gives

$$a^{-\rho}(u + a^r v) \equiv a^\rho (u' + a^{-r} v') \pmod{\lambda}.$$

This relation reduces modulo $(1-a)^2$ to

$$a^{-\rho}(a + a^r b) \equiv a^\rho (a + a^{-r} b) \quad [\text{mod } (1-a)^2].$$

Also, using the relation

$$a^h \equiv 1 - h(1-a) \quad [\text{mod } (1-a)^2],$$

we obtain

$$(a+b)\rho \equiv br \pmod{\lambda}.$$

Determining k by the congruence

$$(a+b)k \equiv b \pmod{\lambda},$$

we have

$$\rho \equiv kr \pmod{\lambda},$$

and

$$a^{-kr}(u + a^r v) \equiv a^{kr}(u' + a^{-r} v') \pmod{\lambda},$$

for $r = 0, 1, 2, \ldots, \lambda - 1$. This gives for $r = 0$

$$u + v \equiv u' + v' \pmod{\lambda},$$

and since u, v, w are symmetric in the original equation (4), we have

$$\left.\begin{cases} u \equiv u' \\ v \equiv v' \\ w \equiv w' \end{cases}\right\} \pmod{\lambda}.$$

These relations give immediately

$$a^{-kr}(u + a^r v) \equiv a^{kr}(u + a^{-r} v) \pmod{\lambda}.$$

Taking $r = 1$ and $r = 2$ in turn, there are obtained relations from which we can infer that $k \equiv 1$ or $2k \equiv 1 \pmod{\lambda}$, noting that $\lambda > 3$. These relations, combined with $(a+b)k \equiv b$ show that

$$a \equiv 0 \pmod{\lambda} \qquad \text{or} \qquad a \equiv b \pmod{\lambda},$$

hence $a \equiv c$ and $b \equiv c \pmod{\lambda}$. From (4) we also have

$$0 \equiv u^\lambda + v^\lambda + w^\lambda \equiv a + b + c \pmod{\lambda},$$

which gives

$$3a \equiv 3b \equiv 3c \equiv 0 \pmod{\lambda},$$

which is impossible since $\lambda > 3$.

We now proceed to the second part of the demonstration, in which it is supposed that one of the three integers u, v, w, is divisible by $1-\alpha$. In this case it is convenient to write (4) in the generalized form

$$u^\lambda + v^\lambda = E(\alpha)(1-\alpha)^{m\lambda} w^\lambda, \tag{6}$$

in which the integers u, v, w, are prime each to each and where $1-\alpha$ and $E(\alpha)$ designate a unit in the field. We have immediately

$$(u+v) \cdot (u+\alpha v) \cdot (u+\alpha^2 v) \ldots (u+\alpha^{\lambda-1} v) = E(\alpha)(1-\alpha)^{m\lambda} w^\lambda.$$

It is first shown that each of the factors on the left hand side of the equation is divisible by $1-\alpha$ but none of them is divisible by $(1-\alpha)^2$ except $u+v$, so that we have

$$u+v = (1-\alpha)^{m\lambda-\lambda+1} \cdot \phi$$

and

$$u+\alpha^r v = (1-\alpha^r)\phi_r,$$

so that

$$\phi \cdot \phi_1 \cdot \phi_2 \ldots \phi_{\lambda-1} = E(\alpha) w^\lambda,$$

where $\phi, \phi_1, \phi_2, \ldots, \phi_{\lambda-1}$ are integers in the field which are prime each to each and to $(1-\alpha)$.

It is concluded from this that

$$u+v = e_0(\alpha)(1-\alpha)^{m\lambda-\lambda+1} \cdot w_1^\lambda,$$
$$u+\alpha^r v = e_r(\alpha)(1-\alpha^r) t_r^\lambda$$

for $r = 1, 2, 3, \ldots, (\lambda-1)$. Setting s in place of r we have

$$u+\alpha^s v = e_s(\alpha)(1-\alpha^s) t_s^\lambda,$$

and eliminating u and v from these three equations, we find

$$t_r^\lambda - \frac{e_s(\alpha)}{e_r(\alpha)} t_s^\lambda = \frac{e_0(\alpha)(\alpha^r-\alpha^s)(1-\alpha)}{e_r(\alpha)(1-\alpha^r)(1-\alpha^s)}(1-\alpha)^{(m-1)\lambda} \cdot w_1^\lambda;$$

which we write in the form

$$t_r^\lambda + \epsilon(\alpha) t_s^\lambda = E_1(\alpha)(1-\alpha)^{(m-1)\lambda} w_1^\lambda.$$

By considering this equation modulo λ, we find $\epsilon(\alpha)$, which is a unit in the field, to be such that

$$\epsilon(\alpha) \equiv c \pmod{\lambda},$$

hence

$$u_1^\lambda + v_1^\lambda = E_1(\alpha)(1-\alpha)^{(m-1)\lambda} w_1^\lambda,$$

where u_1, v_1, w_1, are integers in the field. This equation is of exactly the same type as (6) except that the exponent of $(1-a)^\lambda$ is decreased by 1. We may proceed as before and still further decrease this exponent and finally obtain

$$u^\lambda{}_{m-1}+v^\lambda{}_{m-1}=E(a)(1-a)^\lambda w^\lambda{}_{m-1},$$

but this relation is easily seen to be impossible from the remarks made in the first part of the demonstration.

Kronecker[19] obtained in another way Kummer's[18] criterion for the divisibility of the first factor of the class number of the field $\Omega(a)$, where $a^\lambda=1$, $a\neq 1$, λ an odd prime. Retaining Kummer's notation, the problem reduces to the question as to whether the congruence

$$\psi(\gamma^{2n-1})=b_0+b_1\gamma^{2n-1}+\ldots+b_{\lambda-2}\gamma^{(\lambda-2)(2n-1)}\equiv 0 \pmod{\lambda}$$

is or is not satisfied for one of the values $n=1, 2, 3, \ldots, \mu$. Setting

$$\lambda b_k=\gamma\cdot\gamma_{k-1}-\gamma_k,$$

the above gives

$$\lambda\cdot\psi(\gamma^{2n-1})=\Sigma(\gamma\gamma_{k-1}-\gamma_k)\gamma^{(2n-1)k}\equiv 0 \pmod{\lambda^2},$$

the summation extending over the values

$$k=0, 1, 2, 3, \ldots, (\lambda-2).$$

Using the identity

$$\gamma^k-(\gamma^k-\gamma_k)=\gamma_k$$

for k, and also $k-1$ in lieu of k, we obtain, after some transformations,

$$2n\cdot\Sigma(\gamma\gamma_{k-1}-\gamma_k)\gamma^{(2n-1)k}\equiv\gamma^{2n}\Sigma\gamma_{k-1}{}^{2n}-\Sigma\gamma_k{}^{2n} \pmod{\lambda^2},$$

which gives immediately

$$2n\cdot\Sigma(\gamma\gamma_{k-1}-\gamma_k)\gamma^{(2n-1)k}$$
$$\equiv(\gamma^{2n}-1)[1^{2n}+2^{2n}+\ldots+(\lambda-1)^{2n}] \pmod{\lambda^2}.$$

In the case $n=\mu$ he shows that the right-hand member is never divisible by λ^2, since we may select γ so that $\gamma^{2\mu}-1$ is divisible by λ but not by λ^2; hence, since

$$1^{2n}+2^{2n}+\ldots+(\lambda-1)^{2n}\equiv\pm B_n\cdot\lambda \pmod{\lambda^2}$$

for $n=1, 2, \ldots, \mu-1$, we have the criterion desired.

Kummer[20] made a further investigation of Fermat's last theorem. For the purposes of this report his long discussion will be divided into four parts, each part being concerned with the proof of a certain theorem

[19] J. de Math., (2), 1: 396-398 (1856).

[20] Abhandlungen der Königlichen Akademie der Wissenschaften zu Berlin, Math.-Phys. Klasse, 1857: 41-74. Abstract in Berlin Monatsberichte, 1857: 275-282.

involving algebraic numbers. He attempts to prove that (1) for $p=\lambda$, is impossible for any rational integers x, y, z, under the three assumptions:

Assumption I: The first factor of the class number H is divisible by λ but not by λ^2.

Assumption II: If $B_\nu \equiv 0 \pmod{\lambda}$, $\nu < \frac{1}{2}(\lambda-1)$, there exists an ideal in the field $\Omega(a)$, $a^\lambda = 1$, $a \neq 1$, with respect to which as a modulus the unit

$$E_\nu(a) = \prod_{k=0}^{\mu-1} e(a^{\gamma^k})^{\gamma^{-2k\nu}}$$

is not congruent to the λ-th power of an integer in $\Omega(a)$.

Assumption III: The Bernoulli number $B_{\nu\lambda}$ is not divisible by λ^3.

The first of the above-mentioned theorems is

Theorem (I): If there is but one of the first $\mu-1$ Bernoulli numbers divisible by λ, say $B_\nu \equiv 0 \pmod{\lambda}$, and the second factor of the class number of the field defined by the λ-th root of unity is also divisible by λ, then $E_\nu(a)$ is the λ-th power of a unit in the field $\Omega(a)$.

Here a is a primitive λ-th root of unity and when we speak of a Bernoulli number being divisible by an integer, we mean the numerator is divisible by the integer. Also, λ is an odd prime and $\mu = (\lambda-1)/2$. For the demonstration of this, he first remarked that under the assumption that the first factor of the class number is divisible by λ, it will follow from the investigations in Kummer[17] that there is but one of the first $\mu-1$ Bernoulli numbers divisible by λ. He calls this particular Bernoulli number B_ν. (Incomplete, cf. Vandiver.[64])

As from Kummer,[17] p. 480, if the second factor of the class number is divisible by λ then we have

$$\epsilon(a)^{h\lambda} = e(a)^{r_1} \cdot e(a^\gamma)^{r_2} \cdot e(a^{\gamma^2})^{r_3} \cdots e(a^{\gamma^{\mu-2}})^{r_{\mu-1}} \tag{7}$$

γ being a primitive root of λ and

$$e(a) = \sqrt{\frac{(1-a^\gamma)(1-a^{-\gamma})}{(1-a)(1-a^{-1})}}$$

and the integers $r_1, r_2, \ldots, r_{\mu-1}$ are not all divisible by λ, $\epsilon(a)$ being a fundamental unit. From this it follows that

$$r_1 + \gamma^{2n} r_2 + \gamma^{4n} r_3 + \cdots + \gamma^{2(\mu-2)n} r_{\mu-1} \equiv 0, \bmod \lambda,$$

for all values of n in the series $1, 2, 3, \ldots, \mu-1$, for which the n-th Bernoulli number B_n is not divisible by λ. For the case $n=\nu$ we have

$$r_1 + \gamma^{2\nu} r_2 + \gamma^{4\nu} r_3 + \cdots + \gamma^{2(\mu-2)\nu} r_{\mu-1} \equiv \mu m, \bmod \lambda,$$

where m is a rational integer. From the last two sets of congruences we obtain by elimination

$$r_{k+1} = m\gamma^{-2k\nu} - m\gamma^{2\nu} + \lambda s_{k+1},$$

where s_{k+1} is an integer. Applying this to the relation (7) we have

$$\epsilon(a)^{h\lambda}=(e(a)e(a^{\gamma})^{\gamma^{-2n}}e(a^{\gamma^2})^{\gamma^{-4n}}\dots e(a^{\gamma^{\mu-1}})^{\gamma^{-2(\mu-1)n}})^m U(a)^{\lambda},$$

where $U(a)$ is some unit in the field $\Omega(a)$. Setting

$$E_n(a)=e(a)e(a^{\gamma})^{\gamma^{-2n}}e(a^{\gamma^2})^{\gamma^{-4n}}\dots e(a^{\gamma^{\mu-1}})^{\gamma^{-2(\mu-1)n}},$$

we have

$$\epsilon(a)^{h\lambda}=E_{\nu}(a)^m U(a)^{\lambda}.$$

Since m is prime to λ, we obtain easily

$$E_{\nu}(a)=\mathfrak{E}(a)^{\lambda}.$$

Theorem II. If $B_{\nu}\equiv 0 \pmod{\lambda}$ but $B_{\nu\lambda}\not\equiv 0 \pmod{\lambda^3}$, then a unit in $\Omega(a)$ which is congruent modulo λ^2 to a rational integer is the λth power of a unit in $\Omega(a)$.

To show this he takes any unit in the field $E(a)$ and sets

$$E(a)^t=\pm a^s e(a)^m e(a^{\gamma})^{m_1} e(a^{\gamma^2})^{m_2}\dots e(a^{\gamma^{\mu-1}})^{m_{\mu-1}}$$

where $s, m, m_1, \dots, m_{\mu-1}$ and t are rational integers, the latter integer being the least exponent to which $E(a)$ must be raised in order to be expressed as the product of integral powers of the e's. He then applies to this relation the congruence

$$\text{(7a)}\qquad (\lambda-1)l\left(\frac{\phi(a)}{\phi(1)}\right)\equiv l\left(\frac{N\phi(a)}{[\phi(1)]^{\lambda-1}}\right)+\sum_{i=0}^{\lambda-2}\frac{d_0{}^{i\lambda n}l\phi(e^{v})}{dv^{i\lambda n}}\chi_i(a)$$

modulo λ^{n+1}. In this formula $\phi(a)$ is an algebraic integer in the field $\Omega(a)$, and the symbol

$$l\left(\frac{\phi(a)}{\phi(1)}\right)$$

modulo λ^{n+1}, represents that part of the logarithmic series

$$\frac{\phi(a)-\phi(1)}{\phi(1)}-\frac{1}{2}\left(\frac{\phi(a)-\phi(1)}{\phi(1)}\right)^2+\frac{1}{3}\left(\frac{\phi(a)-\phi(1)}{\phi(1)}\right)^3\dots$$

none of whose terms are divisible by λ^{n+1}. The symbol $N\phi(a)$ stands for the norm of $\phi(a)$ and

$$\frac{d_0{}^{s}l\phi(e^{v})}{dv^{s}}$$

indicates that $\log\phi(e^{v})$ is to be differentiated s times and zero substituted for v in the result. Further,

$$\chi_i(a)=a+\gamma^{-i\lambda^n}a^{\gamma}+\gamma^{-2i\lambda^n}a^{\gamma^2}+\dots+\gamma^{-(\lambda-2)i\lambda^n}a^{\gamma^{\lambda-2}},$$

which KUMMER [20a] had attempted to prove in another article. (Error, cf. Vandiver.[64])

[20a] J. reine angew. Math., 44: 134 (1852).

We then proceed to

Theorem III. If $F(a)$ is an integer in the field $\Omega(a+a^{-1})$, and if

$$\frac{d_0{}^{2\nu}lF(e^v)}{dv^{2\nu}} \equiv 0 \pmod{\lambda},$$

then a unit $E(a)$ in $\Omega(a)$ can be found such that

$$E(a)F(a) \equiv a \pmod{\lambda},$$

where a is a rational integer.

In the argument covering this (pp. 48-50), the incorrect formula just mentioned is also used. He then considered

Theorem IV. Under Assumptions I and II, if P is an ideal such that P^λ is the actual integer $F(a)$ and $B_\nu \equiv 0 \pmod{\lambda}$, then P is or is not an actual integer according as

$$\frac{d_0{}^{\lambda-2\nu}lF(e^v)}{dv^{\lambda-2\nu}} \equiv \text{ or } \not\equiv 0 \pmod{\lambda}.$$

To demonstrate this, Kummer uses first the following congruence

$$\text{(7b)} \quad \text{Ind } E_n(a) \equiv \frac{\gamma^{2n}-1}{2(1+r^{\lambda-2n}-(r+1)^{\lambda-2n})} \cdot \frac{d_0{}^{\lambda-2n}l\Psi_r(e^v)}{dv^{\lambda-2n}}, \mod \lambda,$$

established in Kummer[20a] (p. 103), in which $f(a)$ is an ideal prime in the field $\Omega(a)$ and ind $E_n(a)$ is the integer i in the relation

$$(E_n(a))^{(q-1)/\lambda} \equiv a^i \pmod{f(a)},$$

q being the rational prime which $f(a)$ divides, $q \equiv 1 \pmod{\lambda}$,

$$\psi_r(a) = \Sigma a^{-(r+1)h+\text{ind}(g^h+1)}$$

where g is a primitive root of $f(a)$ such that

$$g^{(q-1)/\lambda} \equiv a \pmod{f(a)};$$

h ranges over the integers 0, 1, 2, ..., $q-2$, excepting $(q-1)/2$. (This relation is proved only for $f(a)$ an ideal of the first degree, whereas Kummer applies Theorem IV to ideals not necessarily of the first degree. Cf. Vandiver.[64])

He writes for the class number $H = H_1\lambda$ where H_1 is not divisible by λ, and we may put

$$f(a)^{H_1\lambda} = F(a)$$

where $F(a)$ is an integer in the field $\Omega(a)$. This gives by a known property of the function $\Psi_r(a)$

$$\Psi_r(a)^{H_1\lambda} = \pm \Pi F(a^{\gamma^h})$$

where the product runs over all those values of h in the series 0, 1, 2, . . ., $\lambda-2$, for which

$$\gamma_{\mu-h}+\gamma_{\mu-h+\text{ind }r}>\lambda$$

where γ_i is the least positive integer which is congruent to γ^i (mod λ).

Then using the relation, (not proved, cf. Vandiver [64]) where

$$\phi(a)\equiv\phi_1(a)\quad(\text{mod }\lambda^{r+1}),$$

$$\frac{d_0{}^{m\lambda^r}l\phi(e^v)}{dv^{m\lambda^r}}\equiv\frac{d_0{}^{m\lambda^r}l\phi_1(e^v)}{dv^{m\lambda^r}},\text{ mod }\lambda^{r+1},$$

he obtains

$$H_1\lambda\text{ Ind }E_n(a)\equiv\frac{\gamma^{2n}-1}{2(1+r^{\lambda-2n}-(r+1)^{\lambda-2n})}\cdot\frac{d_0{}^{(\lambda-2n)\lambda}lF(e^v)}{dv^{(\lambda-2n)\lambda}}\cdot\sum\gamma^{(\lambda-2n)\lambda h}$$

Comparing this with the congruence (7b) above, we obtain

$$H_1\lambda\frac{d_0{}^{(\lambda-2n)\lambda}l\Psi_r(e^v)}{dv^{(\lambda-2n)\lambda}}\equiv\sum\frac{d_0{}^{(\lambda-2n)\lambda}lF(e^{v\gamma^h})}{dv^{(\lambda-2n)\lambda}},$$

modulo λ^2, where the summation extends over all the values of h as defined above.

Kummer then goes through a special investigation involving rational integers only which leads him to

$$\sum\gamma^{(\lambda-2n)\lambda}\equiv(1+r^{(\lambda-2n)\lambda}-(r+1)^{(\lambda-2n)\lambda})(-1)^{\mu+\nu}B_{\nu\lambda-\mu},\text{ mod }\lambda^2,$$

which yields

$$\text{Ind }E_\nu(a)\equiv\frac{(-1)^{\nu+\mu}(\gamma^{2\nu}-1)B_{\nu\lambda-\mu}}{2H_1\lambda}\cdot\frac{d_0{}^{\lambda-2\nu}lF(e^v)}{dv^{\lambda-2\nu}},\text{ mod }\lambda.$$

Kummer, in §5, employs the symbol

$$\left(\frac{\Phi(a)}{f(a)}\right)$$

and defines it to have the value a^i where

$$\Phi(a)^{Nf(a)-1/\lambda}\equiv a^i,\quad\text{mod }f(a),$$

and we also write $i\equiv\text{Ind }\Phi(a)$, modulo λ. If $\phi(a)$ is a composite ideal so that $\phi(a)=f(a)\cdot f_1(a)\cdot f_2(a)\ldots$, we write

$$\left(\frac{\Phi(a)}{\phi(a)}\right)=\left(\frac{\Phi(a)}{f(a)}\right)\cdot\left(\frac{\Phi(a)}{f_1(a)}\right)\cdot\left(\frac{\Phi(a)}{f_2(a)}\right)\cdots.$$

If

$$\left(\frac{E_\nu(a)}{\phi(a)}\right)=a^i$$

and $i=\text{ind }E_\nu(a)$, then

$$\text{Ind }E_\nu(a)\equiv\frac{(-1)^{\nu+\mu}(\gamma^{2\nu}-1)B_{\nu\lambda-\mu}}{2H_1\lambda}\cdot\frac{d_0{}^{\lambda-2\nu}\phi(e^v)^{H_1\lambda}}{dv^{\lambda-2\nu}},\text{ mod }\lambda.$$

It is then noted that if $\phi(\alpha)$ is an actual integer in the field $\Omega(\alpha)$,

$$\left(\frac{E_\nu(\alpha)}{\phi(\alpha)}\right)=1.$$

Also, if $\phi(\alpha)$ and $\phi_1(\alpha)$ are two equivalent ideals, then

$$\left(\frac{E_\nu(\alpha)}{\phi(\alpha)}\right)=\left(\frac{E_\nu(\alpha)}{\phi_1(\alpha)}\right).$$

Using Assumption II, it follows that

$$\left(\frac{E_\nu(\alpha)}{X(\alpha)}\right)=\alpha^i, \quad \text{where } i\not\equiv 0, \quad \text{mod } \lambda,$$

where $X(\alpha)$ is a prime ideal in the field $\Omega(\alpha)$ which belongs to the exponent $h\lambda$ where h is not divisible by λ and therefore

$$\left(\frac{E_\nu(\alpha)}{\phi(\alpha)^m}\right)=\alpha^{him}, \quad \text{Ind } E_\nu(\alpha)\equiv him, \quad \text{mod } \lambda,$$

where $\phi(\alpha)=X(\alpha)^h$ and m is any integer. If $f(\alpha)$ is any ideal which belongs to the exponent λ it is equivalent to one of the ideals

$$\phi(\alpha), \quad \phi(\alpha)^2, \quad \phi(\alpha)^3, \quad \ldots, \quad \phi(\alpha)^{\lambda-1}.$$

If $f(\alpha)$ is equivalent to $\phi(\alpha)^m$, then

$$\text{Ind } E_\nu(\alpha)\equiv him, \quad \text{mod } \lambda,$$

where the index is taken with respect to the ideal $f(\alpha)$. Since hi is not divisible by λ, then the index of $E_\nu(\alpha)$ is necessarily congruent to 0 or not congruent to 0 according as m is congruent to 0 or not congruent to 0, or, what is the same thing, according as $f(\alpha)$ is an integer or an ideal in the field. Setting $f(\alpha)^\lambda=F(\alpha)$, then

$$\text{Ind } E_\nu(\alpha)\equiv\frac{(-1)^{\nu+\mu}(\gamma^{2\nu}-1)B_{\nu\lambda-\mu}}{2\lambda}\cdot\frac{d_0{}^{\lambda-2\nu}lF(e^v)}{dv^{\lambda-2\nu}}, \quad \text{mod } \lambda,$$

from which it follows that $\text{Ind } E_\nu(\alpha)\equiv 0 \pmod{\lambda}$ only if the second factor of the right-hand member of this congruence is divisible by λ, which completes the discussion of Theorem IV.

Kummer also derives from what has just been given the result that if the λth power of an ideal belonging to the field $\Omega(\alpha+\alpha^{-1})$ is an integer in that field, then the ideal is also an integer in the field.

He then applies these results to Fermat's last theorem, assuming that $x^\lambda+y^\lambda+z^\lambda=0$ where x, y, z, are rational integers prime to each other and to λ. Assume first that x, y, z are each prime to λ as in Kummer [18]

$$x+\alpha y=\epsilon(\alpha)f(\alpha)^\lambda$$

whence

$$x+\alpha^{\gamma^h}y=\epsilon(\alpha^{\gamma^h})f(\alpha^{\gamma^h})^\lambda$$

where h is not divisible by λ. Giving h all those values in the set 0, 1, 2, ..., $\lambda-2$, for which

$$\gamma_{\mu-h}+\gamma_{\mu-h+\text{ind } r}>\lambda$$

we obtain by multiplication

$$\Pi(x+a^{\gamma^h}y)=\Pi\epsilon(a^{\gamma^h})(\Pi f(a^{\gamma^h}))^\lambda$$

where the products range over all the values of h just mentioned. The product $\Pi f(a^{\gamma^h})$ is an integer in the field $\Omega(a)$. Also, he finds that $\Pi\epsilon(a^{\gamma^h})$ is a power of a which gives

$$\Pi(x+a^{\gamma^h}y)=\pm a^k\phi(a)^\lambda.$$

Replacing this equality by an identity with e^v in lieu of a, and taking the $(\lambda-2n)$-th derivative of the logarithm of both members and substituting $v=0$, we have

$$\frac{d_0{}^{\lambda-2n}l(x+e^vy)}{dv^{\lambda-2n}}\sum\gamma^{(\lambda-2n)h}\equiv 0, \quad \text{mod } \lambda,$$

where the summation extends over all those values of h used in the above product and n is any integer in the set 1, 2, 3, ..., $\mu-1$.

By previous results it is noted that

$$\sum\gamma^{(\lambda-2n)h}\equiv(-1)^n(1+r^{\lambda-2n}-(r+1)^{\lambda-2n})\frac{B_n}{2n}, \quad \text{mod } \lambda,$$

and since we may choose r so that the factor in the above congruence involving $r\not\equiv 0 \pmod{\lambda}$, then for all values of n other than $n=\nu$, by using Assumption I, we have

$$\frac{d_0{}^{\lambda-2n}l(x+e^vy)}{dv^{\lambda-2n}}\equiv 0, \quad \text{mod } \lambda.$$

Kummer then examines this congruence for $n=\mu-1$ and $n=\mu-2$, as well as those congruences obtained by substituting z in place of x, x in place of y, etc., and finds that all the congruences cannot be satisfied for either of these two values of n, which establishes a contradiction. These results are equivalent to the statement that if (1) for $p=\lambda$, is satisfied in Case I, then $B_{\mu-1}\equiv B_{\mu-2}\equiv 0 \pmod{\lambda}$. He notes that the first of these criteria is equivalent to that given by Cauchy.[12a]

Kummer then considers (1) for $p=\lambda$, in which x, y, z are prime to each other, $z=\lambda^k z_1$, where z_1 is prime to λ. He uses this relation in the more general form

$$U^\lambda+V^\lambda=E(a)(2-a-a^{-1})^{m\lambda}W^\lambda, \tag{8}$$

where U, V, W are integers in the field $\Omega(a+a^{-1})$ prime to each other and to $(1-a)$, $E(a)$ is a unit in the field $\Omega(a)$, and $m>1$. By a method analogous to that used in Kummer,[18] Case II, we obtain

$$U+a^rV=\epsilon_r(a)(1-a^r)\Theta_r(a)^\lambda, \tag{9}$$

where $r=1, 2, 3, \ldots, \lambda-1$, and

$$U+V=\epsilon(a)(2-a-a^{-1})^{m\lambda-\mu}T(a)^\lambda \tag{10}$$

where $\epsilon_r(a)$ and $\epsilon(a)$ are units in the field $\Omega(a)$, $\Theta_r(a)$ is an ideal in the field $\Omega(a)$, and $T(a)$ is an ideal in the field $\Omega(a+a^{-1})$.

Eliminating U from the last two relations we have

$$V=-\epsilon_r(a)\Theta_r(a)^\lambda+\frac{\epsilon(a)(2-a-a^{-1})^{m\lambda-\mu}T(a)^\lambda}{1-a^r}$$

whence we obtain

$$\frac{d_0{}^{\lambda-2\nu}lV(e^v)}{dv^{\lambda-2\nu}}\equiv\frac{d_0{}^{\lambda-2\nu}l\epsilon_r(e^v)}{dv^{\lambda-2\nu}}+\frac{d_0{}^{\lambda-2\nu}l(\Theta_r(e^v)^\lambda)}{dv^{\lambda-2\nu}}, \quad (\text{mod } \lambda),$$

which reduces to

$$\frac{d_0{}^{\lambda-2\nu}l(\Theta_r(e^v)^\lambda)}{dv^{\lambda-2\nu}}\equiv 0, \quad \text{mod } \lambda,$$

showing by the use of Theorem IV that $\Theta_r(a)$ is an integer in the field $\Omega(a)$. It also follows that $T(a)$ is an integer in the field $\Omega(a+a^{-1})$.

Setting a^{-1} in lieu of a in the last relation involving V, and comparing with the original relation, we obtain a result which reduces to

$$\Theta_r(a)^\lambda-\Theta_r(a^{-1})^\lambda=\epsilon'(a)(1-a)^{(2m-1)\lambda}T(a)^\lambda,$$

where $\epsilon'(a)$ is a unit in $\Omega(a)$. From this relation we find

$$\Theta_r(a)-a^t\Theta_r(a^{-1})=\epsilon''_t(a)(1-a^t)P_t(a)^\lambda$$

for $t=1, 2, 3, \ldots, \lambda-1$, and

$$\Theta_r(a)-\Theta_r(a^{-1})=\epsilon''(a)(1-a)^{(2m-2)\lambda+1}Q(a)^\lambda,$$

where $P_t(a)$ and $Q(a)$ are ideals in the field $\Omega(a)$, and $\epsilon''_t(a)$, $\epsilon''(a)$, are units in the field $\Omega(a)$. Eliminating $\Theta_r(a^{-1})$ we obtain

$$\Theta_r(a)\equiv\epsilon''_t(a)P_t(a)^\lambda, \quad \text{mod } (1-a)^{(2m-2)\lambda}$$

and

$$\Theta_r(a^{-1})\equiv\epsilon''_t(a^{-1})P_t(a^{-1})^\lambda, \quad \text{mod } (1-a)^{(2m-2)\lambda}$$

whence

$$\Theta_r(a)\Theta_r(a^{-1})\equiv\epsilon''_t(a)\epsilon''_t(a^{-1})(P_t(a)P_t(a^{-1}))^\lambda, \quad \text{mod } (1-a)^{(2m-2)\lambda}$$

From the last relation we obtain by setting $a=e^v$ and changing the relation into an identity, differentiating 2ν times,

$$\frac{d_0{}^{2\nu}l(\Theta_r(e^v)\Theta_r(e^{-v}))}{dv^{2\nu}}\equiv 0, \quad \text{mod } \lambda,$$

which shows by Theorem III that $\Theta_r(a)$ and $\Theta_r(a^{-1})$ may be multiplied by a certain unit so that the product is congruent to a rational integer modulo λ.

From relations (9) and (10) we obtain

$$U^2+(a^r+a^{-r})UV+V^2=\epsilon_r(a)\epsilon_r(a^{-1})(2-a^r-a^{-r})(\Theta_r(a)\Theta_r(a^{-1}))^\lambda,$$
$$U^2+(a^s+a^{-s})UV+V^2=\epsilon_s(a)\epsilon_s(a^{-1})(2-a^s-a^{-s})(\Theta_s(a)\Theta_s(a^{-1}))^\lambda,$$
$$U^2+2UV+V^2=\epsilon(a)^2(2-a-a^{-1})^{2m\lambda-2\mu}T(a)^{2\lambda}.$$

Eliminating the two quantities U^2+V^2 and UV, we obtain, after some reductions, and making use of the last mentioned property of $\Theta_r(a)$ and $\Theta_r(a^{-1})$,

$${}_r(a)T_r(a)^\lambda-\mathfrak{e}_s(a)T_s(a)^\lambda=\frac{\epsilon(a)^2(2-a-a^{-1})^{2m\lambda-2\mu}(a^r+a^{-r}-a^s-a^{-s})T(a)^{2\lambda}}{(2-a^r-a^{-r})(2-a^s-a^{-s})}$$

where $\mathfrak{e}_r(a)$ and $\mathfrak{e}_s(a)$ are units in the field $\Omega(a)$, $T_r(a)$ and $T_s(a)$ are integers in the field $\Omega(a+a^{-1})$, which are congruent to rational integers modulo λ. It is then shown that the unit $\dfrac{\mathfrak{e}_s(a)}{\mathfrak{e}_r(a)}$ is congruent to a rational integer modulo λ^2, and using Theorem III, we infer that this unit is the λth power of a unit in the field $\Omega(a)$, hence the last relation may be written

$$U_1{}^\lambda+V_1{}^\lambda=E_1(a)(2-a-a^{-1})^{(2m-1)\lambda}W_1{}^\lambda,$$

where U_1, V_1, W_1 are integers in the field $\Omega(a+a^{-1})$, prime to each other, and $E_1(a)$ is a unit in the field $\Omega(a)$. This equation has the same form as (8) with $2m-1$ in lieu of m. Comparing the value of W_1 with the value of W we see that since $W_1=T(a)^2$ then W_1 necessarily contains a lesser number of distinct prime ideal factors than does W, aside from the exceptional case when W is equal to $T(a)$ times a unit in the field, in which event

$$\frac{U+a^rV}{1-a^r}$$

is a unit in the field $\Omega(a)$ for $r=1, 2, 3, \ldots, \lambda-1$, whence

$$\frac{U+a^rV}{1-a^r}=\frac{a^k(U+a^{-r}V)}{1-a^{-r}}$$

which gives, using $U+V\equiv 0 \pmod{\lambda}$,

$$(1-a^k)(1-a^r)\equiv 0, \quad \text{mod } \lambda,$$

and this is impossible for $\lambda>3$. Hence we obtain by repetitions of our processes a series of integers in the field $\Omega(a)$, W, W_1, W_2, W_3, $\ldots$, in each of which the number of distinct ideal factors is less than in the preceding, which is impossible.

Kummer then tests Assumptions I, II, III, for $\lambda=37$, 59 and 67, and finds all of them satisfied in each case; hence he concludes that (1) is impossible for any odd prime $p=\lambda<100$.

SMITH[21] reported on Kummer's[17] derivation of the criterion of the divisibility of the first factor of the class number by λ. In the part of the demonstration where the expression

$$\gamma^{-(2n-1)}\psi(\gamma^{2n-1})$$

is transformed, Smith employs in lieu of Kummer's work the identity

$$\sum_{x=1}^{x=\lambda-1} I\frac{\gamma x}{\lambda}\cdot f(x)+\sum_{x=1}^{x=\gamma-1} F\left(I\frac{\lambda x}{\gamma}\right)=(\gamma-1)F(\lambda-1),$$

where $f(x)$ is any function of x and $F(x)=\sum_{x=1}^{x} f(x)$. He establishes this relation by a geometric method and obtains therefrom Kummer's[18] relation

$$\sum_{x=1}^{x=\gamma-1} F_{2n-1}\left(-\frac{x}{\gamma}\right)=\frac{(-1)^n B_n(\gamma^{2n}-1)}{2n\gamma^{2n-1}}.$$

He also reproduced[21a] Kummer's demonstration that

$$x^\lambda+y^\lambda+z^\lambda=0$$

has no non-zero solutions in rational integers x, y, z, where λ is a regular prime >3.

SMITH[22] stated that if λ is an exceptional prime satisfying the Assumptions I, II, III of Kummer,[20] then Kummer showed that the equation

$$x^\lambda+y^\lambda+z^\lambda=0$$

is insolvable for x, y, z integers in the field $\Omega(a+a^{-1})$, one of the integers x, y, z being divisible by $1-a$, a being a primitive λ^{th} root of unity. Kummer's work as it stands, however, only gives this result under the assumption that there is no common factor of all the integers x, y, z

KUMMER[23] considers further the subject of irregular primes, observing "Eine nähere Untersuchung der besonderen Eigenschaften derjenigen Primzahlen λ, für welche die Klassenzahl durch λ theilbar ist, hat mich schon oft und dauernd beschäftigt." He computes the numerical value of the first factor of the class number of the λth roots of unity, λ an odd

[21] Report on the Theory of Numbers, Collected Works, I, 1894, 114-117. Report of the British Association, Part II, 1860: 136-138.

[21a] L. c., 131-137; 148-152, respectively.

[22] Report on the Theory of Numbers, Collected Works, Vol. I, 134-135, footnote. Report of British Assn., Part II, 1860: 150-151.

[23] Berlin Monatsberichte, 1874: 239-248.

prime, for $100<\lambda<164$. The method employed depends on expressing this first factor, multiplied by $(2\lambda)^{\mu-1}$, $\mu=(\lambda-1)/2$ in the form

$$P=N\phi(\beta)\cdot N\phi(\beta^m)\cdot N\phi(\beta^{m'})\ldots$$

where $1, m, m', m'', \ldots$ range over all the odd divisors of $\lambda-1$. It is found that the only irregular primes between the limits mentioned are 101, 103, 131, 149, 157. For $\lambda=157$, the first factor of the class number is divisible by 157^2 and not by 157^3, but in the other cases by the first power of λ only. For $\lambda=101$, the 34th Bernoulli number is divisible by λ; for $\lambda=103$, the 12th Bernoulli number; for $\lambda=131$, the 11th Bernoulli number; for $\lambda=149$, the 65th Bernoulli number; for $\lambda=157$, the 31st and 55th Bernoulli numbers.

Kummer concludes the article with some speculations (p. 248) on the frequency of irregular primes. Cf. Kummer,[39] Jensen,[58] Vandiver,[66] Hensel.[40]

Mirimanoff[24] gave a new criterion for the divisibility of the second factor of the class number of the field defined by θ where θ is a root of $x^\lambda=1$, $\theta\neq 1$, λ an odd prime, by λ. Set

$$\lambda=2\nu+1, \qquad e(\theta)=\frac{(1-\theta^g)(1-\theta^{-g})}{(1-\theta)(1-\theta^{-1})}, \qquad e_\kappa=e(\theta^{g^\kappa})$$
$$(\kappa=0, 1, 2, \ldots, \nu-1),$$

where g is a primitive root of λ. The second factor of the class number is divisible by λ if there exists a set of integral exponents $m_0, m_1, \ldots, m_{\nu-3}, m_{\nu-2}$, such that $e_0^{m_0}e_1^{m_1}\ldots e_{\nu-2}^{m_{\nu-2}}$ is equal to the λ-th power of a unit in the field $\Omega(\theta)$ and not all the m's are divisible by λ. Cf. Kummer,[17] pp. 480-481.

Using Kronecker's[24a] notation of symbolic powers, we put

$$e_0^{m_0}e_1^{m_1}\ldots e_{\nu-2}^{m_{\nu-2}}=e^{m_0+m_1x+\ldots+m_{\nu-2}x^{\nu-2}}=e^{m(x)};$$

whence

$$\left(e^{m(x)}\right)^{n(x)}=e^{m(x)\cdot n(x)},$$

where the exponents are reduced by the use of the formula

$$x^{\nu-1}+x^{\nu-2}+\ldots+x+1=0.$$

Let d be an arbitrary divisor of ν; p, q, etc., the distinct prime divisors of d; set $\nu=\delta d$. A unit ϵ is said to belong to the divisor d if

$$\epsilon_\kappa=\epsilon_{d+\kappa}=\ldots=\epsilon_{(\delta-1)d+\kappa},$$
$$\epsilon_\kappa\cdot\epsilon_{d/p+\kappa}\cdots\epsilon_{(p-1)d/p+\kappa}=1,$$
$$\epsilon_\kappa\cdot\epsilon_{d/q+\kappa}\cdots\epsilon_{(q-1)d/q+\kappa}=1,$$

[24] J. reine angew. Math., 109: 82-88 (1892).
[24a] J. reine angew. Math., 93: 32 (1882).

in which ϵ_κ is put in place of $\epsilon(\theta^{g^\kappa})$. If ϵ belongs to the divisor d, the symbol $\epsilon^{m(x)}$ may be replaced by $\epsilon^{m(r_d)}$, r_d being a primitive root of the equation $z^d-1=0$. Set

$$\overset{(d)}{\epsilon}=e^{(1+x^d+\ldots+x^{(\delta-1)d})(1-x^{d/p})(1-x^{d/q})\ldots}$$

If $d_1, d_2, \ldots, d_\kappa$ are the different divisors of ν, we have the theorem that if $e^{m(x)}$ is the λ-th power of a unit in the field, $m(x)$ being prime to λ, one or more of the units $\overset{(d_i)}{\epsilon}{}^{m(r_{d_i})}$ satisfies the condition

$$\overset{(d_i)}{\epsilon}{}^{m(r_{d_i})}=\lambda^{\text{th}} \text{ power}$$

provided $m(r_{d_i})$ is not divisible by λ, and conversely if the unit $\overset{(d_i)}{\epsilon}{}^{m(r_{d_i})}$ is the λ-th power of a unit in the field and λ does not divide $m(r_{d_i})$, there exists always an exponent $n(x)$ prime to λ and such that $e^{n(x)}$ is the λ-th power of a unit in the field. Hence, if the second factor b of the class number is divisible by λ, we have for a particular i

$$\overset{(d_i)}{\epsilon}{}^{m(r_{d_i})}=\lambda^{\text{th}} \text{ power,}$$

the exponent $m(r_{d_i})$ being prime to λ. It is stated that this condition is necessary and sufficient. If $\overset{(d_i)}{\epsilon}{}^{m(r_{d_i})}$ is the λ-th power of a unit in the field, then the unit $\overset{(d_i)}{\epsilon}{}^{Nm(r_{d_i})}$ is also the λ-th power of a unit where $Nm(r_{d_i})$ is the norm of $m(r_{d_i})$ taken with respect to all the primitive roots of $z^{d_i}-1=0$.

Consider the decomposition of λ into prime factors in the field $\Omega(z)$ in Kummer's [13] sense. Further, suppose that these are also integers in the field and let $f_1, f_2, \ldots, f_j$ be the factors of this type of λ which also divide $m(r_{d_i})$ and set

$$R(r)=f_1^{n_1}f_2^{n_2}\ldots f_j^{n_j},$$

where f_k is contained exactly n_k times in $m(r_{d_i})$, $k=1, 2, \ldots, j$, hence

$$\overset{(d_i)}{\epsilon}{}^{R(r)}=\lambda^{\text{th}} \text{ power,}$$

and this gives, after some transformations, the result that if $\overset{(d_i)}{\epsilon}{}^{m(r_{d_i})}$ is the λ-th power of a unit in the field such that $m(r_{d_i})$ is not divisible by λ, it is necessary and sufficient that $\overset{(d_i)}{\epsilon}{}^{\frac{\lambda}{f_l}}$ be a λ-th power of a unit in the field for some value of l. Set $\nu=\delta_i d_i$ and let $c_0=1, c_1, c_2, \ldots, c_{\psi(d_i)-1}$ be the numbers less than and prime to d_i, then

$$\Pi_j(g^{2\delta_i\kappa}-r^{c_j})\equiv 0 \pmod{\lambda}$$

where r is a primitive root of $x^{d_i}-1=0$ and the κ is prime to d_i.

Mirimanoff then considers the unit obtained by replacing the f's which occur in the relation

$$\overset{(d_i)}{\epsilon}{}^{f_1 f_2 \ldots f_l} = \lambda^{\text{th}} \text{ power}$$

by the corresponding factors $g^{2\delta_i\kappa} - r^{c_j}$. Let ϵ_0 be the unit $\overset{(d_i)}{\epsilon}$ or a symbolic power of this unit, develop ϵ_0 in ascending powers of $t=1-\theta$, so that

$$\epsilon_0 \equiv 1 + at^a + bt^{a+1} + \ldots \pmod{\lambda}, \qquad a \not\equiv 0 \pmod{\lambda},$$

and we have

$$\epsilon_j = \epsilon_0(\theta^{g^j}) \equiv 1 + ag^{ja}t^a + \ldots \pmod{\lambda}$$
$$(j=1, 2, \ldots, \phi(d_i)-1).$$

These relations are then used to examine the congruence

$$\overset{(d_i)}{\epsilon}{}^{\frac{\lambda}{f_l}} \equiv 1 \pmod{\lambda}$$

which must hold if the left-hand member is the λ-th power of a unit. If the congruence does hold, he observes that if $\gamma_0, \gamma_1, \ldots, \gamma_{d_i-1}$ are the periods of $2\delta_i$ terms, and setting

$$M_\kappa = \sqrt[\lambda]{\overset{(d_i)}{\epsilon}{}_{d_i-\kappa}^{\frac{\lambda}{f_{c_j}}}} \qquad (\kappa=0, 1, 2, \ldots, d_i-1)$$

and

$$M_\kappa = a_0\gamma_{d_i-\kappa} + a_1\gamma_{d_i+1-\kappa} + \ldots + a_{d_i-1}\gamma_{2d_i-1-\kappa};$$
$$(\kappa=0, 1, \ldots, d_i-1)$$

then in order that the unit $\overset{(d_i)}{\epsilon}{}^{\frac{\lambda}{f_{c_j}}}$ is the λ-th power of a unit, it is necessary and sufficient that the coefficients $a_0, a_1, \ldots, a_{d_i-1}$ are rational integers.

These criteria are then applied to the particular case $\lambda=37$ and yield the result that the second factor of the class number of the field defined by a primitive 37th root of unity is prime to 37. Cf. Kummer,[20] p. 73. Other special results, p. 88, concerning units in this field are obtained.

Mirimanoff[25] applied the results of his[24] previous paper to the relation

$$x^{37} + y^{37} + z^{37} = 0$$

where x, y, z, are integers in the field defined by $(\theta+\theta^{-1})$, θ being a primitive root of $u^{37}-1=0$ and where z, assumed prime to x and y, is divisible by $\beta=(1-\theta)(1-\theta^{-1})$. In lieu of this equation we consider the more general form

(11) $$x^{37} + y^{37} = \epsilon\beta^\kappa z^{37},$$

[25] J. reine angew. Math., 111: 26-30 (1893).

where ϵ is some unit in the field $\Omega(\theta+\theta^{-1})$, κ is a multiple of 37, and x, y, z, are defined as above and are also prime to β. Further, assume that the numbers $(x+y)^2$ and xy belong to the field $\Omega(\theta+\theta^{-1}+\theta^{g^9}+\theta^{-g^9})$, g being a primitive root of 37, and we have

$$x^{37}+y^{37}=(x+y)\prod_{i=1}^{i=18}(x^2+y^2+\delta_i xy),$$

where

$$\delta_i=\theta^i+\theta^{-i},$$

whence

(12) $$\begin{cases} x+y=e_0\beta^{\kappa-18}u_0^{37}, \\ (x+y)^2-(2-\delta_i)xy=e_i\beta u_i^{37}, \end{cases}$$

$$(i=1,\ 2,\ \ldots,\ 18)$$

where e_0, e_i are units and u_0, u_i are integers in the field $\Omega(\theta)$ prime to β. For $i=1$, this gives

(13) $$(x+y)^2-\beta xy=\epsilon^{36}\beta\nu_1^{37},$$

where ϵ is a unit in the field $\Omega(\theta+\theta^{-1})$ and $\nu_1=e_1u_1$. Putting

$$\frac{\epsilon^{36}}{\epsilon_9^{\ 6}\epsilon_3^{\ 2}}=E(\theta),$$

also, if ϵ_a belongs to the divisor a of 18,

$$x=\epsilon_9^{\ 3}\epsilon_3x'; \qquad y=\epsilon_9^{\ 3}\epsilon_3y'; \qquad z=\epsilon_9^{\ 3}\epsilon_3z',$$

it is shown by means of the results of his previous[24] paper that $E(\theta)$ is the 37-th power of a unit so that (13) becomes

$$(x'+y')^2-\beta x'y'=\beta\xi^{37}.$$

In this relation set θ^{g^9} in place of θ and let β'' and ξ'' be the conjugates of β and ξ. These give, with (12),

$$\xi^{37}+\eta^{37}=\epsilon_0\frac{\beta''-\beta}{\beta''}\beta^{2k-37}\zeta^{37},$$

where $u_0^{\ 2}=\zeta$ and $-\xi''=\eta$ and ϵ_0 is a unit in the field $\Omega(\theta+\theta^{-1})$. This equation belongs to the class of equations (11) and the numbers $(\xi+\eta)^2$ and $\xi\eta$ belong to the field $\Omega(\theta+\theta^{-1}+\theta^{g^9}+\theta^{-g^9})$.

It may be proved by this manner of descent that we reach a contradiction. We have

$$\text{Mod. }(x^2+y^2+\delta_i xy)>\text{Mod. }\frac{(x+y)^2}{2},\ \text{for } \delta_i>0$$

and

$$\text{Mod. }(x^2+y^2+\delta_i xy)>\text{Mod. }\frac{(x-y)^2}{2},\ \text{for } \delta_i<0,$$

and these give

$$\text{Mod. }(\epsilon\beta^{\kappa}z^{37})>\frac{1}{2^{18}}\text{ Mod. }(x+y)^{19}\text{ Mod. }(x-y)^{18}.$$

Similar inequalities are obtained by taking the equations conjugate to (11) and they give on multiplication

$$37^{\kappa}\text{ Mod. }N(z)^{37} > \frac{1}{2^{18.18}}\text{ Mod. }N(x+y)^{19}\text{ Mod. }N(x-y)^{18},$$

where N designates the norm. Then, since

$$x+y=e_0\beta^{\kappa-18}u_0^{37},\qquad u_0^2=\zeta\qquad\text{and}\qquad \kappa\geqq 37,$$

we have

$$\text{Mod. }N(z^{37}) > \left(\frac{37}{2}\right)^{18.18}\text{ Mod. }N(\zeta^{37}),$$

from which we infer that the modulus of the norm of ζ is less than the modulus of the norm of z, and the moduli of the norms of z, ζ, etc., are always greater than $\left(\frac{37}{2}\right)^{18.18}$. Using the method of descent we obtain finally a number ζ such that

$$\text{Mod. }N(\zeta) < \left(\frac{37}{2}\right)^{18.18},$$

which yields the result that the equation (11) is never satisfied if the numbers x, y, z belong to the field $\Omega(\theta+\theta^{-1})$ and if the numbers $(x+y)^2$ and xy belong to the field $\Omega(\theta+\theta^{-1}+\theta^{g^9}+\theta^{-g^9})$, x, y, z being prime to each other in the field $(\theta+\theta^{-1})$.

Next, Mirimanoff considers the equation $x^{37}+y^{37}+z^{37}=0$ in which x, y, z are prime to $a=1-\theta$. Let η_3 be the period $(\theta+\theta^{g^{12}}+\theta^{g^{24}})$ and η_6 the period $\eta_3(\theta)+\eta_3(\theta^{-1})$. It is assumed that the numbers x, y, z are prime to each other and prime to $t=1-\theta$, and belong to the field $\Omega(\eta_6)$. We then have, if a, b and c are rational integers,

$$\left.\begin{aligned} x&\equiv a\\ y&\equiv b\\ z&\equiv c\end{aligned}\right.\quad(\text{mod. }t^6),$$

and

$$x^{37}+y^{37}=(x+y)\prod_{i=1}^{i=11}\left(x^3+x^2y\eta_3(\theta^{g^i})+xy^2\eta_3(\theta^{-g^i})+y^3\right)$$

which yields

$$x^3+x^2y\eta_3(\theta)+xy^2\eta_3(\theta^{-1})+y^3=\epsilon u_0^{37},$$

where ϵ is a unit in the field $\Omega(\eta_3)$ and since the number of classes of ideals in this field is not divisible by 37, u_0 is an integer in the field. Replacing θ by θ^{-1} in this relation, we find

$$a^3+a^2b\eta_3(\theta)+ab^2\eta_3(\theta^{-1})+b^3\equiv a^3+ab^2\eta_3(\theta^{-1})+ab^2\eta_3(\theta)+b^3\quad(\text{mod. }t^6)$$

and therefore

$$(a-b)\left(\eta_3(\theta)-\eta_3(\theta^{-1})\right)\equiv 0\,(\text{mod. }t^6),$$

which yields the result that $(a-b)$ is divisible by 37. In the same wa[y] we find

$$a-c\equiv 0 \pmod{37} \qquad \text{and} \qquad b-c\equiv 0 \pmod{37},$$

which are inconsistent with $a+b+c\equiv 0 \pmod{37}$, and Mirimano[ff] then states the conclusion that $x^{37}+y^{37}+z^{37}=0$ is never satisfied i[n] integers x, y, z belonging to the field $\Omega(\eta_6)$ prime to each other an[d] to $1-\theta$. In particular, these results show that (1) is not satisfied i[n] rational integers for $p=37$.

WENDT[26] proved that if $m=2^\nu p^k$ can be so chosen that $mp+1$ is [a] prime not dividing D_m where ν is not divisible by the prime p, then (1) is impossible in Case I. Cf. Vandiver.[84] Here

$$D_m=\begin{vmatrix} 1 & \binom{m}{1} & \binom{m}{2}\cdots\cdots\binom{m}{m-1} \\ \binom{m}{m-1} & 1 & \binom{m}{1}\cdots\cdots\binom{m}{m-2} \\ & \cdots\cdots\cdots\cdots\cdots & \\ & \cdots\cdots\cdots\cdots\cdots & \\ \binom{m}{1} & \binom{m}{2} & \binom{m}{3}\cdots\cdots\quad 1 \end{vmatrix}$$

HILBERT[27] reproduced Kronecker's derivation of the criterion for th[e] divisibility of the first factor of the class number of the field $k(\zeta)$ wher[e] $\zeta=e^{2i\pi/l}$.

He also proved that the second factor of the class number is divisibl[e] by l only if the first factor is divisible by l. Let $\gamma_1, \gamma_2, \ldots, \gamma_{l^*}$ be [a] system of real fundamental units of the field $k(\zeta)$, $s=(\zeta:\zeta^r)$ then w[e] may set, if $l^*=(l-3)/2$,

$$(14) \qquad s^t\epsilon=\gamma_1^{m_{1t}}\gamma_2^{m_{2t}}\cdots\gamma_{l^*}^{m_{l^*t}}$$

for $t=0, 1, 2, \ldots, l^*-1$, and the exponents $m_{1t}, m_{2t}, \ldots, m_{l^*t}$ ar[e] integers and ϵ is defined by

$$\epsilon=\sqrt{\frac{(1-\zeta^r)(1-\zeta^{-r})}{(1-\zeta)(1-\zeta^{-1})}}$$

whence

$$(14a) \quad \log|s^t\epsilon|=m_{1t}\log|\gamma_1|+m_{2t}\log|\gamma_2|+\ldots+m_{l^*t}\log|\gamma_{l^*}|,$$

where the symbol $\log|\gamma|$ stands for the real value of the logarithm

[26] J. reine angew. Math., 113: 335-347 (1894).

[27] Die Theorie der algebraischen Zahlkörper, Jahresber., deut. math. Verein[.] 1897: 429-432, 435-437.

Set also

$$\epsilon_t = \epsilon^{n_{1t}} (s\epsilon)^{n_{2t}} \dots (s^{l^*-1}\epsilon)^{n_{l^*t}}$$
$$(t=1, 2, \dots, l^*)$$

where

$$\epsilon_t = \eta^{(r^2-s)(r^4-s)(r^6-s)\dots(r^{2t-2}-s)(r^{2t+2}-s)(r^{2t+4}-s)\dots(r^{l-3}-s)}$$

then

$$(15) \qquad \log \epsilon_t = n_{1t} \log |\epsilon| + n_{2t} \log |s\epsilon| + \dots + n_{l*t} \log |s^{l^*-1}\epsilon|$$
$$(t=1, 2, \dots, l^*)$$

where the exponents are symbolic powers. Combining (14a) and (15) gives

$$(15a) \qquad \log \epsilon_t = M_{1t} \log |\gamma_1| + M_{2t} \log |\gamma_2| + \dots + M_{l*t} \log |\gamma_{l*}|,$$
$$(t=1, 2, \dots, l^*)$$

where $M_{1t}, M_{2t}, \dots, M_{l^*t}$ are known bilinear combinations of the $2l^{*2}$ rational integers $n_{11}, n_{21}, \dots, n_{l*, l*}; m_{10}, m_{20}, \dots, m_{l^*, l^*-1}$. From (14a) and (15) we obtain in each case l^*-1 other equations after we make the substitutions $s, s^2, \dots, s^{l^*-1}$. Setting

$$R = \begin{vmatrix} \log |\gamma_1|, & \dots, & \log |\gamma_{l*}| \\ \log |s\gamma_1|, & \dots, & \log |s\gamma_{d*}| \\ \dots & \dots & \dots \\ \log |s^{l^*-1}\gamma_1|, & \dots, & \log |s^{l^*-1}\gamma_{l*}| \end{vmatrix}$$

$$\Delta = \begin{vmatrix} \log |\epsilon|, & \log |s\epsilon|, & \dots, & \log |s^{l^*-1}\epsilon| \\ \log |s\epsilon|, & \log |s^2\epsilon|, & \dots, & \log |s^{l^*}\epsilon| \\ \dots & \dots & \dots & \dots \\ \log |s^{l^*-1}\epsilon|, & \log |s^{l^*}\epsilon|, & \dots, & \log |s^{2l^*-2}\epsilon| \end{vmatrix}$$

$$\bar{\Delta} = \begin{vmatrix} \log \epsilon_1, & \log \epsilon_2, & \dots, & \log \epsilon_{l*} \\ \log s\epsilon_1, & \log s\epsilon_2, & \dots, & \log s\epsilon_{l*} \\ \dots & \dots & \dots & \dots \\ \log s^{l^*-1}\epsilon_1, & \log s^{l^*-1}\epsilon_2, & \dots, & \log s^{l^*-1}\epsilon_{l*} \end{vmatrix}$$

we obtain

$$(16) \qquad \frac{\bar{\Delta}}{R} = \frac{\bar{\Delta}}{\Delta} \cdot \frac{\Delta}{R} = \begin{vmatrix} M_{11}, & M_{21}, & \dots, & M_{l*1} \\ M_{12}, & M_{22}, & \dots, & M_{l*2} \\ \dots & \dots & \dots & \dots \\ M_{1l*}, & M_{2l*}, & \dots, & M_{l*l*} \end{vmatrix}$$

after using the theorem for the multiplication of determinants. Assuming that the first factor of the class number is prime to l, we can then show that the above determinant in the M's is prime to l, for if this determinant is divisible by l, then there exist l^* rational integers N_1, $N_2, \ldots, N_{l^*}$, not all divisible by l so that

$$\sum_{(t)} N_t M_{1t}, \qquad \sum_{(t)} N_t M_{2t}, \qquad \ldots, \qquad \sum_{(t)} N_t M_{l^*t}$$
$$(t=1, 2, \ldots, l^*)$$

are each divisible by l. Using (15a) we have

$$N_1 \log \epsilon_1 + N_2 \log \epsilon_2 + \ldots + N_{l^*} \log \epsilon_{l^*} = l \log E$$

where E is a positive unit in the field $k(\zeta)$, and this gives immediately

$$\epsilon_1^{N_1} \epsilon_2^{N_2} \ldots \epsilon_{l^*}^{N_{l^*}} = E^l.$$

Writing this equation as an identity in an indeterminate x by adding the proper multiple of $(x^l-1)/(x-1)$, setting $x=e^v$, and finding the $2t$-th derivative of the logarithm of each side of the resulting equation with respect to v and setting $v=0$, we have

$$(-1)^{t+l^*} \frac{B_t}{4tr^{2t}} N_t \equiv 0 \pmod{l},$$
$$(t=1, 2, \ldots, l^*),$$

where the B's are the Bernoulli numbers. This gives a contradiction since not all the N's are divisible by l. The desired result then follows from (16). Cf. Mirimanoff,[25] Kummer.[20]

HILBERT[28] proved that if l is a regular prime and α, β, γ, are integers in the field $\Omega(\zeta)$ where

$$\zeta = e^{2i\pi/l},$$

none zero, then the equation

$$\alpha^l + \beta^l + \gamma^l = 0 \tag{17}$$

is never satisfied. He divides the discussion into two cases according as one of the three integers α, β, γ, is or is not divisible by $\mathfrak{l}$ where $\mathfrak{l}$ is the ideal (λ), $\lambda = 1-\zeta$.

In the first case he employs a simple argument to show the truth of the theorem for $l=3$ and 5. Assume $l \geqq 7$. Since any of the integers α, β, γ, may be multiplied by a power of ζ without altering (17), we may assume that α, β, γ, are semi-primary. By means of the decomposition

$$(\alpha+\beta)(\alpha+\zeta\beta)(\alpha+\zeta^2\beta)\ldots(\alpha+\zeta^{l-1}\beta) = -\gamma^l,$$

it is shown that

$$\alpha+\beta = \mathfrak{j}^l \mathfrak{a},$$
$$\alpha+\zeta\beta = \mathfrak{j}_1^l \mathfrak{a},$$
$$\alpha+\zeta^2\beta = \mathfrak{j}_2^l \mathfrak{a},$$
$$\ldots\ldots\ldots\ldots$$
$$\alpha+\zeta^{l-1}\beta = \mathfrak{j}^l_{l-1} \mathfrak{a};$$

[28] Jahresber. Deut. Math. Verein., 1897: 517-525.

where $\mathfrak{a}$ is the greatest common ideal divisor of α, β and $\mathfrak{j}, \mathfrak{j}_1, \mathfrak{j}_2, \ldots, \mathfrak{j}_{l-1}$ are ideals in $\Omega(\zeta)$.

Since $\alpha+\zeta^{l-1}\beta$ is prime to $\mathfrak{l}$, we can determine a power of ζ, say ζ^*, so that $\zeta^*(\alpha+\zeta^{l-1}\beta)$ is semi-primary and we may set

$$\mu=\frac{\alpha}{\zeta^*(\alpha+\zeta^{l-1}\beta)}, \qquad \rho=\frac{\beta}{\zeta^*(\alpha+\zeta^{l-1}\beta)},$$

whence

$$\mu+\rho=\left(\frac{\mathfrak{j}}{\mathfrak{j}_{l-1}}\right)^l,$$
$$\mu+\zeta\rho=\left(\frac{\mathfrak{j}_1}{\mathfrak{j}_{l-1}}\right)^l,$$
$$\cdots\cdots\cdots\cdots\cdots$$
$$\mu+\zeta^{l-2}\rho=\left(\frac{\mathfrak{j}_{l-2}}{\mathfrak{j}_{l-1}}\right)^l.$$

As l is a regular prime, it follows that

$$\frac{\mathfrak{j}}{\mathfrak{j}_{l-1}}\sim 1, \qquad \frac{\mathfrak{j}_1}{\mathfrak{j}_{l-1}}\sim 1, \ldots, \qquad \frac{\mathfrak{j}_{l-2}}{\mathfrak{j}_{l-1}}\sim 1,$$

hence

$$\mu+\zeta^u\rho=\zeta^{e_u}\epsilon_u\alpha_u{}^l, \qquad (u=0, 1, 2, \ldots, l-2),$$

where e_u is a rational integer, ϵ_u is a real unit in $\Omega(\zeta)$ and α_u is a fraction in $\Omega(\zeta)$ with numerator and denominator prime to $\mathfrak{l}$. Since the lth power of the number α_u is congruent to a rational integer a_u (modulo $\mathfrak{l}^l$), we then have

$$\mu+\zeta^u\rho=\zeta^{e_u}\epsilon_u a_u, \qquad (\mathfrak{l}^l), \qquad (u=0, 1, 2, \ldots, l-2).$$

In this relation use the substitution $(\zeta : \zeta^{-1})$. We obtain a result which, when taken in connection with the above, yields, noting that $\epsilon_u=\epsilon_{-u}$,

(17a) $$\mu+\zeta^u\rho\equiv\zeta^{2e_u}\mu'+\zeta^{2e_u-u}\rho' \qquad (\mathfrak{l}^l)$$
$$(u=0, 1, 2, \ldots, l-2)$$

where μ' and ρ' are the conjugate imaginaries of μ and ρ respectively. Since μ and ρ are semi-primary, then

$$\mu\equiv m, \qquad \rho\equiv r \qquad (\text{mod } \mathfrak{l}^2),$$

where m and r are rational numbers and we have

$$m+\zeta^u r\equiv\zeta^{2e_u}m+\zeta^{2e_u-u}r, \qquad (\mathfrak{l}^2),$$

which gives

$$2e_u(m+r)\equiv 2ru, \qquad (l),$$

and also

$$e_u\equiv ru, \qquad (l), \qquad (u=0, 1, 2, \ldots, l-2).$$

Then (17a) gives, by elimination, a congruence involving ζ only (mod $\mathfrak{l}^l$). This is shown to be impossible for $l \geqq 7$.

For the proof in Case II, assume γ is divisible by $\mathfrak{l}$ so that γ is divisible $\mathfrak{l}^m$ but not by $\mathfrak{l}^{m+1}$, hence we may write

$$\alpha^l + \beta^l = \epsilon \lambda^{lm} \delta^l, \tag{18}$$

where δ is an integer in the field $\Omega(\zeta)$ prime to $\mathfrak{l}$ and $\epsilon = -1$. We shall generalize this relation and prove it is impossible for ϵ any unit in $\Omega(\zeta)$.

We take, as before, α and β as semi-primary, and by taking the above relation modulo $\mathfrak{l}^{l+1}$ it is seen that $m > 1$. Proceeding by a method similar to that used in connection with the first case, we obtain

$$\begin{cases} \alpha + \beta = \lambda^{l(m-1)+1} \mathfrak{j}^l \mathfrak{a}, \\ \alpha + \zeta\beta = \lambda \mathfrak{j}_1{}^l \mathfrak{a}, \\ \dots\dots\dots\dots\dots \\ \alpha + \zeta^{l-1}\beta = \lambda \mathfrak{j}^l{}_{l-1} \mathfrak{a}, \end{cases}$$

where $\mathfrak{j}, \mathfrak{j}_1, \dots, \mathfrak{j}_{l-1}, \mathfrak{a}$, are ideals in $\Omega(\zeta)$ prime to $\mathfrak{l}$. If $l > 3$, we set

$$\mu = \frac{\alpha\lambda}{\alpha + \zeta^{l-1}\beta}, \qquad \rho = \frac{\beta\lambda}{\alpha + \zeta^{l-1}\beta};$$

and obtain from the above relations

$$\begin{cases} \mu + \rho = \lambda^{l(m-1)+1} \left(\dfrac{\mathfrak{j}}{\mathfrak{j}_{l-1}}\right)^l, \\ \mu + \zeta\rho = \lambda \left(\dfrac{\mathfrak{j}_1}{\mathfrak{j}_{l-1}}\right)^l. \\ \mu + \zeta^2\rho = \lambda \left(\dfrac{\mathfrak{j}_2}{\mathfrak{j}_{l-1}}\right)^l, \end{cases}$$

and as in Case I, we have

$$\frac{\mathfrak{j}}{\mathfrak{j}_{l-1}} \sim 1, \qquad \frac{\mathfrak{j}_1}{\mathfrak{j}_{l-1}} \sim 1, \dots, \qquad \frac{\mathfrak{I}_{l-2}}{\mathfrak{j}_{l-1}} \sim 1.$$

The case $l = 3$ in Case II is treated separately and we find for any odd l the relation

$$\begin{cases} \mu + \rho = \dfrac{\epsilon^* \lambda^{l(m-1)+1} \gamma^{*l}}{\nu}, \\ \mu + \zeta\rho = \dfrac{\lambda \alpha^{*l}}{\nu}, \\ \mu + \zeta^2\rho = \dfrac{\epsilon\lambda\beta^{*l}}{\nu}, \end{cases}$$

where $\nu, \alpha^*, \beta^*, \gamma^*$, are integers prime to $\mathfrak{l}$ and ϵ and ϵ^* are units in the field $\Omega(\zeta)$. Elimination of μ and ρ gives

$$\alpha^{*l} + \eta\beta^{*l} = \eta^* \lambda^{l(m-1)} \gamma^{*l},$$

where η and η^* are units in $\Omega(\zeta)$.

Using the theorem that if l is a regular prime and E is a unit in the field $\Omega(\zeta)$ which is congruent to a rational integer modulo l, then E is the lth power of a unit in $\Omega(\zeta)$, we obtain an equation of the same form as (18) with the number $m-1$ occurring in the exponent of λ in lieu of m. Repeating our operations as from the beginning of our treatment of Case II, we obtain ultimately equation (18) with $m=1$, and this states a contradiction.

Note that in Kummer's [18] proof he assumed that the three integers α, β, γ in (17) had no common factor, a restriction which does not occur in Hilbert's argument. Also, Kummer excepts the case $l=3$, which is included in Hilbert's treatment.

Hilbert also proves that the relation

$$\alpha^4+\beta^4=\gamma^2$$

is impossible in integers α, β, γ in the field $\Omega(i)$, $i=\sqrt{-1}$.

CELLERIER [29] obtained results which are transformations of the Kummer [23] criteria. He also showed that if

$$x^p+y^p+z^p=0$$

where p an odd prime then

$$B_{\mu-3}\equiv B_{\mu-4}\equiv 0 \pmod p,$$

where the B's are Bernoulli numbers with the exception of a finite number of specified values of p. Cf. Kummer,[20] Mirimanoff.[33]

MAILLET [30] proved that if λ^{t-1} is the highest power of the prime λ which divides the class number H of ideals in the field defined by a primitive λ-th root of unity, then the equation

$$x^{\lambda^t}+y^{\lambda^t}+z^{\lambda^t}=0$$

is impossible in integers, in the field formed by this root, prime to each other and to λ for $\lambda>3$. The demonstration of this result is an immediate extension of the argument employed by Kummer for $t=1$.

MAILLET [31] obtained a number of results concerning the equation

$$x^\lambda+y^\lambda=cz^\lambda$$

where λ is a regular prime, using in the main Kummer's [20] methods. He first establishes the lemma that the equation

$$\text{(19)} \qquad u^\lambda+v^\lambda=E(\alpha)(1-\alpha)^{\mu\lambda-\beta}Aw^\lambda \qquad (\mu>0,\ \beta=0 \text{ or } 1)$$

is impossible if u, v are integers in the field $\Omega(\alpha)$, and w an ideal in

[29] Mem. soc. phys. d'Hist. nat. Geneve, 32, No. 7: 16-42 (1894-1897).

[30] Association Francaise pour l'avancement des sciences, 26th Session, 1897: 162-166.

[31] Acta Math., 24: 247-256 (1901). Compt. Rend., 129: 198-199 (1899).

the field, prime each to each and to λ, where a is a primitive λ-th root of unity, $E(a)$ is a unit in the field $\Omega(a)$, A is an ideal in the field $\Omega(a)$ prime to λ and equal to 1, or of the form $q_1^{a_1}q_2^{a_2}\ldots q_i^{a_i}$, where q_1, q_2, $\ldots$, q_i are distinct ideal primes with $i\leqq\lambda-3$. We have

$$(20)\qquad u^\lambda+v^\lambda=(u+v)(u+av)\ldots(u+a^{\lambda-1}v);$$

and if we put

$$u=a+(1-a)^2Q,$$
$$v=b+(1-a)^2R,$$

where a, b are rational integers, which is always possible, we have

$$u+v\equiv 0 \mod (1-a)^2.$$

Now $u+a^r\cdot v$ and $u+a^n\cdot v$, $(r\neq n)$, have for their greatest common divisor $(1-a)$, hence we can find among the factors in the second member of (20) $u+a^r\cdot v$, $u+a^s\cdot v$ $(r>0,\ s>0,\ r\neq s)$, which are not divisible by any of the numbers $q_1, q_2, \ldots, q_i$, such that

$$(21)\qquad \begin{cases} u+a^rv=(1-a)e_r(a)t_r^\lambda(a), \\ u+a^sv=(1-a)e_s(a)t_s^\lambda(a), \end{cases}$$

where $e_r(a)$ and $e_s(a)$ are units in the field $\Omega(a)$, $t_r^\lambda(a)$ and $t_s^\lambda(a)$ are the λ-th powers of integers in the field prime to each other. We also have

$$(22)\qquad u+v=(1-a)^{\mu\lambda-\lambda+1-\beta}E'(a)A_1w_1(a)^\lambda,$$

where $E'(a)$ is a unit in the field, $A_1w_1(a)^\lambda$ is an integer in the field $\Omega(a)$, t_r, t_s, w_1 are prime each to each and to λ. The relation (19) is impossible for $\mu=1$: suppose $\mu>1$, then (21) and (22) give

$$\begin{vmatrix} 1 & a^r & e_rt_r^\lambda \\ 1 & a^s & e_st_s^\lambda \\ 1 & 1 & (1-a)^{\mu\lambda-\lambda-\beta}E'A_1w_1^\lambda \end{vmatrix}=0,$$

or

$$t_r^\lambda-\epsilon t_s^\lambda=E_1(a)A_1(1-a)^{\mu\lambda-\lambda-\beta}w_1^\lambda,$$

where

$$\epsilon=\frac{e_s(1-a^r)}{e_r(1-a^s)}$$

$$E_1=\frac{E'(a^r-a^s)}{e_r(1-a^s)}$$

ϵ and E_1 being units in the field. This gives

$$t_r^\lambda-\epsilon t_s^\lambda\equiv 0 \pmod{\lambda},$$

and we also have

$$t_r^\lambda\equiv c, \qquad t_s^\lambda\equiv c' \pmod{\lambda}$$

where c and c' are rational integers, and these give

$$c-\epsilon c'\equiv 0 \pmod{\lambda},$$

hence ϵ is the λ-th power of a unit ϵ' in the field. Setting

$$t_r=u_1, \qquad -\epsilon' t_s=v_1,$$

we obtain

$$u_1^\lambda+v_1^\lambda=E_1A_1(1-a)^{\mu\lambda-\lambda-\beta}w_1^\lambda,$$

and this equation is of the same form as (19) except that the power of $(1-a)$ has been diminished by λ. The repetition of this process leads to a contradiction.

The theorem just proved is then applied to various equations of the type $x^\lambda+y^\lambda=cz^\lambda$, which is shown to be impossible for a number of different rational integral values of c; x, y and z being rational integers.

Gambioli [32] gave an abstract of a paper by Kummer,[18] a list of references on Bernoulli numbers and ideal numbers.

Mirimanoff [33] showed that the result of Kummer [30] (p. 65) is equivalent to the following theorem:

If (1) is satisfied in Case I, then

$$(23) \qquad \begin{cases} B_{\frac{(p-i)}{2}} f_i(t)\equiv 0 \pmod{p} \\ f_{p-1}(t)\equiv 0 \pmod{p} \end{cases}$$

$i=3, 5, \ldots, p-2; \qquad -t=x/y, y/x, x/z, z/x, y/z, z/y.$

Also

$$f_i(t)=\sum_{k=1}^{p-1} k^{i-1}t^k,$$

$i=2, 3, \ldots, p-1.$

He also derived the criteria (equivalent to (23))

$$(23a) \qquad f_{p-1}(t)\equiv f_{p-i}(t)f_i(t)\equiv 0 \pmod{p},$$

$i=2, 3, \ldots, \nu;\ \nu=\dfrac{p-1}{2}$, and

$$B_{\nu-3}\equiv B_{\nu-4}\equiv 0 \pmod{p}.$$

Cf. Cellerier,[29] Wieferich,[37] Mirimanoff,[41] Frobenius,[56] Vandiver,[55, 62, 73, 77, 83, 86] Furtwängler,[46] Pollaczek.[61]

Dickson [34] discussed the problem: Given an odd prime n to find the odd prime moduli p for which $\xi^n+\eta^n+\zeta^n\equiv 0 \pmod{p}$ has no solutions

[32] Periodico di Mat., 16: 145-192 (1901); 17: 48-50 (1902).
[33] J. reine angew. Math., 128: 45-68 (1905).
[34] J. reine angew. Math., 135: 134-141, 181-188 (1909).

each prime to p. He also proved that the above relation, for n and p odd primes, has integral solutions each prime to p if

$$p \geqq (n-1)^2(n-2)^2+6n-2.$$

Cf. Legendre,[1] Wendt,[26] Furtwängler,[50] Vandiver.[84]

DICKSON[35] showed that (2) is not satisfied for various values of n and p, and using Sophie Germain's theorem (Legendre[1]), he proved that (1) is not satisfied in Case I for any prime exponent <7000. Cf. Beeger.[79]

SCHÖNBAUM[36] reproduced Hilbert's proof of Fermat's last theorem for regular primes and reviewed some of the results in the theory of cyclotomic fields which lead up to it. He noted that it follows from Kummer,[23] that there are five irregular primes >100 and <167. Cf. Vandiver.[66]

WIEFERICH[37] proved by means of the criteria (23) that if (1) is satisfied in Case I, then $2^{p-1} \equiv 1 \pmod{p^2}$.

LINDEMANN[38] attempted a proof of Fermat's last theorem, using algebraic numbers. Assume $x^n-y^n-z^n=0$, n an odd prime. On page 74, the relation 302 is proved only if n is a regular prime as it is obtained from

$$\mathfrak{p}^n \equiv \mathfrak{p} \pmod{1-\zeta}; \qquad \zeta = e^{2i\pi/n},$$

and this cannot be given any meaning unless $\mathfrak{p}$ is a principal ideal.

KUMMER[39] mentioned results which he had obtained concerning irregular primes and Fermat's last theorem, in letters to Kronecker. All of said results are included in Kummer,[17, 18, 20] with the exception of the following statements which occur without proof in the letter dated December 28, 1849:

If a unit exists which is congruent to a rational integer c_1, modulo λ and B_n, $B_{n'}$, $B_{n''}$, ... are the Bernoulli numbers in the set $B_1, B_2, \ldots, B_{\mu-1}$ whose numerators are divisible by λ, where

$$\mu = \frac{\lambda-1}{2},$$

then

$$e(a)^{rm(\beta)}e(a)^{r'm'(\beta)}e(a)^{r''m''(\beta)}\ldots \equiv c \pmod{\lambda},$$

where c, r, r', r'', etc., are certain integers and

$$m(\beta) = 1+\gamma^{-2n}\beta+\ldots+\gamma^{-2n(\mu-1)}\beta^{\mu-1},$$
$$m'(\beta) = 1+\gamma^{-2n'}\beta+\ldots+\gamma^{-2n'(\mu-1)}\beta^{\mu-1},$$

and similarly for $m''(\beta)$.

[35] Messenger of Math., (2), 38: 14-32 (1908). Quar. J. Math., 40: 27-45 (1908).
[36] Casopsis, Prag, 37: 384-506 (1908).
[37] J. reine angew. Math., 136: 272-292 (1909).
[38] Über den sogenannten letzten Fermatschen Satz. Leipzig, Veit and Co., 1909. 83 p.
[39] Abhandlungen zur Geschichte der Mathematik. 29: 75, 84-85, 88, 91 (1910).

In this formula Kummer is using Kronecker's [24a] notation of symbolic powers and β stands for the substitution (a/a^{γ}), γ being a primitive root of λ. The unit above which is congruent to c, modulo λ, is not the λ-th power of a unit unless each of the units

$$e(a)^{rm(\beta)},\ e(a)^{r'm'(\beta)},\ e(a)^{r''m''(\beta)},\ \ldots,$$

is the λ-th power of a unit. Kummer refers to this result as follows: "Sehr wichtiger satz, welcher eine grosse Schwierigkeit hebt!"

HENSEL [40] commented on Kummer's various results concerning Fermat's last theorem.

MIRIMANOFF [41] making use of the criteria (23) proved that if (1) is satisfied in Case I, then

$$\text{(23b)} \qquad \prod_{i=1}^{m-1}(a_i-t)\sum_{i=1}^{m-1}\frac{R_i}{a_i-t}\equiv 0 \pmod{p},$$

$$R_i=\frac{f_{p-1}(a_i)}{(1-a_i)^{p-1}}$$

where $a_1, a_2, \ldots, a_{m-1}$ are the roots $\neq 1$ of $z^m=1$. For m=2 and 3 we obtain $2^{p-1}\equiv 3^{p-1}\equiv 1 \pmod{p^2}$.

GOT [42] reproduced with explanations Kummer's memoir of 1857 on Fermat's last theorem. No errors are noted, but compare pages 43-44 with Vandiver,[74] page 404.

FURTWÄNGLER [43] gave many properties of ideals and units in relative irregular cyclotomic fields in connection with investigations concerning the class field and laws of reciprocity. Full reports on these papers will be given in later sections of the report of Algebraic Numbers and we shall state here only those results of Furtwängler which have been used by various writers in developing properties of the class number and results on Fermat's last theorem.

In the following definitions and theorems, k is a field containing the field defined by a primitive l-th root of unity ζ, as a sub-field, where l is an odd prime and $\lambda=(1-\zeta)$.

Definition 1. An integral or fractional number a of k whose numerator and denominator are prime to l is called primary when the congruence $x^l\equiv a$ modulo $l\lambda$ has a solution x in the field k.

Definition 2. An integral or fractional number a of k whose numerator and denominator are prime to l is called hyper-primary if the congruence

[40] Abhandlungen zur Geschichte der Mathematik, 29: 18-32 (1910).

[41] Compt. Rend., 150: 204-206 (1910). J. reine angew. Math., 139: 309-324 (1911).

[42] Annales de la faculté des sciences de Toulouse, 25: 21-62 (1911).

[43] Math. Ann., 58: 1-50 (1904); 63: 1-37 (1906); 67: 1-29 (1909); 72: 346-386 (1912). Göttingen Nachr., Math.-Physik. Kl., 1911: 293-317. (These papers are cited as F. I-V respectively.)

$x^l \equiv a$ modulo $l\lambda\mathfrak{L}$ has a solution x in k. The $\mathfrak{L}$ is defined as the product $\mathfrak{L}=\mathfrak{L}_1\mathfrak{L}_2\ldots\mathfrak{L}_z$ where $(\lambda)=\mathfrak{L}_1^{a_1}\mathfrak{L}_2^{a_2}\ldots\mathfrak{L}_z^{a_z}$ is the decomposition of the ideal (λ) in the field k, the $\mathfrak{L}$'s being distinct prime ideals in k. (F. I., §13, Def. 12.)

Definition 3. An integral or fractional number ω in k is called a singular primary number of k when it is primary and in addition the principal ideal (ω) is the l-th power of an ideal in k without ω being the l-th power of a number in k. (F. II, §3, p. 9.)

Let the class number of the field k be $H=l^h q\,(q\not\equiv 0$, modulo $l)$. Let also a normal basis for the group of the q-th powers of the ideal classes of k be $c_1, c_2, \ldots, c_e$ whose orders are respectively $l^{h'_1}, \ldots, l^{h'_e}$, that is, the q-th power of any ideal class in the field can be represented in the form $c_1^{j_1}c_2^{j_2}\ldots c_e^{j_e}$ where

$$c_s^{l^{h_s}}\sim 1$$
$$(s=1, 2, \ldots, e).$$

We then have the theorems:

Theorem A: In the field k there are exactly e singular primary numbers $\omega_1, \omega_2, \ldots, \omega_e$ which are, aside from l-th powers, independent under multiplication, that is, from any equation

$$\omega_1^{x_1}\omega_2^{x_2}\ldots\omega_e^{x_e}=a^l,$$

where a is a number in k we have $x_1\equiv x_2\equiv\ldots\equiv x_e\equiv 0$, modulo l. (F. II, §7, p. 18.)

Theorem B: Let ω_0 be a singular primary number in k, then there belongs to ω_0 a uniquely determined subgroup $\mathfrak{G}_{\omega_0}$ of order H/l of the complete class group $\mathfrak{H}$ of k with the property that for all ideals $\mathfrak{j}_{\omega_0}$ of the group $\mathfrak{G}_{\omega_0}$

$$\left(\frac{\omega_0}{\mathfrak{j}_{\omega_0}}\right)=1$$

is satisfied while for all other ideals $\mathfrak{j}$ of $\mathfrak{H}$

$$\left(\frac{\omega_0}{\mathfrak{j}}\right)\neq 1$$

will hold. All singular primary numbers which belong to $\mathfrak{G}_{\omega_0}$ in this sense may be expressed in the form $\omega_0^x a^l$, a being a number in k. (F. III, §10, Th. 10, p. 26); (F. III, §4, Th. 6, p. 364). The symbols in the last relation represent l-th power characters.

Theorem C: When c is an ideal class that does not belong to the subgroup $\mathfrak{G}_{\omega_0}$ of Theorem B, and if $\mathfrak{H}$ is expressed as the totality of accessory groups (Nebengruppen) with respect to $\mathfrak{G}_{\omega_0}$, that is,

$$\mathfrak{H}=\mathfrak{G}_{\omega_0}+c\mathfrak{G}_{\omega_0}+\ldots+c^{l-1}\mathfrak{G}_{\omega_0}$$

then $\left(\frac{\omega_0}{\mathfrak{j}}\right)$ assumes the same value for all ideals belonging to the same accessory groups; in particular $\left(\frac{\omega_0}{\mathfrak{j}}\right)$ has the same value for two equivalent ideals $\mathfrak{j}$.

Theorem D: If the number μ of k is not a singular primary number and not an l-th power in k, then in every ideal class of k there exist prime ideals $\mathfrak{j}_p$, for which $\left(\frac{\mu}{\mathfrak{j}_p}\right)=1$.

Let K be the field obtained by adjoining to k the number $\sqrt[l]{\mu}$ where μ is a number defined as in theorem D. Let S be the substitution of the relative group of K, $S=(\sqrt[l]{\mu}:\zeta_1\sqrt[l]{\mu})$. If $\mathfrak{j}_p$ is an ideal in k, prime to l then it follows from $\left(\frac{\mu}{\mathfrak{j}_p}\right)=1$ that $\mathfrak{j}_p$ decomposes into the product of l prime ideals in $K(\sqrt[l]{\mu}, k)$ and from $\left(\frac{\mu}{\mathfrak{j}_p}\right)\neq 1$ we infer that $\mathfrak{j}_p$ is prime in the field $K(\sqrt[l]{\mu}, k)$, hence Theorem B gives

Theorem E: If ω_0 is a singular primary number in k, then only those prime ideals $\mathfrak{j}_p$ in k decompose into l distinct prime ideals in $K(\sqrt[l]{\omega_0}, k)$ which belong to the ideal classes of the subgroup $\mathfrak{G}_{\omega_0}$. (F. V, §1, Th. III.)

From Theorem D we obtain

Theorem F: If the number μ in k is not a singular primary number and not the l-th power of a number in k, then there exist prime ideals in each ideal class of k which are composite in K.

If $c_1, c_2, \ldots, c_h$ are those classes of a relative cyclic field $K(\sqrt[l]{\mu}, k)$ which contain the ideals of k and let C be an arbitrary ideal class of K, a system of ideal classes $P=\{Cc_1, \ldots, Cc_{h'}\}$ will be designated as the class-complex generated by C and the system $I=\{c_1, \ldots, c_{h'}\}$ will be termed the principal complex. The class C_1C_2 defines the complex P_1P_2.

Definition 4. The complex P_A which is identical with the relative conjugate complex $P_A{}^S$ is called an ambiguous complex. A complex is evidently ambiguous if and only if for one of its generated classes C_A we have $C_A{}^{1-S}=c_i$ where c_i is a class of I. From

$$C_A^{1-S}=c_i \qquad \text{and} \qquad C_A^{1+S+\ldots+S^{l-1}}$$

we have

$$C_A{}^l=c_i \qquad \text{and} \qquad P_A{}^l=I.$$

We call any ambiguous complex $P_{A,1}, P_{A,2}, \ldots, P_{A,n}$, independent if from any relation $P_{A,1}^{x_1}P_{A,2}^{x_2}\ldots P_{A,n}^{x_n}=I$ we have

$$x_1\equiv x_2\equiv \ldots \equiv x_n\equiv 0, \bmod l$$

The greatest number of distinct independent complexes in K will be indicated by a. We then have, if e has the same meaning as in Theorem B,

Theorem G: If ω_0 is a singular primary number in k, then in $K(\sqrt[l]{\omega_0}, k)$,

$$a = e - 1$$

(F. II, §8, Th. 6, p. 19).

Theorem H: If the number μ is a non-singular primary number in k, then in $K(\sqrt[l]{\mu}, k)$,

$$a \geqq e.$$

(F. III, §2, pp. 8, 9.)

Theorem J: If the relative discriminant of $K(\sqrt[l]{\mu}, k)$ does not contain two distinct ideal prime factors in k, then

$$a = e.$$

(F. III, §2, pp. 8, 9.)

Let the class number H_K of $K(\sqrt[l]{\mu}, k) = l^m Q$ $(Q \not\equiv 0, \bmod l)$, then we have

Theorem K: The system of the Q-th powers of the ideal classes of $K(\sqrt[l]{\mu}, k)$ can be expressed uniquely in the form

$$C_1^{F_1(S)} C_2^{F_2(S)} \ldots C_a^{F_a(S)} c$$

where $C_1, C_2, \ldots, C_a$ constitute a certain set of a classes of K and c is the Q-th power of a class included in the principal complex. For these classes C_i we have

$$C_i^{(1-S)^{p_i}} = c_i, \qquad C_i^{(1-S)^{p_i - 1}} \neq c$$
$$(i = 1, 2, \ldots, a)$$

for rational integers $p_i > 0$. The expressions $F_i(S)$, $i = 1, 2, \ldots, a$ are polynomials in S with rational integral coefficients. (F. II, §6, Th. 4, p. 15.)

Hecke[44] considered the properties of irregular fields and their applications to Fermat's last theorem. Let H be the class number of the field K defined by a primitive l-th root of unity, l being an odd prime, $H = h_1 \cdot h$ where h is the class number of the real sub-field k of K of degree $(l-1)/2$. Let l^a be the highest power of l dividing h and l^{a_1} the highest power of l dividing h_1, and set

$$h = l^a q, \qquad h_1 = l^{a_1} q_1.$$

Consider the group of all ideal classes in the field k which are q-th powers so that for each class c in k we have the equivalence

$$c^q \sim c_1^{x_1} c_2^{x_2} \ldots c_e^{x_e} \qquad (x_i = 0, 1, \ldots, l^{b_i} - 1).$$

[44] Göttingen Nachr., Math.-Physik. Kl., 1910: 420-424.

Also, if G is the class group of those ideals in K whose relative norms with respect to k belong to the principal class, then G is of degree h_1, hence there exists classes $C_1, C_2, \ldots, C_e$ so that for any class C in the group G we have

$$C^{q_1} \sim C_1^{y_1} C_2^{y_2} \ldots C_{e_1}^{y_{e_1}} \qquad (y_i = 0, 1, \ldots, l^{b_i} - 1).$$

The group of all classes C^{q_1} is called the group G_1. It is then shown that

$$e_1 \geqq e.$$

If $q_1 \cdot q = q_2$, then the q_2-th power of all classes in K may be expressed in the form

$$C \cdot c_1^{x_1} c_2^{x_2} \ldots c_e^{x_e}$$

where C is a class in G_1.

Hecke then constructs with respect to k for $e > 0$ the relative cyclic enlarged field of relative degree l that is indecomposable (unverzweigt), (cf. Furtwängler [43] II, 2, 21-2), which leads to the proof of the theorem. Using this result it is then proved that if $e_1 = e$, then the relation $x^l + y^l + z^l = 0$ is not satisfied with integers in K prime to l, and also, this relation is not satisfied under the conditions mentioned if the first factor of the class number is divisible by l but not by l^2. Cf. Hecke [38] of Chapter I of this report; Furtwängler,[46] Bernstein,[45] of the present chapter.

Bernstein [45] proved that (1) is impossible in Case I under the assumptions

I. The second factor $h_2 = l^{\mu} h'_2$ of the class number, $h = h_1 h_2$, of the cyclotomic field $k(\zeta)$ defined by a primitive l-th root of unity, l being an odd prime, is divisible by l.

II. In the sub-class field (Teilklassenkörper) of l^{μ}-th degree which belongs to the factor l^{μ} of h_2, all ideals of $k(\zeta)$ whose l-th powers are principal ideals in $k(\zeta)$ are themselves principal ideals.

It was shown, however, by Pollaczek [76] that this result is equivalent to that of Hecke [44] (cf. also Vandiver [66]).

Furtwängler [46] examined the equation

$$(24) \qquad \alpha^l + \beta^l + \gamma^l = 0$$

where l is an odd prime and α, β, γ are three integers in the field $k(\zeta)$, where ζ is a primitive l-th root of unity. An ideal $\mathfrak{q}$ in the field $k(\zeta)$

[45] Göttingen Nachr., Math.-Physik. Kl., 1910: 482-488.

[46] Göttingen Nachr., Math.-Physik. Kl., 1910: 554-562.

is said to belong to the exponent n when it is prime to the ideal $\mathfrak{l}=(\zeta-1)$ and a number k exists in the field such that

$$\kappa=\mathfrak{q}^l$$

and

$$\kappa\equiv r_1(\mathfrak{l}^n),$$

and if there is no unit η in $k(\zeta)$ such that

$$\eta\kappa\equiv r_2(\mathfrak{l}^{n+1})$$

where r_1, r_2, are rational numbers. (This use of the phrase "belongs to the exponent n should not be confused with the other use made of this term in the present report; cf. Kummer.[13])

The equation (24) gives, if $\mathfrak{a}$ is the greatest common ideal divisor of a and β,

$$a+\zeta^i\beta=\mathfrak{q}_i{}^l\mathfrak{a} \qquad (i=0,\ 1,\ \ldots,\ l-1)$$

and setting (cf. Hilbert [28])

$$a+\zeta^{l-1}\beta=\rho,$$

we have, if ϵ_i is a unit in $k(\zeta)$, $a^*=a/\rho$, $\beta^*=\beta/\rho$, $\kappa_i=\mathfrak{q}_i{}^l$,

$$a^*+\zeta^i\beta^*=\epsilon_i\kappa_i \qquad (i=0,\ 1,\ \ldots,\ l-1),$$

and to simplify the notation we write this as

$$a+\zeta^i\beta=\epsilon_i\kappa_i \qquad (i=0,\ 1,\ \ldots,\ l-1).$$

Assume first that in the field $k(\zeta)$ no ideal exists which belongs to the exponent 3. If r is a primitive root of l and s is the substitution (ζ/ζ^r), then

$$(a+\zeta^i\beta)^{(s-r)(s-r^2)}\equiv a_0(\mathfrak{l}^4)$$
$$(i=0,\ 1,\ \ldots,\ l-1)$$

where the exponent in the left-hand member is to be interpreted symbolically and a_0 is a rational number. From (24) we have

$$(sa)^l+(s\beta)^l+(s\gamma)^l=0,$$

and writing a and β as functions of ζ, we have

$$[a(\zeta^m)+\zeta^i\beta(\zeta^m)]^{(s-r)(s-r^2)}\equiv a_0(\mathfrak{l}^4)$$
$$(i=0,\ 1,\ \ldots,\ l-1)$$
$$(m=1,\ 2,\ \ldots,\ l-1).$$

This relation is simplified by expressing the left-hand member in ascending powers of λ where $\lambda=\zeta-1$, giving

$$(a+\zeta^i b)^{(s-r)(s-r^2)}\equiv a_0(\mathfrak{l}^4)$$
$$(i=0,\ 1,\ \ldots,\ l-1)$$

for $\alpha \equiv a$, $\beta \equiv b$, modulo $\mathfrak{l}$; a, b being rational numbers, and this yields

$$\left[\frac{d^3 \log (a+\zeta^i b)^{(s-r)(s-r^2)}}{(d\zeta)^3}\right]_{\zeta=1} \equiv 0 \quad (l)$$

$$(i=0, 1, \ldots, l-1).$$

Setting $\zeta^i = e^v$, we have

$$\frac{d_0{}^3 \log (a+e^v b)}{(dv)^3} \equiv 0 \quad (l),$$

and this relation is impossible if we replace the number pair (a, b) by (a, c) and (b, c).

This work is then extended, and if we assume that in the field $k(\zeta)$ no ideal exists which belongs to the exponent $2j+1\left(j \leqq \frac{l-3}{2}\right)$, then

$$(a+\zeta^i b)^{g(s)} \equiv a_0(\mathfrak{l}^{2j+2}) \qquad (i=0, 1, \ldots, l-1),$$

which gives

$$\frac{d_0{}^{2j+1} \log (a+e^v b)^{g(s)}}{(dv)^{2j+1}} \equiv 0 \quad (l),$$

where

$$g(s) = (s-r)(s-r^2) \ldots (s-r^j)$$

whence

$$\frac{d_0{}^{2j+1} \log (a+e^v b)}{(dv)^{2j+1}} \equiv 0 \quad (l).$$

According to Kummer and Mirimanoff this congruence is not satisfied for $j=1, 2, 3, 4$, which proves that if in the field $k(\zeta)$ there exists no ideal belonging to the exponents 3, 5, 7, 11, modulo $\mathfrak{l}$, then (24) is not satisfied for any integers in the field $k(\zeta)$ prime to (l). Using this result it is then shown, through a consideration of the group of classes of $k(\zeta)$, that if the number class sets (Klassenverbände) of $k(\zeta)$ is l^f and $k'(\zeta+\zeta^{-1})$ is l^e, and if $f-e \leqq 3$, then (24) cannot be satisfied by integers in the field $k(\zeta)$ prime to l and in particular if the class number of the field $k(\zeta)$ is divisible by l^3 but not by l^4, then (24) is not satisfied by integers in the field $k(\zeta)$ prime to l. Cf. Hecke.[44]

Bernstein[47] investigated Case II of Fermat's last theorem. He quotes (p. 508) Kummer's results concerning the last theorem and states Kummer's three assumptions. He then remarks that the first assumption is equivalent to the statement that the first factor of the class number of the field $k(\zeta)$, ζ being a primitive l-th root of unity, l an odd prime, is divisible by l but not by l^2. Concerning this statement, cf. Vandiver, Bachmann,[59] review.

[47] Göttingen Nachr., Math.-Physik. Kl., 1910: 507-516.

Bernstein then states

Theorem I. The class field of the l-th degree of $k(\zeta)$ is obtained from a unit ϵ.

For proof, he refers to HILBERT.[48] He proves Theorem II: Every primary unit is real. He then gives Theorem III: Under the assumption that the class number of the cyclotomic field $k(Z)$ formed by a primitive l^2-th root of unity, is divisible by l but not by l^2, then if

$$\epsilon \equiv \alpha^{l^2} \pmod{l^2 \mathfrak{l}}, \tag{25}$$

where $\mathfrak{l} = (1-\zeta)$ and α is an integer or fraction in the field $k(\zeta)$, then ϵ is the l-th power of a unit.

For proof it is observed that ϵ is a primary number, so that $E = \sqrt[l]{\epsilon}$ defines an indecomposable (unverzweigten) field. From (25) we may write

$$\epsilon \equiv a^{l^2} \pmod{l^2 \mathfrak{l}},$$

where a is a rational number and we may take ϵ and E real, and then from (25) we have the decomposition

$$\mathfrak{l} = \mathfrak{L} \cdot S\mathfrak{L} \ldots S^{l-1}\mathfrak{L}$$

in the field $k(\sqrt[l]{\epsilon})$ where $\mathfrak{L}$ is defined as in Hilbert (l. c., p. 400). We also have

$$E - \zeta^u a^l \equiv 0 \qquad (\mathrm{mod}\ \mathfrak{l} \cdot (\mathrm{S}^u \mathfrak{L})^{l-1})$$

or

$$E \equiv (Z^u a)^l \qquad (\mathrm{mod}\ (S^u \mathfrak{L})^l) \qquad (u = 0, 1, \ldots, l-1).$$

It is then shown from this that the class number of the field $k(Z)$ is divisible by l^2, which is contrary to the assumption and the theorem follows.

Using these theorems, Bernstein, following in the main the method of Kummer,[20] proved that under the assumption that the class number of the field $k(Z)$ is divisible by l and not by l^2, then

$$a^l + b^l + c^l = 0 \tag{26}$$

is not possible in rational integers a, b, c, none zero, and one of them divisible by l.

He then proves

Theorem IV. Under the assumption that the field $k(\zeta)$ contains no class belonging to the exponent l^2, and the class number h_2 of the field $k(\zeta + \zeta^{-1})$ is prime to l, then every primary number which is the l-th power of an ideal in the field is the product of a primary unit and the l-th power of a number in the field.

[48] Jahresber. deut. math. Verein, 4: 432 *et seq.* (1894).

For proof we note that the classes whose l-th powers give the principal class may be expressed in the form

$$C_1^{X_1}\ldots C_G^{X_G}\ldots c_1^{x_1}\ldots c_g^{x_g}D^l \qquad (X_i,\, x_i=0,\, 1,\, \ldots,\, l-1)$$

and this reduces to the simplified form

$$C_1^{X_1}\ldots C_G^{X_G}D^l,$$

using the assumption that the class number of the field $k(\zeta+\zeta^{-1})$ is prime to l.

Corresponding to the congruence

$$X_i \equiv 0 \quad (l)$$

there is a singular primary number M and the conjugate imaginary $\overline{M}$ of M belongs to the same congruence. From the properties of singular primary numbers (cf. Furtwängler [43, 46]) we have

$$M=\overline{M}^a\beta^l$$

and

$$M=M^{a\cdot a}(\beta\overline{\beta}^a)^l,$$

giving

$$a^2-1\equiv 0 \quad (l).$$

It is then shown that

$$a\equiv -1 \quad (l)$$

is impossible so that we have

$$a\equiv +1 \quad (l)$$

and this is shown to yield, if η is a unit in k,

$$M=\eta\cdot\kappa^l.$$

It is then observed that following the method used in the proof of the first theorem concerning Fermat's last theorem, and by the use of the theorem just proved, we obtain the result that under the assumption that the field $k(Z)$ contains no class belonging to the exponent l^2 and the class number h_2 of the field $k(\zeta+\zeta^{-1})$ is prime to l, then (26) is impossible, with a, b, c, restricted as before.

Vandiver [66] (p. 420) showed, however, that Bernstein's first theorem concerning Fermat's last theorem constitutes no advance over Kummer's [18] result. Pollaczek [76] (p. 37) also pointed this out and in addition arrived at the conclusion that Bernstein's second result did not include Kummer's [20] as it does not exclude the exponents 37, 59 and 67.

FURTWÄNGLER [49] proved that if l is any prime, then the class numbers of the field defined by a primitive l^κ-th root of unity is divisible by l if, and

[49] J. reine angew. Math., 140: 29-32 (1911).

only if, the class number of the field defined by a primitive l-th root of unity is divisible by l.

For a proof of this theorem the field defined by the l^{κ}-th roots of unity is compared with the field defined by the $l^{\kappa+1}$-th roots of unity.

We have the theorem: If the class number of the field of the primitive l^{κ}-th roots of unity is prime to l, then every unit of this field is the relative norm of a unit of the field defined by a primitive $l^{\kappa+1}$-th root of unity.

For proof, we note that if $l' = l^{\kappa-1}\left(\frac{l-1}{2}\right)$ and k is defined by a primitive l^{κ}-th root of unity ζ_{κ}, then there are $l'-1$ fundamental units in k. Also, there exist l' independent unit systems (Einheitenverbände) in k, and therefore the number of distinct unit systems in k is $l^{l'}$. In the field K defined by a primitive $l^{\kappa+1}$-th root of unity, there are l' relative fundamental units with respect to k. Calling these $H_1, H_2, \ldots, H_{l'}$, and designating a substitution of the relative group of K with respect to k by S, then a unit of the form

$$H_1^{F_1(S)} \ldots H_{l'}^{F_{l'}(S)} \zeta^{e}_{\kappa+1}\eta$$

is the symbolic $(S-1)$-th power of a unit in K only if

$$F_1(1) \equiv F_2(1) \equiv \ldots \equiv F_{l'}(1) \equiv e \equiv 0 \quad (l).$$

Here the function F is a polynomial in S with rational integral coefficients, $\zeta_{\kappa+1}$ is a primitive $l^{\kappa+1}$-th root of unity and η is an arbitrary integer in k. Since the relative norm of $\zeta^{e}_{\kappa+1}\eta = 1$, we have $e \equiv 0$ (modulo l). It follows from the property of the fundamental units just mentioned that among the unit systems in k

(27) $$H_1^{e_1} \ldots H_{l'}^{e_{l'}} \zeta^{e}_{\kappa+1} H^{l}$$
$$(e_i,\ e = 0, 1, \ldots, l-1)$$

there are at most l' units having the relative norm 1 taken with respect to k. If H' and H'' are two such units which are not l-th powers of a unit, then

$$H' = A^{S-1}, \qquad H'' = B^{S-1}$$

where A and B are integers in K. It is then shown that

$$A = a\Lambda^{m} H_a, \qquad B = \beta\Lambda^{n} H_b,$$

where H_a and H_b are units in K, m and n are integers prime to l, a and β are integers in k, and $\Lambda = 1 - \zeta_{\kappa+1}$. From this it is shown that

$$H'' = (H')^{f} \bar{H}^{l}$$

where f is prime to l, and $\bar{H}$ is a unit in K. It follows from this that there are at most l' unit systems in (27) with the relative norm 1 with respect to k. Forming the relative norm of the unit (27) with respect to k we have, from what precedes, that these relative norms in k yield $l^{r'}$ distinct unit systems. As this is the exact number of unit systems in k, the theorem is proved. It is then shown that if J is an ideal in K, and

$$J^{S-1} \sim j$$

where j is an ideal in k, then J is equivalent to an ideal in k.

For the proof of the first theorem mentioned in this paper, take an arbitrary ideal J in K, and it is always possible to find an exponent q prime to l so that J^q is equivalent to some ideal in k. This follows from the fact that $J^{q(1-S)}$ is equivalent to an ideal in k since an $(S-1)^l$-th symbolic power of an ideal is always actually the l-th power of an ideal; hence by the preceding theorem, J^q is itself equivalent to an ideal in k. Hence, if the class number of k is prime to l, then the class number of K is prime to l. The converse of this result, namely, that if the class number of the field k is divisible by l, then the class number of K is divisible by l is a consequence of Furtwängler's (§29 of Chap. I, p. 91) theorem.

FURTWÄNGLER[50] considered the Fermat relation in the form

$$x_1{}^l + x_2{}^l + x_3{}^l = 0 \tag{27a}$$

where the x's are rational integers prime to each other, whence, if x_3 is prime to l,

$$x_1 + \zeta^i x_2$$

is the lth power of an ideal in the field $k(\zeta)$ where $\zeta = e^{2i\pi/l}$. Also

$$\left(\frac{a}{x_1+\zeta^i x_2}\right) = 1$$

where a is an arbitrary integer in $k(\zeta)$ prime to $(x_1+\zeta^i x_2)$ and the symbol in the left hand member of the equation indicates the lth power character of a with respect to $(x_1+\zeta^i x_2)$. Using Eisenstein's law of reciprocity between the power characters involving a rational integer r and a semi-primary integer in the field $k(\zeta)$, we obtain

$$\left(\frac{r}{x_1\zeta^{x_2}+x_2\zeta^{-x_1}}\right) = \left(\frac{x_1\zeta^{x_2}+x_2\zeta^{-x_1}}{r}\right) = 1.$$

If r is a factor of x_1, then

$$\left(\frac{x_2\zeta^{-x_1}}{r}\right) = \left(\frac{\zeta^{-x_1}}{r}\right) = 1$$

which gives if x_1 is prime to l,

$$r^{l-1} \equiv 1 \quad (l^2).$$

[50] Wiener Berichte, Abt. IIa, 121: 589-592 (1912).

This proves that if x_1, x_2, x_3, are three rational integers none zero, and prime to each other, connected by the relation (27a) and l is an odd prime, then

$$r^{l-1} \equiv 1 \quad (l^2)$$

where r is any factor of x_i $(i=1, 2, 3)$, if x_i is prime to l. Setting $r=2$, which is evidently a factor of $x_1 x_2 x_3$, we obtain

$$2^{l-1} \equiv 1 \quad (l^2).$$

Taking r as a factor of $x_1 \pm x_2$ in the above relations, we find that x_1, x_2, x_3, are three rational integers none zero, prime to each other and connected by the relation (27a) where l is an odd prime, then

$$r^{l-1} \equiv 1 \quad (l^2)$$

where r is any factor of $x_i \pm x_k$ $(i, k=1, 2, 3)$ and $x_i + x_k$ and $x_i - x_k$ are prime to l. These results are used to prove that

$$3^{l-1} \equiv 1 \quad (l^2)$$

and to derive Legendre's theorem that the Fermat relation with the exponent l and in case I will not hold for any l for which $2l+1$ is a prime.

BOHNICEK[51] proved if n is an integer >2 and α, β, γ are integers in the field defined by a primitive 2^n-th root of unity, none zero, then

$$\alpha^{2^{n-1}} + \beta^{2^{n-1}} + \gamma^{2^{n-1}} = 0$$

is impossible. For $n=3$ this reduces to a result given by Hilbert.[28] The proof is obtained by the use of the theorem that the class number of the field defined by a primitive 2^n-th root of unity is odd (cf. Weber, Algebra II, Edition 2, 818) also the theorem that if k is a sub-field of the field defined by a primitive 2^n-th root of unity, m is an integer $\leqq n$ and ξ is a unit in k such that

$$\xi \equiv \alpha^{2m} \qquad (2^{m+1}),$$

where α is an integer in k, then ξ is the 2^m-th power of a unit in k, together with an extension of a method employed by Hilbert[28] to establish the theorem for the case $n=3$.

VÉRÉBRUSSOV[52] considered, using Kummer's methods, the classes of ideals to which two conjugate imaginary ideals belong in the field defined by α where α is a primitive λ-th root of unity, λ being an odd prime, and concludes by a meaningless argument that if $f(\alpha)$ is an ideal in the

[51] Wiener Berichte, Abt. IIa, 121: 727-742 (1912).

[52] Mémoire sur les classes des nombres complexes ideaux conjugés avec l'application à la démonstration du dernier théorème der Fermat, Paris and Leipzig, 1912.

field $\Omega(a)$, then $f(a) \cdot f(a^{-1})$ is an integer in the field. Based on this result, he attempts a demonstration of Fermat's last theorem.

FUETER[52a] investigated the solutions of $\xi^3+\eta^3+\zeta^3=0$ in the quadratic imaginary field $k(\sqrt{m})$. If m is congruent to $2 \pmod 3$, then solutions exist only when the class number of the quadratic field is divisible by 3. In particular we have,

$$\left(\frac{9+\sqrt{-31}}{2}\right)^3+\left(\frac{9-\sqrt{-31}}{2}\right)^3+3^3=0.$$

Analogous results are obtained for the case of real quadratic fields.

FABRY[53] attempted to prove that if $xyz \not\equiv 0 \pmod{\lambda}$,

$$x^\lambda+y^\lambda+z^\lambda=0$$

is impossible in rational integers, none zero, where λ is an odd prime.

As Kummer had shown, so he shows that

$$(x+a^{n_1}y)(x+a^{n_2}y)\dots(x+a^{n_\mu}y)=a^r Q^\lambda(a)$$

where a is a primitive λ-th root of unity, $Q(a)$ is an integer in the field defined by a,

$$h \cdot n_h \equiv 1 \quad \text{modulo } \lambda,$$

the h's being the $(\lambda-1)/2=\mu$ integers defined by

$$\frac{q+1}{k+1}\lambda<h<\frac{q+1}{k}\lambda, \qquad q=0, 1, 2, \dots, k-1.$$

Here k is a rational integer,

$$0<k<\lambda-1.$$

He then expresses the left-hand member of the above equation in ascending powers of $1-a$ and obtains therefrom complicated congruences involving multinomial coefficients. MIRIMANOFF,[53a] however, pointed out that these congruences do not cover all possible cases which arise from the development and consequently Fabry's attempted proof is insufficient.

BURNSIDE[53b] extended the results of Fueter[52a] and showed that the equation

$$x^3+y^3+z^3=0$$

has non-trivial solutions in the field $k(\sqrt{n})$ if, and only if, the equation

$$nl^2+12k^3+3=0$$

has solutions in rational numbers l and k, and if this condition holds then the first equation has an infinite number of solutions.

[52a] Sitzungsber. Heidelberger Akad. Wiss., 1913: 25.
[53] Compt. Rend., 156: 1814 (1913).
[53a] Compt. Rend., 157: 491-492 (1913).
[53b] Proc. London Math. Soc., (2), 14: 1-4 (1914).

VANDIVER[54] gave without proof the criteria for (1) in Case I:

$$\sum_{r=1}^{p-1} y_r^{(n)} r^{p-2} t^r \equiv 0 \pmod{p},$$

where $y_r^{(n)} \equiv -r/p \pmod{n}$; $0 \leqq y_r^{(n)} < n$, with n any integer prime to p, and t is defined as in next reference.

VANDIVER[55] proved that if (1) is satisfied in Case I, then $5^{p-1} \equiv 1 \pmod{p^2}$, and $1+\frac{1}{2}+\frac{1}{3}+\ldots+\frac{1}{[\frac{p}{5}]} \equiv 0 \pmod{p}$, where $[p/5]$ is the greatest integer in $p/5$. These results were obtained by transformations of the Kummer Criteria (23) and with the use of the identical congruence in x and y,

$$(28) \quad \left\{ \begin{aligned} &(y^2-x)\sum_{n=1}^{p-1} 2^{p-n-1}\tbinom{p-2}{n-1} f_n(y) f_{p-n}(x) \\ &\quad \equiv x f_{p-1}(y) - x^p y^2 f_{p-1}(y) \\ &\qquad + 2^{p-2} K(x)(y^p x + y^{p+1} x^{\mu+1} - y^2 - y x^{\mu+1}) \\ &\qquad + M(x)(y^{p+1} + y^p x^{\mu+1} - y^2 x^{\mu} - y), \\ &\qquad\qquad \mu = \frac{p-1}{2}, \end{aligned} \right.$$

modulo p, where $K(x)$ and $M(x)$ are polynomials in x with integral coefficients, and $f_n(x)$ is defined as in Mirimanoff.[33]

This leads to the congruences

$$(28a) \qquad \frac{t^m-1}{t-1} \sum{}' \frac{f(a)}{1-a^p} \cdot \frac{1-a^2}{t-a^2} \equiv 0 \pmod{p}$$

where the summation extends over every distinct value of a given by $a^m=1$, $a \neq 1$, $-t = \frac{x}{y}, \frac{y}{x}, \frac{x}{z}, \frac{z}{x}, \frac{y}{z}, \frac{z}{y}$.

FROBENIUS[56] proved the identity

$$(y^k-x)F(x,y) + (y^k-1)f_1(x)f(y) = x(y^p-1)\sum_{l=0}^{k-1} h_l^{(k)}(x) y^l$$

where k is any integer, $h_l^{(k)}(x) = \sum_{r=0}^{p-1} (kr+l)^{p-2} x^r$,

$$F(x,y) = \sum_{n=1}^{p-2} \tbinom{p-2}{n-1} k^{p-n-1} f_{p-n}(x) f_n(y);\ f(y) = f_{p-1}(y);\ f_1(x) = \frac{x^p-1}{x-1}.$$

For $k=2$ we have another form of the relation (28).

[54] Bull. Am. Math. Soc., 21: 68 (1914).
[55] J. reine angew. Math., 144: 314-318 (1914).
[56] Sitzungsber. Akad. Wiss., Berlin, 1914: 653-681.

Using the relations

$$\frac{m^n-1}{n}b_n \equiv -\sum{}' \frac{f_n(\rho)}{1-\rho^p} \pmod{p},$$

and

$$\frac{m^{p-1}-1}{p}=q(m)\equiv -\sum{}' \frac{f(\rho)}{1-\rho^p} \pmod{p},$$

where m is an integer prime to p; $n=1, 2, \ldots, p-1$; the summation extends over all the values ρ other than unity such that $\rho^m=1$ and $b_0=1$, $b_1=-1/2$, $b_2=1/6$, $b_3=0$, $b_4=-1/30$, $\ldots$, are the Bernoulli numbers, he derives the identity in x,

$$(x^p-1)G_m{}^{(k)}(x)-(x^m-1)F_{m:k}(x)\equiv H_m{}^{(k)}(x) \pmod{p},$$

where

$$G_m{}^{(k)}(x)=G(x)=x\frac{x^m-1}{x-1}\sum{}'\frac{f(\rho)}{1-\rho^p}\cdot\frac{1-\rho^k}{x-\rho^k},$$

$$F_{m:k}(x)\equiv -\sum_{n=0}^{p-2}\left(-\frac{m}{k}\right)^n b_n f_{p-n}(x),$$

and

$$H_m{}^{(k)}(x)=x(x^m-1)\sum_{l=0}^{k-1}\sum_{\rho}\frac{h_l{}^{(k)}(x)\rho^l}{x-\rho^k},$$

the ρ summation ranging over all values $\rho^m=1$ including unity, m and k being any integers prime to p. Making use of (23) gives

(29) $$(t^p-1)G_m{}^{(k)}(t)\equiv H_m{}^{(k)}(t) \pmod{p},$$

which is satisfied by

$$-t\equiv x/y,\ y/x,\ x/z,\ z/x,\ y/x,\ z/y \pmod{p}$$

from (1), or the congruence (29) is also satisfied, if in lieu of t we take,

$$t,\ \frac{1}{t},\ 1-t,\ \frac{1}{1-t},\ \frac{t-1}{t},\ \frac{t}{t-1}.$$

By taking various values of m and k in (29) and eliminating the h functions appearing in H, he finds for various small prime values of m

$$G_m{}^{(k)}(t)\equiv 0 \pmod{p}$$

for $k=1, 2, \ldots, (m-1)/2$. For $k=1$, m arbitrary, this gives (23b). For $k=2$, m arbitrary, we have (28a).

It is also proved that (p. 664),

(29a) $$G_m{}^{(1)}+G_m{}^{(2)}+\ldots+G_m{}^{(\nu)}=-\frac{m}{2}q(m)t\frac{t^{m-1}-1}{t-1};$$

$\nu=(m-1)/2$, m prime. With the aid of these relations it is shown that if (1) holds in Case I, then $q(2) \equiv q(3) \equiv q(5) \equiv q(11) \equiv q(17) \equiv 0 \pmod{p}$, and if $p \equiv 1 \pmod{6}$, $q(7) \equiv q(13) \equiv q(19) \equiv 0 \pmod{p}$. Cf. Vandiver.[85]

VANDIVER[57] examined the theory of Fermat's quotient $(m^{p-1}-1)/p$ and called the least positive residues of the integers

$$1^{p-1},\ 2^{p-1},\ 3^{p-1},\ \ldots,\ (p-1)^{p-1}$$

proper residues, modulo p^2, and proved that there are not more than $\left[p-\frac{1+\sqrt{2p-5}}{2}\right]$ and not less than $[\sqrt{p}]$ incongruent proper residues modulo p^2, where p is a prime >2.

It is then noted that the criteria

$$2^{p-1} \equiv 3^{p-1} \equiv 1 \pmod{p^2}$$

in connection with Fermat's last theorem limits the number of incongruent proper residues modulo p^2.

JENSEN[58] proved that there is an infinity of irregular primes of the form $4k+3$. For proof, assume that the distinct irregular primes of this form are restricted to $p_1, p_2, \ldots, p_q$. There exists a prime integer K such that

$$K \equiv 1 \pmod{2p_1(p_1-1)p_2(p_2-1)\ldots p_q(p_q-1)},$$

and therefore by a known formula (cf. Bachmann, Niedere Zahlentheorie, II, 41, relation (107)).

$$-B_1 \equiv \frac{(-1)^K B_K}{K} \pmod{p},$$

for p any of the numbers p_1, p_2, etc., $\neq 3$, $B_1 = 1/6$, $B_2 = 1/30$, etc., being the Bernoulli numbers. Hence all prime factors of the numerator of B_K are of form $4n+1$. Also, by the von-Staudt-Clausen theorem, Bachmann, l. c., p. 43, the denominator of $B_K = 6$. Hence

$$2B_K \equiv -1 \pmod{4}. \tag{30}$$

But the formula

$$\frac{(-1)^{n-1}B_n}{n} \equiv \frac{S_{2n}(2^\rho-1)}{n \cdot 2^\rho} \pmod{2^{\rho+1}}$$

where $S_{2n}(2^\rho-1) = 1^{2n} + 2^{2n} + \ldots + (2^\rho-1)^{2n}$, and $\rho > 1$, $n > 1$, gives for $n = K$, $\rho = 2$,

$$(-1)^{K-1} \cdot 2B_K \equiv 1 \pmod{4},$$

which contradicts (30).

[57] Bull. Am. Math. Soc., 22: 64-67 (1915).
[58] Nyt Tidsskrift für Matematik, 1915 (Afdeling B): 82.

BACHMANN[59] gave an almost complete reproduction of the papers by Dickson,[35] Kummer,[18] Mirimanoff,[33] Wieferich[37] and Furtwängler.[50]

DICKSON[60] gave a history of Fermat's last theorem with abstracts of papers published before 1917. He discussed the origin of the theory of algebraic numbers, in particular the history of the introduction by Kummer of the concept of ideal numbers. The relation of this theory to Fermat's last theorem is brought out.

POLLACZEK[61] used the Kummer criteria (23) in the form

$$B_i\left[\frac{d^{l-2i}\log(1-e^{v}t)}{dv^{l-2i}}\right]_{v=0}\equiv 0 \pmod{l},$$

$i=1, 2, \ldots, (l-3)/2$, and

$$x^l+y^l+z^l=0, \tag{31}$$

l an odd prime, $-t=x/y, y/x, y/z, z/y, x/z, z/x$. Also

$$\left[\frac{d^{l-1}\log(1-e^{v}t)}{dv}\right]_{v=0}\equiv 0 \pmod{l}.$$

Here B_i is the ith Bernoulli number. He also employed the relations

$$\left[\frac{d^{2i}\log\dfrac{e^{ax}-1}{e^{x}-1}}{dx^{2i}}\right]_{x=0}=(-1)^{i+1}\frac{B_i}{2i}(a^{2i}-1)$$

and its equivalent

$$\sum_{\eta}\left[\frac{d^{2i-1}}{dx^{2i-1}}\left(\frac{1}{1-e^{x}\eta}\right)\right]_{x=0}=(-1)^{i}\frac{B_i}{2i}(a^{2i}-1)$$

η ranging over all the values given by $\eta^a=1$, $\eta\neq 1$. He proved that if (31) is satisfied in Case I, then

$$\frac{a}{h}\sum_{\tau}\left[\frac{1}{1-e^{x}\tau}\right]_0^{(l-2)}\frac{1}{1-\dfrac{1}{\tau^a}}$$
$$\equiv\sum_{\eta}\left[\frac{1}{1-e^{x}\eta}\right]_0^{(l-2)}\frac{1}{\dfrac{t}{\eta^h}-1}-\frac{q(a)}{1-t} \pmod{l},$$

where the τ summation ranges over all values, τ defined by $\tau^h=t$; a and h are positive integers, a prime to l; the symbol $[X]_0^{(l-2)}$ indicating that X is to be differentiated $(l-2)$ times with respect to x, and $x=0$ substituted in the result. This relation may be shown to be another form of

[59] Das Fermatproblem in seiner bisherigen Entwicklung, Berlin and Leipzig, 1916, 160 p. Reviewed by Vandiver, Bull. Am. Math. Soc., 27: 373-376 (1921).
[60] Annals of Math., (2), 18: 161-187 (1917).
[61] Sitzungsber. Akad. Wiss., Wien 126, IIa: 45-59 (1917).

Frobenius' (29), if $a=m$, $h=k$, $l=p$. By means of it and (29a) Pollaczek, extending Frobenius' methods, shows that $q(a)\equiv 0 \pmod{l}$ for $a\leqq 31$, except for a finite number of values of l, if (31) is satisfied in Case I. It is also proved that $x^2+xy+y^2\not\equiv 0 \pmod{l}$, or $t^2-t+1\not\equiv 0 \pmod{l}$, if (31) is satisfied in Case I.

VANDIVER[62] proved that if $\mathfrak{P}$ is a prime ideal of the first degree in the algebraic field defined by $\alpha=e^{2i\pi/p}$ then

$$\prod_{\nu=1}^{k-1}\prod_{r=1}^{[\nu p/k]}\mathfrak{P}_{[1:r]}\sim 1,$$
$$k=2,3,\ldots,p-1,$$

or the ideal on the left is a principal ideal, where $\mathfrak{P}_a$ is the ideal obtained from $\mathfrak{P}$ by the substitution (α/α^a); $[x]$ is the greatest integer in x; and $[1:r]$ is the least positive solution m of $mr\equiv 1 \pmod{p}$. Using the results from (1) that $(x+\alpha y)$ is the pth power of an ideal it is shown that:

If (1) is satisfied in Case I, then it is necessary and sufficient that rational integers x, y and z exist which satisfy

$$\prod_{\nu=1}^{k-1}\prod_{r=1}^{[\nu p/k]}(x+\alpha^{[1:r]}y)=\alpha^g\omega^p, \tag{32}$$
$$x+y=v^p; \qquad v \text{ a rational integer,}$$

where k is an integer, $1<k<p$; ω is an integer in $\Omega(\alpha)$ and g is an integer satisfying

$$g\equiv -\frac{kyq(k)}{x+y} \pmod{p}.$$

In Kummer's derivation of his criteria (23) there were a number of steps not explained. Also, he used his own theory of algebraic numbers, definition of ideal and theorems obtained therefrom, and not all of Kummer's processes along these lines are accurate, as pointed out by Dedekind. In the paper now being reported on, a complete derivation of the Kummer criteria is attempted, based on Dedekind's theory of ideals and using (32). The argument begins with the relation

$$\prod_q\prod_s\mathfrak{P}_{[1:s]}\sim 1,$$

where s ranges over the values satisfying

$$\frac{qp}{k+1}<s<\frac{qp}{k}$$

and q ranges over the set $1, 2, \ldots, k$; k being any integer subject to the conditions $0<k<p-1$. This relation was given by Kummer but the

[62] Annals of Math., 21: 72-80 (1919).

modern form of the proof was given by Weber, Lehrbuch der Algebra, II, ed. 2, 749-750.

In this connection Bachmann[59] gave a reproduction of Kummer's[20] derivation and supplied some but not all of the missing steps. (Cf. Vandiver, Bull. Am. Math. Soc., 27: 375 (1921).)

From (32) another proof of Furtwängler's[50] theorem is obtained. (Cf. Fueter.[69])

VANDIVER[63] considered the first factor h of the class number of the field defined by $\zeta = e^{2i\pi/l}$ where

$$h = \frac{f(Z)f(Z^3)\dots f(Z^{l-2})}{(2l)^{\frac{1}{2}(l-3)}},$$

$$f(x) = r_0 + r_1 x + r_2 x^2 + \dots + r_{l-2} x^{l-2},$$

$Z = e^{2i\pi/(l-1)}$, r is a primitive root of l, and r_i is the least positive residue of r^i, modulo l. The decomposition of (l) into prime ideal factors in the field $\Omega(\zeta)$ shows that one of the prime factors is

$$\mathfrak{P} = (Z - r, l),$$

whence

$$Z^{kl^{a'}} \equiv r^{kl^{a'}} \pmod{\mathfrak{P}^{a'+1}}; \qquad a' > \frac{l-3}{2}.$$

This leads to

$$(2l)^{\frac{1}{2}(l-3)} h \equiv \prod_s f(r^{sl^{a'}}) \pmod{\mathfrak{P}^{a'+1}},$$

where $s = 1, 3, \dots, l-2$, whence

$$h \equiv \frac{\prod_s f(r^{sl^{a'}})}{(2l)^{\frac{1}{2}(l-3)}} \pmod{l^{a+1}},$$

where $a = a' - \frac{1}{2}(l-3)$. Using $r_i \equiv r^i \pmod{l}$, and Fermat's theorem, this reduces to

(33) $$h \equiv \frac{\prod_s \sum_{n=1}^{l-1} n^{sl^a+1}}{(2l)^{\frac{1}{2}(l-3)}} \pmod{l^a}.$$

Employing the symbolic method of Blissard concerning Bernoulli numbers, it is then shown that

$$\sum_{n=1}^{l-1} n^{sl^a+1} \equiv (-1)^{(sl^a-1)/2} l B_{(sl^a+1)/2} \pmod{l^{a+1}},$$

where $B_1 = 1/6$, $B_2 = 1/30$, etc., are the Bernoulli numbers; together with (33) this gives

$$h \equiv \frac{l \prod_s (-1)^{(sl^a-1)/2} B_{(sl^a+1)/2}}{2^{\frac{1}{2}(l-3)}} \pmod{l^a}$$

$s = 1, 3, \dots, l-2$. For $a = 1$, this yields a result due to Kummer.[17]

[63] Bull. Am. Math. Soc., 25: 458-461 (1919).

VANDIVER[64] pointed out that the proofs of the results given in Kummer[20] are inaccurate and incomplete in several respects. Under this Assumption I, Kummer proceeds to show that only one of the numbers, B_i, $i=1, 2, \ldots, \mu-1$, is divisible by λ. In this connection he states (p. 42, 5th line from bottom) "...denn der erste Faktor der Klassenanzahl muss, wie aus meiner Untersuchung der Teilbarkeit der Klassenanzahl durch λ (Liouville's Journal, 16, 1851 (473)) unmittelbar folgt, den Faktor λ mindestens so viel mal enthalten, als wie viele der $(\lambda-3)/2$ Bernoullischen Zahlen durch λ theilbar sind." On examining the paper referred to by Kummer we find that he reduces h_1 modulo λ and obtains a residue which may be expressed in the form

$$m \prod_{i=1}^{\mu-1} B_i,$$

where m is an integer prime to λ. At no place in this work, however, does he refer to any reduction of h_1, modulo λ^n, $n>1$. Hence, he is not warranted in making, without additional argument, the statement given above.

Kummer's proofs of Theorems II and III are vitiated because of his use of the formula (7a) of this report, which was shown to be inaccurate by F. MERTENS.[65]

In connection with Theorem IV, note the formula (A) which he gives on page 53 of his article, and (7b) of this report. It was proved by him only for ideals $f(a)$ of the first degree, whereas he applies Theorem IV to ideals not necessarily of the first degree.

VANDIVER[66] examined the divisibility of the first factor of the class number of the field $\Omega(e^{2i\pi/p^n})$ by p, and considered the relation of the results obtained to certain statements made by Bernstein.[47]

WESTLUND[67] reduced the first factor of the class number of the field mentioned for $n>1$ to the form

$$h_1 = k \times \frac{\prod_s \phi(\theta^s)}{2^{\frac{p^{n-2}(p-1)^2}{2}} \, p^{\frac{np^{n-2}(p-1)^2}{2}-1}} = kk_1,$$

where k is the first factor of the class number of $\Omega(e^{2i\pi/m'})$, $\theta=e^{2i\pi/\mu}$, $\mu=\phi(m)=p^{n-1}(p-1)$, $m=p^n$, $m'=p^{n-1}$; r_i is the least positive residue of r^i, modulo p^n, r being a primitive root of p^n. The integer s takes on

[64] Proc. Nat. Acad. Sci., 6: 266-269 (1920).
[65] Wiener Berichte, 126, Abt., IIa: 1337-1343 (1917).
[66] Proc. Nat. Acad. Sci., 6: 416-421 (1920).
[67] Trans. Am. Math. Soc., 4: 201-212 (1903).

all odd values $<\mu$ except multiples of p, and the function $\phi(\theta)$ defined by Westlund may be put in the form

$$\phi(\theta)=r_0+r_1\theta+\ldots+r_{\mu-1}\theta^{\mu-1}.$$

The integer k_1 is reduced modulo p by a modification of the method used by Kronecker[19] in reducing the first factor of the class number of $\Omega(e^{2i\pi/p})$. Set

$$(r-\theta^{-1})\phi(\theta)=p^n g(\theta),$$

where

$$g(\theta)=q_0+q_1\theta+\ldots+q_{\mu-1}\theta^{\mu-1}$$

and

$$q_i=\frac{rr_i-r_{i+1}}{p^n}.$$

From an argument used by Westlund

$$\prod_s(r-\theta^{-s})=\frac{r^{\frac{\mu}{2}}+1}{r^{\frac{\mu'}{2}}+1},\quad \mu'=\phi(m'),$$

which leads after a few transformations to

$$k_1\equiv\prod_s g(\theta^s)\pmod{p}.$$

We have the identity

$$\prod_s g(x^s)=a+V(x)W(x),$$

where $V(x)=\Pi(x-\theta^i)$, i ranging over the $\phi(\mu)$ integers less than and prime to μ, since $V(x)$ is irreducible in the rational field and $W(x)$ is a polynomial in x with integral coefficients. It is then shown that $V(r)\equiv 0$ modulo p, and this gives

$$k_1\equiv\prod_s g(r^s)\pmod{p}.$$

Now

$$\prod_s g(r^s)\equiv\prod_t\left(g(r^{2t-1})\right)^{p^{n-2}(p-1)}\pmod{p},$$

where $t=1, 2, \ldots, (p-1)/2$. To reduce the right-hand member, set

$$rr_i=r_{i+1}+rr_i-r_{i+1},$$

which gives easily

$$2tr_{i+1}^{2t-1}\cdot(rr_i-r_{i+1})\equiv r^{2t}r_i^{2t}-r_i^{2t}\pmod{p^{2n}}$$

and this yields

$$2tp^n r^{2t-1}\sum_i q_i r^{i(2t-1)}\equiv r^{2t}\sum_i r_i^{2t}-\sum_i r^{2t}{}_{i+1}\pmod{p^{2n}}$$

and

$$\prod_t g(r^{2t-1})\equiv\prod_t\frac{(r^{2t}-1)S_{2t}}{2tp^n r^{2t-1}}\pmod{p},$$

where $S_{2t}=a_1^{2t}+a_2^{2t}+\ldots+a_\mu^{2t}$, where the a's are the integers less than p^n and prime to it. The quantity S_{2t} is then reduced modulo p^{n+1} and it is shown that

$$S_{2t}\equiv R_{2t} \pmod{p^{n+1}}$$

for $t<(p-1)/2$ and

$$S_{2t}\equiv R_{2t} \pmod{p^n}$$

for $t=(p-1)/2$ where $R_{2t}=1^{2t}+2^{2t}+\ldots+(p^n-1)^{2t}$. Using the Bernoulli summation formula we then obtain

$$\frac{(r^{2t}-1)S_{2t}}{2tp^nr^{2t-1}}\equiv\frac{(r^{2t}-1)R_{2t}}{2tp^{2t-1}}\equiv\frac{(-1)^{t+1}B_t(r^{2t}-1)}{2tr^{2t-1}} \pmod{p},$$

the B's being the Bernoulli numbers, this congruence holding for any t less than $(p-1)/2$. The expression

$$\frac{(r^{p-1}-1)S_{p-1}}{(p-1)p^nr^{p-2}}$$

may be reduced modulo p to an integer prime to p, hence we have

$$\prod_s g(r^s)\equiv\left(\prod_{t=1}^{(p-3)/2} B_t\right)^{p^{n-2}(p-1)} \pmod{p}.$$

Hence, $\prod_s g(r^s)$ and, therefore, k, is divisible by p if and only if at least one of the numbers B_t, $(t=1, 2, \ldots, (p-3)/2)$ is divisible by p.

Now Bernstein [47] gave the result that under the assumption that the class number of the field $\Omega(e^{2i\pi/p^2})$ is divisible by p but not by p^2, then $x^p+y^p+z^p=0$ is impossible in integers prime to each other for $xyz\equiv 0$ modulo p. In view of the results just obtained, this criterion constitutes no advance over Kummer's [18] result that the Fermat equation does not hold for rational integers if p is a regular prime. Taking this in connection with the errors in Kummer's memoir of 1857, it is noted that Fermat's last theorem is not rigorously proved for all irregular primes less than 100. These irregular primes are 37, 59 and 67. Mirimanoff [25] gave an adequate proof for the case $p=37$, which leaves the cases of 59 and 67 still to be disposed of. Cf. Vandiver.[87]

It is then observed that Bernstein's [45] conclusions concerning the first case of the last theorem do not include Kummer's [20] (p. 65) results on that case but at most supplement them.

It is pointed out that Kummer's [23] computations show that the last theorem is proved for all exponents p such that $100<p<167$, excepting $p=101$, 103, 131, 149, 157. Cf. Schönbaum.[36]

Dickson [67a] gave the history of Fermat's last theorem with detailed abstracts of papers published prior to 1920. Cf. the remarks concerning this history in the introduction to present chapter of this report.

[67a] History of the Theory of Numbers, Vol. II, Ch. XXVI, 731-776 (1920).

MORDELL[68] reproduced part of the work of Kummer.[18, 20] On p. 25 he remarks that it seems that a new application of the laws of reciprocity may be expected to lead to interesting results on Fermat's last theorem. FUETER[69] using methods due to Hilbert, proved that if (1) is satisfied in Case I, then employing the latter's notation of symbolic powers (HILBERT[70]), we have

$$(x+\alpha y)^{r_0+r_{-1}s+\cdots+r_{-p+2}s^{p-2}}=\alpha^g\omega^p$$

where s refers to the substitution $(\alpha:\alpha^r)$, r is a primitive root of p, $\alpha=e^{2i\pi/p}$, r_n is the least positive residue of r^n, modulo p. Here, also, ω is an integer in $\Omega(\alpha)$ and

$$g\equiv-\frac{y}{x+y}\pmod{p}.$$

By means of this relation the theorems of Furtwängler[50] are proved. He obtained a relation II, p. 15, which is a transformation of (32) of this report, deducing therefrom the Kummer criteria (23). He also derived the following transformations of the Kummer criteria:

$$\sum_{n=1}^{l-1}\left[\frac{an}{l}\right]\frac{\sigma^n}{n}\equiv 0\pmod{l},$$
$$(a=1,\ 2,\ \ldots,\ l-1),$$

where $[an/l]$ is the greatest integer in an/l and $-\sigma=x/y,\ y/x,\ x/z,\ z/x,\ y/z,\ z/y$. Also

(33a) $$\sum_{i=0}^{l-2} q(r_{i+k})\sigma^{r_i}\equiv 0\pmod{l},$$
$$(k=0,\ 1,\ \ldots,\ l-1),$$

where r_s is the least positive residue of r^s, modulo l, and

$$q(n)=\frac{n^{p-1}-1}{p}.$$

Cf. Vandiver.[62]

TAKAGI[71] considered the conditions under which a principal ideal is the l-th power of an ideal, using the norm residue symbol $(\mu,\ \nu)$. Let l be an odd prime; $\zeta=e^{2i\pi/l}$; k the cyclotomic field generated by ζ; r a

[68] Three Lectures on Fermat's Last Theorem, Cambridge Univ. Press, 1921.
[69] Math. Ann., 85: 11-20 (1922).
[70] Bericht über die theorie der Algebraischen Zahlkörper, Jahresber. deut. Math. Verein, 1894: 271.
[71] Proc. Physico-Math. Soc. Japan, (3), 4: 170-182 (1922).

primitive root of l; s the substitution $(\zeta|\zeta^r)$; $\lambda=1-\zeta$, the prime divisor of l in k; $\kappa_1, \kappa_2, \ldots, \kappa_l$ are bases such that

$$\mu\equiv\mu^l\kappa_1^{u_1}\kappa_2^{u_2}\ldots\kappa_l^{u_l} \pmod{\lambda^{l+1}},$$
$$\nu\equiv\nu^l\kappa_1^{v_1}\kappa_2^{v_2}\ldots\kappa_l^{v_l} \pmod{\lambda^{l+1}},$$

the κ's being further chosen so that

$$\kappa_a\equiv 1-\lambda^a \pmod{\lambda^{a+1}},$$
$$\kappa_a^{s-r_a}\equiv 1 \pmod{\lambda^{l+1}}.$$

It is sufficient to take

$$\begin{aligned}&\kappa_1=\zeta,\\ &\kappa_{l-1}=1+l,\\ &\kappa_l=1+\lambda^l,\\ &\kappa_a\equiv(1-\lambda^a)^{-r^a(s-1)(s-r)\ldots(s-r^{a-1})(s-r^{a+1})\ldots(s-r^{l-2})}\\ &\qquad (a=2, 3, \ldots, l-2)\end{aligned}$$

where the exponent in the value of κ_a refers to Hilbert's symbolic powers. For any ideal J in the field k we have

$$J^{Q(s)}\sim 1$$

where

$$Q(s)=q_0s^{l-2}+q_1s^{l-3}+\ldots+q_{l-3}s+q_{l-2}.$$

If $(\omega)=J^l$, then

$$\omega^{Q(s)}=\epsilon\alpha^l$$

where ϵ is a unit of k. Set

$$\left.\begin{aligned}\omega\equiv\omega^l\kappa_1^{a_1}\kappa_2^{a_2}\ldots\kappa_{l-1}^{a_{l-1}}\\ \epsilon\equiv\epsilon^l\kappa_1^{e_1}\kappa_2^{e_2}\ldots\kappa_{l-1}^{e_{l-1}}\end{aligned}\right\} \pmod{\lambda^{l+1}},$$

so that

$$e_t=0, \quad (t=3, 5, \ldots, l-2, l-1)$$

then

$$\omega^{Q(s)}\equiv\omega^{lQ(s)}\kappa_1^{a_1Q(r)}\kappa_2^{a_2Q(r^2)}\ldots\kappa_{l-1}^{a_{l-1}Q(r^{l-1})} \pmod{\lambda^l},$$

which gives

$$\left.\begin{aligned}a_1Q(r)&\equiv e_1,\\ a_tQ(r^t)&\equiv e_t, \quad (t=2, 4, \ldots, l-3)\\ a_tQ(r^t)&\equiv 0, \quad (t=3, 5, \ldots, l-2)\\ a_{l-1}Q(r^{l-1})&\equiv 0,\end{aligned}\right\} \pmod{l},$$

yielding

$$(34)\qquad \left\{\begin{aligned}B_{\frac{l-n}{2}}\,a_n&\equiv 0, \quad (n=3, 5, \ldots, l-2)\\ a_{l-1}&\equiv 0,\\ e_t&\equiv 0, \quad (t=2, 4, \ldots, l-1)\end{aligned}\right\} \pmod{l}.$$

This is another form of a result obtained by Kummer[20] (p. 65) for the case where ω is of the form $\omega=x+y\zeta$, x, y being rational integers, but whose method may be immediately applied to any integer in the field k.

He derives also another criterion for the existence of l-th powers of ideals, which criterion was obtained by MIRIMANOFF[72] for a special case.

If μ, ν are the l-th powers of any ideals or units in the field k, then

$$(\mu^{s^n}, \nu)=1, \quad (n=0, 1, \ldots, l-2). \tag{35}$$

Set

$$\left.\begin{array}{l}\mu\equiv\mu^l\kappa_1^{e_1}\kappa_2^{e_2}\ldots\kappa_{l-1}^{e_{l-1}}\\ \nu\equiv\nu^l\kappa_1^{e'_1}\kappa_2^{e'_2}\ldots\kappa_{l-1}^{e'_{l-1}}\end{array}\right\} \pmod{\lambda^l},$$

whence

$$\mu^{s^n}\equiv\mu^{ls^n}\mu^{e_1r^n}\kappa_2^{e_2r^{2n}}\ldots\kappa_{l-1}^{e_{l-1}r^{(l-1)n}} \pmod{\lambda^l}$$

and from (35) we obtain

$$r^ne_1e'_{l-1}+2r^{2n}e_2e'_{l-2}+\ldots+ar^{an}e_ae'_{l-a} +\ldots+(l-1)r^{(l-1)n}e_{l-1}e'_1\equiv 0 \pmod{l}.$$
$$(n=0, 1, \ldots, l-2).$$

These $l-1$ congruences give by elimination

$$e_ae'_{l-a}\equiv 0 \pmod{l},$$
$$(a=1, 2, \ldots, l-1).$$

Taking

$$\nu=\frac{1-\zeta^r}{1-\zeta}$$

these relations give another proof of (34).

VANDIVER[73] stated without proof a number of results concerning (1). The proofs of most of these theorems were published later. Cf. Vandiver,[80, 82, 85, 88] Fueter,[69] formula (33a) for $k=0$.

VANDIVER[74] proved Theorems I and IV of Kummer.[20] To complete Kummer's proof of Theorem I it is necessary to prove only the statement that if h_1 is divisible by λ but not by λ^2, then one and only one Bernoulli number B_ν in the set B_i, $i=1, 2, \ldots, \mu-1$, is divisible by λ. Using the relation (cf. Vandiver[63])

$$h_1\equiv\lambda\prod_s\frac{(-1)^{(s\lambda^2-1)/2}B_{(s\lambda^2+1)/2}}{2^{(\lambda-3)/2}} \pmod{\lambda^2}, \tag{36}$$
$$(s=1, 3, \ldots, \lambda-2).$$

[72] J. reine angew. Math., 128: 67 (1905). Cf. (23a) of this report.
[73] Bull. Am. Math. Soc., 28: 258-260 (1922).
[74] Bull. Am. Math. Soc., 28: 400-407 (1922).

with the assumption that $\lambda > 5$, $B_a \equiv B_b \equiv 0 \pmod{\lambda}$ where a, b are each included in the set $1, 2, \ldots, \mu-1$, we obtain, after using

$$\frac{B_c}{c} \equiv (-1)^{k\mu} \frac{B_{c+k\mu}}{c+k\mu} \pmod{\lambda},$$

k being an integer and c not a multiple of μ (cf. Kummer [20]) for $a = (s+1)/2$,

$$B_{(s\lambda^2+1)/2} \equiv 0 \pmod{\lambda}.$$

Similarly,

$$B_{(s_1\lambda^2+1)/2} \equiv 0 \pmod{\lambda},$$

where $(s_1+1)/2 = b$. Applying these relations to (36), we obtain $h_1 \equiv 0 \pmod{\lambda^2}$.

Kummer's Theorem IV is then stated but without the inclusion of Assumption II, as is necessary. For the proof the formula a on page 53 of Kummer's memoir is examined and also the corresponding formula for the generalized function $\psi_r(a)$,

$$\text{ind}\, E_n(a) \equiv \frac{\gamma^{2n}-1}{2(1+r^{\lambda-2n}-(r+1)^{\lambda-2n})} \cdot \frac{d_0{}^{\lambda-2n} \log \psi_r(e^v)}{dv^{\lambda-2n}} \pmod{\lambda},$$

where r is an integer, $1 < r < \lambda-1$, $E_n(a)$ and γ are defined as before and ind $(E_n(a))$ is i in the relation

$$(E_n(a))^{(q^t-1)/\lambda} \equiv a^i \pmod{\mathfrak{P}},$$

$\mathfrak{P}$ being an ideal prime factor of the odd prime q, and t the exponent to which q belongs modulo λ. Further

$$\psi_r(a) = \sum_h a^{-(r+1)h + \text{ind}(g^h+1)},$$

where g is a primitive root of $\mathfrak{P}$ such that $g^{(q^t-1)/\lambda} \equiv a \pmod{\mathfrak{P}}$, h ranges over the integers $0, 1, 2, \ldots, q^t-2$, excepting $(q^t-1)/2$; $\text{ind}(g^h+1)$ being defined as i in the relation $(g^h+1) \equiv g^i \pmod{\mathfrak{P}}$.

The case $q=2$ is exceptional and MITCHELL'S [75] definition of $\psi_r(a)$ is used in that case. Using the latter's decomposition of $\psi_r(a)$ into ideal factors, it is shown that

(37) $$\psi_r(a)^{H_1\lambda} = \pm a^d \Pi F(a^{\gamma^h})$$

where $H_1\lambda$ is the class number of $\Omega(a)$, H_1 prime to λ and h ranges over the values in the set $0, 1, 2, \ldots, \lambda-2$, such that

$$\gamma_{\mu-h} + \gamma_{\mu-h+\text{ind}\, r} > \lambda,$$

using Kummer's notation.

[75] Trans. Am. Math. Soc., 17: 165 (1916).

Since Kummer employs (p. 54 of his article) without proof or reference the relation

$$(38)\qquad \frac{d_0{}^{m\lambda^r}\log\phi(e^v)}{dv^{m\lambda^r}}\equiv\frac{d_0{}^{m\lambda^r}\log\phi_1(e^v)}{dv^{m\lambda^r}}\pmod{\lambda^{r+1}},$$

m not being a multiple of $\lambda-1$, and $\phi(a)\equiv\phi_1(a) \pmod{\lambda^{r+1}}$, a special case of this theorem is here proved. Using

$$\phi(e^v)=\phi_1(e^v)+W(e^{vp}-1)+cV,$$

where c is a rational integer and $V=(e^{vp}-1)(e^v-1)$, differentiating $m\lambda$ times with respect to V, then the relation (38) is obtained under the assumptions that $\phi(1)=\phi_1(1)$ and $\phi(a)$ is prime to λ. Applying this to (37) after raising to the power $\lambda-1$, we obtain Kummer's relation

$$\text{ind}\,E_\nu(a)\equiv-\frac{(-1)^{\lambda+\mu}(\gamma^{2\nu}-1)B_{\nu\lambda-\mu}}{2H_1\lambda}\cdot\frac{d_0{}^{\lambda-2\nu}lG(e^v)}{dv^{\lambda-2\nu}}\pmod{\lambda}.$$

(Cf. Kummer,[20] p. 57.)

Bliss[75a] commented on Fermat's last theorem stating that one may with justice feel very uncertain of its validity.

Pollaczek[76] considered at length the properties of irregular fields defined by primitive l-th roots of unity and primitive l^2-th roots of unity and considered the relation of these properties to Fermat's last theorem. He quotes the theorems A to K of Furtwängler.[43] The first field referred to he designates by $K(\zeta)$ and the second field by $K(\epsilon)$. He notes first that it follows from Furtwängler, VI, p. 29, that the class number of $K(\epsilon)$ is divisible by l if, and only if, l is an irregular prime. He indicates two other methods for proving this, the last of which involves the use of Furtwängler's theorem H. He then notes that the method of proof can also be carried over and yields

Theorem I. When the class number H_1 of the field $K(\zeta)$ is prime to l, then also the class number of the field obtained by adjoining the l-th root of η to $K(\zeta)$ where η is a unit in $K(\zeta)$, is also prime to l.

Pollaczek then considers the canonical expressions for units and the ideal classes in both $K(\zeta)$ and $K(\epsilon)$. In what follows, η defines a unit in $K(\zeta)$, H is a unit in $K(\epsilon)$; the ideals and classes belonging to $K(\zeta)$ will be designated by small German letters and the ideals and classes in $K(\epsilon)$ with large German letters. Further, r is a primitive root modulo l^2 and s stands for the substitution $(\zeta:\zeta^r)$ in $K(\zeta)$ and also for the substitution $(\epsilon:\epsilon^r)$ in $K(\epsilon)$. He then proves

[75a] Bull. Am. Math. Soc., 29: 161-162 (1923).

[76] Math. Zeit., 21: 1-38 (1924).

Theorem II. In the field $K(\zeta)$ there exists a system of fundamental real units η_i which have the property

$$\eta_i^{s-r^{2i}} = \eta'^{\,l}_i \qquad \left(i=1, 2, \ldots, \frac{l-3}{2}\right).$$

The proof of this theorem will be given in full as the method used is similar to a number of others used in this paper. Select a fundamental system of real units $\tilde{\eta}_1, \tilde{\eta}_2, \ldots, \tilde{\eta}_{\frac{l-3}{2}}$, and apply to them the substitution s. We may then write

$$(39) \qquad \begin{cases} \tilde{\eta}_1^{\,s} = \pm \tilde{\eta}_1^{\,a_{11}} \tilde{\eta}_2^{\,a_{12}} \ldots \tilde{\eta}_{\frac{l-3}{2}}^{\,a_{1,\frac{l-3}{2}}}, \\ \cdots\cdots\cdots\cdots\cdots\cdots\cdots\cdots \\ \tilde{\eta}^{\,s}_{\frac{l-3}{2}} = \pm \tilde{\eta}_1^{\,a_{\frac{l-3}{2},1}} \tilde{\eta}_2^{\,a_{\frac{l-3}{2},2}} \ldots \tilde{\eta}_{\frac{l-3}{2}}^{\,a_{\frac{l-3}{2},\frac{l-3}{2}}} \end{cases}.$$

We then apply to each of these equations the substitution s and obtain the units $\tilde{\eta}_i^{\,s^2}$ as products of the $\tilde{\eta}_i^{\,s}$ which in turn may be replaced as the products of powers of the $\tilde{\eta}_i$. We proceed further in this manner but since

$$\tilde{\eta}_i^{\,s^{\frac{l-1}{2}}} = \tilde{\eta}_i$$

it follows that the matrix A of the rational integers a_{ik} satisfies the relation

$$A^{\frac{l-1}{2}} = E_{\frac{l-3}{2}}$$

where $E_{\frac{l-3}{2}}$ is the unit matrix of degree $\dfrac{l-3}{2}$.

The characteristic equation of A will then have as roots $\left(\dfrac{l-1}{2}\right)$-th roots of unity. We shall assume temporarily that the characteristic equation of A is

$$(40) \qquad \frac{t^{\frac{l-1}{2}} - 1}{t-1} = 0.$$

Considering this relation as a congruence modulo l, we will have all the distinct quadratic residues of l as roots with the exception of unity. We may therefore select a matrix T' with rational integers as elements t'_{ik}, whose determinant $|T'| \equiv 1 \bmod l$ so that in $T'A(T')^{-1}$ the elements of the principal diagonal are the $\dfrac{l-3}{2}$ quadratic residues not equal to 1 and the other elements congruent to zero, that is $T'A(T')^{-1}$ is congruent to a diagonal matrix modulo l. Corresponding to a matrix T'' for which

$|T'| \equiv 1 \pmod{N}$ there exists, because of a theorem of Minkowski's, a matrix whose determinant $|T|=1$ and $T \equiv T' \pmod{N}$ where N is an arbitrary rational integer. Applying this result to the case $N=l$, there will therefore exist a system of fundamental units η_i so that

$$\eta_i = \tilde{\eta}_i^{t_{11}} \tilde{\eta}_2^{t_{12}} \cdots \tilde{\eta}_{\frac{l-3}{2}}^{t_{1,\frac{l-3}{2}}},$$

$$\cdots\cdots\cdots\cdots\cdots\cdots\cdots\cdots\cdots$$

$$\eta_{\frac{l-3}{2}} = \tilde{\eta}_1^{t_{\frac{l-3}{2},1}} \tilde{\eta}_2^{t_{\frac{l-3}{2},2}} \cdots \tilde{\eta}_{\frac{l-3}{2}}^{t_{\frac{l-3}{2},\frac{l-3}{2}}}$$

where the determinant of the rational integers $t_{ik}=1$. Applying the substitution s to the foregoing we obtain

$$\eta_1^s = \pm \eta_1^{b_{11}} \eta_2^{b_{12}} \cdots \eta_{\frac{l-3}{2}}^{b_{1,\frac{l-3}{2}}},$$

$$\cdots\cdots\cdots\cdots\cdots\cdots\cdots\cdots\cdots$$

$$\eta^s_{\frac{l-3}{2}} = \pm \eta_1^{b_{\frac{l-3}{2},1}} \eta_2^{b_{\frac{l-3}{2},2}} \cdots \eta_{\frac{l-3}{2}}^{b_{\frac{l-3}{2},\frac{l-3}{2}}}$$

and if B designates the matrix of the b_{ik} then $B=(TA(T')^{-1})$ and by the known property of this matrix we have by a properly selected notation $b_{ii} \equiv r^{2i}$, $b_{ik} \equiv 0 \pmod{l}$; $i \neq k$. Setting these values in the last set of equations we obtain our theorem under the assumption made as to the characteristic equation.

To complete the demonstration we show that (40) is the characteristic equation of A. Assume that this is not true, then the equation of lowest degree with rational integral coefficients which A satisfies,

$$G(x) = g_0 + g_1 x + \ldots + g_n x^n = 0,$$

is such that $n < \dfrac{l-3}{2}$.

Consider the expressions $\tilde{\eta}_1^{G(s)}$, $\left(i=l,\ 2,\ \ldots,\ \dfrac{l-3}{2}\right)$ and transform them by means of the equations (39), so that

$$\tilde{\eta}_1^{G(s)} = \pm \tilde{\eta}_1^{n_{11}} \tilde{\eta}_2^{n_{12}} \cdots \tilde{\eta}_{\frac{l-3}{2}}^{n_{1,\frac{l-3}{2}}},$$

$$\cdots\cdots\cdots\cdots\cdots\cdots\cdots\cdots\cdots$$

$$\tilde{\eta}_{\frac{l-3}{2}}^{G(s)} = \pm \tilde{\eta}_1^{n_{\frac{l-3}{2},1}} \tilde{\eta}_2^{n_{\frac{l-3}{2},2}} \cdots \tilde{\eta}_{\frac{l-3}{2}}^{n_{\frac{l-3}{2},\frac{l-3}{2}}}.$$

For the matrix $N=(n_{ik})$ we have

$$N = g_0 + g_1 A + \ldots + g_n A^n = G(A) = 0$$

because of the hypothesis concerning $G(A)$.

We therefore have for the units $\tilde{\eta}_i$, as well as for all real units of the field $k(\zeta)$,

$$\tilde{\eta}^{G(s)} = \pm 1.$$

Since $G(x)$ is a polynomial of degree $n < \frac{l-3}{2}$, it follows that the regulator of the field $k(\zeta)$ vanishes showing that our assumption that (40) was not the characteristic equation of A, leads to a contradiction. An extension of this method yields a proof of:

Theorem IIa. In the field $K(\zeta)$, there exists for every integer $c \geq 1$, a fundamental system of real units $\eta_{i,c}$ with the property

$$\eta_{i,c}^{s-r^{2i}l^{c-1}} = \eta'^{\,l^c}_{i,c}$$

$$(i = 1, 2, \ldots, (l-3)/2).$$

Since $K(\zeta)$ is irregular, the class number $H_l = l^h q$, $q \not\equiv 0$ modulo l. In considering the group of classes in this field it is sufficient for the purposes of this paper to consider only the q-th powers of the ideal classes of $K(\zeta)$, which will be termed the irregular class group. In this sense, two ideal classes $\mathfrak{j}$, $\mathfrak{j}'$ are the same if $\mathfrak{j}^q = \mathfrak{j}'^q$. For the class of an ideal $\mathfrak{j}$ contained in an irregular group of ideal classes, we may take the class to which the ideal $\mathfrak{j}^{q \cdot q'}$ $(q \cdot q' \equiv 1$, modulo $l^h)$ belongs. With these definitions we have

Theorem III. In $K(\zeta)$ we may select for the group of the q-th powers of the ideal classes a normal basis

$$\mathfrak{j}_1, \ldots, \mathfrak{j}_e, \; \mathfrak{j}_i^{l^{h_i}} = 1, \; \mathfrak{j}_i^{l^{h_i - 1}} \neq 1, \qquad (41)$$

$$(i = 1, 2, \ldots, e)$$

such that

$$\mathfrak{j}_1^{s-c_1} = 1, \; \ldots, \; \mathfrak{j}_e^{s-c_e} = 1, \qquad (41a)$$

where the c's are rational integers.

The demonstration of this theorem is analogous to that of Theorem II, depending on the symbolic matrix method as there employed. The proof is carried out for the case $e = 4$, but the method is general.

Theorem IV is then stated and proved by Pollaczek. He states a result for the field $K(\epsilon)$ which is analogous to the result given in Theorem II for the case $K(\zeta)$.

In the same way Theorem V is stated and proved and it contains a result for the field $K(\epsilon)$ which is analogous to that stated in Theorem III for the field $K(\zeta)$.

Pollaczek next examines the connection between the irregular class group as expressed in Theorem III with the singular primary numbers of the field $K(\zeta)$. Using Theorems IIa and III of this paper, together with Theorems B and C of Furtwängler,[43] there is obtained

Theorem VI. If among the elements of a normal basis of the irregular class group of $K(\zeta)$ there exists for a certain quadratic non-residue b_0 exactly z_{b_0} classes

$$\mathfrak{p}_{m_1}, \mathfrak{p}_{m_2}, \ldots, (\mathfrak{p}_{m_i}{}^{s-b_{m_i}}=1)$$

such that $b_{m_i} \equiv b_0$, modulo l, then there are either z_{b_0} or $z_{b_0}-1$ basis classes

$$\mathfrak{q}_{n_1}, \mathfrak{q}_{n_2}, \ldots, (\mathfrak{q}_n{}^{s-a_{n_i}}=1)$$

where $a_{n_i} \equiv r/b_0$ modulo l. In particular, if the second case holds, the unit $\eta_{\frac{1}{2}\,\mathrm{ind}\,r/b}$ is a singular primary unit of the type given in Theorem II. In the above, we designate by $\mathfrak{p}_1, \mathfrak{p}_2, \ldots, (\mathfrak{p}_i{}^{s-b_i} \sim 1)$ the ideals of those classes $\mathfrak{j}$ in (41), (41a), in which the c_i's are quadratic non-residues b_i; we designate also by $\mathfrak{q}_1, \mathfrak{q}_2, \ldots, (\mathfrak{q}_i{}^{s-a_i} \sim 1)$ the ideals of those classes $\mathfrak{j}_i$ in (41), (41a), in which the c_i's are quadratic residues a_i.

In the above theorem it follows that for the classes $\mathfrak{p}$ we have

$$\mathfrak{p}_i{}^{s^{\frac{l-1}{2}}-b_i^{\frac{l-1}{2}}} = \mathfrak{p}_i{}^{s^{\frac{l-1}{2}}+1} = 1.$$

Also, for the $\mathfrak{q}$-classes we have from Theorem VI

$$\mathfrak{q}_i{}^{s^{\frac{l-1}{2}}-1} = 1, \quad \mathfrak{q}_i{}^{s^{\frac{l-1}{2}}+1} = \mathfrak{q}_i{}^2$$

in $K(\zeta)$ and $K(\zeta+\zeta^{-1})$. It then follows that the $\mathfrak{q}$-classes contain only real ideals in $K(\zeta)$ and the $\mathfrak{p}$-classes only imaginary ideals. Since the second factor of the class number $K(\zeta)$ is equal to the class number of $K(\zeta+\zeta^{-1})$, it follows that the order of the group of the $\mathfrak{q}$-classes is equal to the highest power of l in the second factor of the class number of $K(\zeta)$, and the order of the $\mathfrak{p}$-class group is equal to the highest power of l in the first factor.

Pollaczek then notes that, analogous to Theorem VI, we have a theorem concerning what he terms $\mathfrak{P}$-basis-classes containing only imaginary ideals in the field $K(\epsilon)$, and $\mathfrak{Q}$-classes which contain only real ideals and are therefore in the field $K(\epsilon+\epsilon^{-1})$. Analogous to the results for the field $K(\zeta)$ we then have the theorem that since the second factor of the class number of $K(\epsilon)$ is equal to the class number of $K(\epsilon+\epsilon^{-1})$, (cf. Weber, Algebra, II: 784), then the order of the $\mathfrak{P}$-class group and the $\mathfrak{Q}$-class group are equal to the highest powers of l contained in the first and second factors of the class number of $K(\epsilon)$, respectively.

By means of Furtwängler's[43] theorem "F," it is then shown that the number of $\mathfrak{P}$-classes is not less than the number of $\mathfrak{p}$-basis-classes in

(41), and also that the number of $\mathfrak{Q}$-classes is not less than the number of $\mathfrak{q}$-classes in the irregular class field of $K(\zeta)$. In particular, we have (cf. Furtwängler [40])

Theorem Ia: If the class number of the field $K(\zeta+\zeta^{-1})$ is prime to l then the class number of the field $K(\epsilon+\epsilon^{-1})$ is prime to l.

The following theorem is then proved:

Theorem VII: An ideal of the $\mathfrak{p}$-class group which does not belong to the principal class in $K(\zeta)$, also does not belong in the principal class in the field $K(\epsilon)$.

Pollaczek then proceeds to the investigation of necessary conditions for the existence of a $\mathfrak{p}$-class of given order as well as a $\mathfrak{P}$-class of given order. We have the equivalence

(42) $$\mathfrak{j}^{q_0+q_1s^{-1}+\dots+q_{l-2}s^{-(l-2)}}\sim 1$$

(cf. Hilbert, Bericht., p. 360) where $\mathfrak{j}$ is any ideal in the field $K(\zeta)$,

$$q_k=\frac{rr_k-r_{k+1}}{l}$$
$$(k=0,1,\dots,l-2)$$

and r_k is the least positive residue of r^k modulo l. If an ideal $\mathfrak{p}_i$ of the $\mathfrak{p}$-basis-class of order l^{h_i} exists, then

(43) $$\mathfrak{p}_i^{s-b_i}\sim 1$$

where

$$b_i\equiv r^{-Tl^{h_i-1}},\quad \bmod l^{h_i}$$

and $T\leqq l-2$, which follows from Theorem III.

Combination of (42) and (43) gives

$$\mathfrak{p}_i^{q_0+q_1b_1^{-1}+\dots+q_{l-2}b_i^{-(l-2)}}\sim 1$$

and

$$\sum_{k=0}^{l-2} q_k b_i^{-k}\equiv\sum_k q_k r^{kTl^{h_i-1}}\equiv 0,\quad \bmod l^{h_i}.$$

By extension of a method employed by Kronecker [19] in connection with obtaining the criterion that the first factor of the class number of $K(\zeta)$ is divisible by l (cf. Hilbert, Bericht., p. 431), we have

$$\sum_{k=0}^{l-2} q_k r^{kTl^{h_i-1}}\equiv\frac{r^{l^{h_i-1}T+1}-1}{r^{l^{h_i-1}T}(l^{h_i-1}T+1)}\cdot\frac{1}{l}\sum_{x=1}^{l-1}x^{l^{h_i-1}T+1},\quad \bmod l^{h_i},$$

and using the Bernoulli summation formula and the Von Staudt-Clausen theorem (cf. Vandiver,[63] 459-460), we have

$$\sum_{k=0}^{l-2} q_k r^{kTl^{h_i-1}}\equiv\frac{r^{l^{h_i-1}T+1}-1}{r^{l^{h_i-1}T}(l^{h_i-1}T+1)}\cdot(-1)^{\frac{lT+3}{2}}B_{\frac{l^{h_i-1}T+1}{2}},\quad \bmod l^{h_i}$$

and therefore we have proved

Theorem VIII: A necessary condition that there exists an imaginary ideal belonging to the exponent l^{h_t} in $K(\zeta)$ is that one of the $(l-3)/2$ Bernoulli numbers

$$B_{\frac{l^{h_t-1}T+1}{2}}, \qquad T=l-4, l-6, \ldots$$

is divisible by l^{h_t}.

It is then noted that this theorem is not sufficient for the existence of an ideal of the type mentioned. However, it is shown that we have

Theorem IX: If for every odd $T<l-2$ such that

$$B_{\frac{T+1}{2}} \equiv 0, \quad \text{mod } l,$$

$h^{(T)}$ is the greatest integer for which

$$B_{\frac{l^{h(T)-1}T+1}{2}} \equiv 0, \quad \text{mod } l^{h(T)},$$

then the order of the group of classes of the imaginary ideals in $K(\zeta)$ is equal to

$$l^{\sum_T h^{(T)}}.$$

For proof, the first factor A_l of the class number of $K(\zeta)$ is used in the form

$$\text{(43a)} \qquad A_l = \frac{g(Z)g(Z^3)g(Z^5)\ldots g(Z^T)\ldots g(Z^{l-2})}{(-1)^{\frac{l-1}{2}} 2^{\frac{l-3}{2}} \cdot \dfrac{r^{\frac{l-1}{2}}+1}{l}},$$

where Z is a primitive $(l-1)$-th root of unity and

$$g(Z) = \sum_{k=0}^{l-2} q_k Z^k.$$

Pollaczek states that the criterion follows from the reduction of A_l modulo $\mathfrak{L}^{h_t}$ where $\mathfrak{L}=(l, r-Z)$. (Cf. Vandiver.[63])

Pollaczek then considers analogous problems in $K(\epsilon)$. He refers to Hilbert's Bericht., p. 376, and remarks that a form of the class number of the field defined by m-th roots of unity reduces for $m=l^2$ to

$$A_{l^2} = \frac{G(\bar{Z})G(\bar{Z}^3)G(\bar{Z}^5)\ldots g(\bar{Z}^{l^2-l-1})}{(-1)^{\frac{l-1}{2}} 2^{\frac{l^2-1}{2}-1} \cdot \dfrac{r^{\frac{l^2-l}{2}}+1}{l^2}}$$

where

$$G(\bar{Z}) = \sum_{k=0}^{l^2-l-1} Q_k \bar{Z}^k$$

and $\bar{Z}$ is a primitive (l^2-l)-th root of unity,

$$Q_k=\frac{rR_k-R_{k+1}}{l^2}$$

and R_k is the least positive residue of r^k modulo l^2. Setting $Z=Z\zeta$, we find

$$G(Z^T)=g(Z^T).$$

Corresponding to each factor $G(Z^T)$ in the numerator of (43a) which is divisible by $\mathfrak{L}$, there is a factor of $G(Z^T\zeta)$, namely

$$\mathfrak{L}'=(\mathfrak{L},1-\zeta),\qquad \mathfrak{L}'^{l-1}=\mathfrak{L},$$

contained to at least the first power; consequently A_{l^2}/A_l is divisible by at least l^{n_l} where n_l is the number of distinct Bernoulli numbers in the set $B_1, B_2, \ldots, B_{(l-3)/2}$ which are divisible by l.

The possibility of A_{l^2}/A_l being divisible by a higher power of l than l^{n_l} is then investigated. If this condition holds, then

$$G(Z^T\zeta)\equiv 0,\quad \mathrm{mod}\ \mathfrak{L}'^2.$$

Developing the left-hand member of this congruence in ascending powers of $1-\zeta$ gives

$$\sum_{k=0}^{l^2-l-1} kQ_kZ^{kT}\equiv 0,\quad \mathrm{mod}\ \mathfrak{L}.$$

This congruence is then transformed by methods analogous to those used in the proof of Theorem VIII and there is obtained

$$\sum_{k=0}^{l^2-l-1} kQ_kr^{kT}\equiv\frac{1}{1-r^{l-1}}\cdot\frac{r^{T+1}-1}{2Tr^T}\left(B'_{\frac{T+1}{2}+\frac{l-1}{2}}-B'_{\frac{T+1}{2}}\right),\quad \mathrm{mod}\ l,$$

where

$$B'_n=\frac{(-1)^nB_n}{n}$$

and this yields

Theorem X: When there are exactly n_l numbers among the first $(l-3)/2$ Bernoulli numbers divisible by l, then A_{l^2}/A_l is at least divisible by l^{n_l} and in order that A_{l^2}/A_l is divisible by l^{n_l+1}, it is necessary and sufficient that

$$(44)\quad \begin{cases}\dfrac{B_{\frac{T+1}{2}+\frac{l-1}{2}}}{\frac{T+l}{2}}\equiv\dfrac{(-1)^{\frac{l-1}{2}}B_{\frac{T+1}{2}}}{\frac{T+1}{2}},\quad \mathrm{mod}\ l^2,\\[2ex] B_{\frac{T+1}{2}}\equiv 0,\quad \mathrm{mod}\ l,\end{cases}$$

for some $T<l-2$.

For fixed T, then the $\mathfrak{p}$-basis ideals in (41) in which $c \equiv r^{-T}$ (modulo l), have relative norms which give an equal number of $\mathfrak{P}$-basis classes in the irregular class group of $K(\epsilon)$ with $c \equiv r^{-T}$ and for such ideal we have

$$\mathfrak{P}^{sS-r^{-l^{\nu}T}} \sim 1,$$

as well as

$$\mathfrak{P}^{Q_0+Q_1s^{-1}+\ldots+Q_{l^2-l-1}s^{-(l^2-l-1)}} \sim 1,$$

the latter relation, which is analogous to (42), being satisfied by any ideal of $K(\epsilon)$. Using these two equivalences, the following theorem is obtained:

Theorem Xa: The existence of the congruences (44) is a necessary condition that there exists at least one $\mathfrak{P}$-class $\mathfrak{P}^{sS-r^{-l^{\nu}T}}=1$ of the type that the class $\mathfrak{P}^{1-S}$ contains no ideals in $K(\zeta)$.

The case where the class number of $K(\zeta)$ is divisible by l but not by l^2 is then treated and there is obtained

Theorem XI: If the class number of the field $K(\zeta)$ is divisible by l but not by l^2, and $B_\nu \equiv 0$, modulo l, $\nu < (l-1)/2$, and

$$B_{\nu+\frac{l-1}{2}} \not\equiv B'_\nu, \quad \text{mod } l^2,$$

then the sub-group of the irregular classes of $K(\epsilon)$ is cyclic and of order l^2, and for an ideal $\mathfrak{P}$ of a basis-class of this group we have

$$\mathfrak{P}^{s-r^{1-2\nu-(l-1)y}} \sim 1$$

and also

$$\frac{B_{\nu+y\cdot\frac{l-1}{2}}}{\nu+y\cdot\dfrac{l-1}{2}} \equiv 0, \quad \text{mod } l^2.$$

In the field $K(\epsilon)$ there exists a unit which is congruent to the l^2-th power of another unit modulo $l^2 \cdot \lambda$ which is not itself an l-th power of a unit. The proof depends on special applications of Pollaczek's methods previously described.

The above results are then applied to Fermat's last theorem and Pollaczek concludes that Bernstein's[45] results on the first case of the last theorem are equivalent to Hecke's.[44] He also points out that the criterion given by Bernstein[47] (p. 508, Assumption I), is never satisfied. (Cf. Vandiver.[66]) He shows also that the second assumption of Bernstein (p. 508) is not satisfied for $l=37$, 59, 67, hence the results of Bernstein do not include those of Kummer.[20]

VANDIVER [77] transformed the Kummer criteria (23), starting with the obvious identity

$$f_1(x)f_1(y)=\frac{(x^p-1)f_1(y)}{x/y-1}-\frac{x/y(y^p-1)f_1(x)}{x/y-1},$$

where $f_1(u)=1+u+u^2+\ldots+u^{p-1}$. Setting $x=xe^{hv}$, $y=ye^{kv}$, h and k being indeterminates not zero, multiplying through by $(x/y)^p-1$, differentiating a times ($a\leqq p-2$), with respect to v, and putting $v=0$, we have an identity in x and y which, after setting $x=xe^v$, $y=ye^v$, differentiating $p-2-a$ times with respect to v, setting $v=0$, gives another identity in x and y.

In the last identity we set $y=\rho$, where ρ is an mth root of unity, $\neq 1$, and $x=t$, where $-t=\frac{u}{v},\frac{v}{u},\frac{u}{w},\frac{w}{u},\frac{v}{w},\frac{w}{v}$; $u^p+v^p+w^p=0$. This gives

$$(t^{pm}-1)\sum{}'\frac{A_1(t,\rho)}{((t/\rho)^p-1)(\rho^p-1)}$$
$$=\sum{}'\frac{(t^{pm}-1)}{(t/\rho)^p-1}B_2-\sum{}'\frac{(t^{pm}-1)}{(t/\rho)^p-1}C_2+G_3p,$$
$$=B_3-C_3+G_3p,$$

where

$$B_3=(t^p-1)\Sigma'\sum_{n=1}^{a+1}\binom{a}{n-1}k^{a+1-n}(h-k)^{n-1}F_n\left(\frac{t}{\rho}\right)\frac{f_{p-n}(\rho)}{\rho^p-1},$$
$$C_3=\Sigma'\sum_{n=1}^{a+1}\binom{a}{n-1}h^{a+1-n}(h-k)^{n-1}F'_n\left(\frac{t}{\rho}\right)f_{p-n}(t),$$

Σ' represents a summation over all distinct values of $\rho\neq 1$,

$$F_n(z)=\sum_{r=1}^{pm-1}r^{n-1}z^r,\quad (n>1),\quad F_1(z)=\sum_{r=0}^{mp-1}z^r,$$
$$F'_1(z)=\sum_{s=1}^{pm}z^s,\quad F'_n=F_n,\quad (n>1),$$
$$f_n(z)=\sum_{r=1}^{p-1}r^{n-1}z^r,\quad n>1.$$

Using the Kummer criteria (23) in connection with this we obtain

$$k^a(t^{pm}-1)\sum\frac{f_1(t)f_{p-1}(\rho)}{\rho^p-1}\equiv B_3-C_3\pmod p,$$

which, for $a=1$, gives

$$k(t^{pm}-1)\Sigma'f_1(t)\frac{f_{p-1}(\rho)}{\rho^p-1}\equiv(t^p-1)k\Sigma'F_1\left(\frac{t}{\rho}\right)\frac{f_{p-1}(\rho)}{\rho^p-1}$$
$$+(t^p-1)(h-k)\Sigma'F_2\left(\frac{t}{\rho}\right)\frac{f_{p-2}(\rho)}{\rho^p-1}$$
$$-h\Sigma'F_1\left(\frac{t}{\rho}\right)f_{p-1}(t)-(h-k)\Sigma'F_2\left(\frac{t}{\rho}\right)f_{p-2}(t)\pmod p.$$

[77] Annals of Math., (2), 26: 88-94 (1924).

In this relation put $h \equiv 0 \pmod p$ and $h \not\equiv k \pmod p$. We have for $k=1$, $f_{p-2}(t) \equiv 0$, and hence

$$(45) \qquad \Sigma' F_2 \left(\frac{t}{\rho}\right) \frac{f_{p-2}(\rho)}{\rho^p - 1} \equiv 0 \pmod p.$$

This congruence is reduced for $m=3$ to a relation which yields the criterion

$$1 + \frac{1}{2^2} + \ldots + \frac{1}{\left[\frac{p}{3}\right]^2} \equiv 0 \pmod p$$

for the solution of (1) in Case I. Cf. Pollaczek,[61] p. 59.

It is noted that this criterion is not satisfied for any $p<32$. It is possible that analogous criteria may be obtained by setting $m=4$, 5, etc., in (45).

Pomey [78] investigated Fermat's last theorem by elementary methods. Of his three principal results (theorems IV ter, V ter, and III bis) given without reference, the first two were known previously (cf. Vandiver, Trans. Am. Math. Soc., 15: 203 (1914), relations (5) and (6), Frobenius,[56] pp. 661-3) and the third may be derived immediately from them. By means of these theorems he proved Fermat's last theorem in Case I, for various prime exponents less than 100. By employing the criterion of Sophie Germain (Legendre [1]), he proved Fermat's last theorem in Case I for eleven prime exponents between 9048 and 10000 as well as for twenty-four other exponents between 5000000 and 5003250.

Beeger [79] computed the residue r of the quotient $(2^\xi - 1)/p \pmod p$ where ξ is the least exponent satisfying the congruence $2^\xi \equiv 1 \pmod p$, for all primes $p<14000$ and >2000. By means of these results, which are tabulated in the paper, he found that 3511 was the only prime number >2000 and <14000 that satisfies the congruence $2^{p-1} \equiv 1 \pmod{p^2}$. As Dickson had proved that (1) had no solution in Case I for all exponents $p<7000$, the present work shows that (1) has no solutions in Case I for any exponent $p<14000$.

Vandiver [80] took the norm residue symbol

$$\left\{\frac{\nu, \mu}{\mathfrak{p}}\right\} = a^L$$

[78] J. de Math., (9), 1925: 1-22; Abstract in Compt. Rend., 1923, 1187.
[79] Mess. of Math., 55: 17-26 (1925).
[80] Proc. Nat. Acad. Sci., 11: 292-298 (1925).

in the form given by HILBERT [81] where

$$L \equiv \sum_{s=1}^{p-1} (-1)^{s-1} l^{(s)}(\nu) l^{(p-s)}(\mu) \pmod{p},$$

$$l^{(g)}(\omega) = \left[\frac{d^g \log(\omega(e^v))}{dv^g}\right]_{v=0}$$

$g=1, 2, \ldots, p-1$; $\mathfrak{p}=(1-a)$; $\nu \equiv 1 \pmod{\mathfrak{p}}$, $\mu \equiv 1 \pmod{\mathfrak{p}}$; ν and μ integers in the field $\Omega(a)$, $a=e^{2i\pi/p}$. The symbol $\omega(x)$ is defined as follows: If

$$\omega = c_0 + c_1 a + \ldots + c_{p-2} a^{p-2},$$

then

$$\omega(x) = \sum_{r=0}^{p-2} c_r x^r - \frac{\sum_{r=0}^{p-2} c_r - 1}{p} \cdot \frac{x^p - 1}{x-1}.$$

If ν and μ are any integers in the field prime to $\mathfrak{p}$ then

$$\left\{\frac{\nu, \mu}{\mathfrak{p}}\right\} = \left\{\frac{\nu^{p-1}, \mu^{p-1}}{\mathfrak{p}}\right\}. \tag{46}$$

Now if (γ) is a principal ideal and the pth power of any ideal in $\Omega(a)$ then (γ), $(x+a^a y)$ being prime to each other and to $\mathfrak{p}$,

$$\left\{\frac{\gamma}{x+a^a y}\right\} = 1 = \left\{\frac{x+a^a y}{\gamma}\right\}, \tag{47}$$

since $(x+a^a y)$ is the pth power of an ideal in $\Omega(a)$. Furtwängler gave a law of reciprocity between two integers in a field containing $\Omega(a)$, which for the special case where the field is $\Omega(a)$ itself becomes

$$\left\{\frac{\omega}{\theta}\right\}\left\{\frac{\theta}{\omega}\right\}^{-1} = \left\{\frac{\theta, \omega}{\mathfrak{p}}\right\}, \tag{48}$$

ω and θ being any two integers in $\Omega(a)$ such that (ω) and (θ) are prime to each other and to $\mathfrak{p}$. Setting $\omega = \gamma^{p-1}$ and $\theta = (x+a^a y)^{p-1}$ then (46) (47) and (48) give

$$\left\{\frac{x+a^a y, \gamma}{\mathfrak{p}}\right\} = 1$$

or

$$L \equiv 0 \pmod{p},$$

for

$$\nu = \theta, \quad \mu = \omega.$$

It is then shown that $l^{(p-1)}(\omega) \equiv 0 \pmod{p}$

and $l^{(p-1)}(\theta) \equiv 0 \pmod{p}$

and thence (cf. Takagi [71])

$$\sum_{s=2}^{p-2} (-1)^{s-1} a^s \left[\frac{d^s \log(x+e^v y)}{dv^s}\right]_{v=0} \left[\frac{d^{p-s} \log \gamma(e^v)}{dv^{p-s}}\right]_{v=0} \equiv 0 \pmod{p}.$$

[81] Bericht über die Theorie der algebraischen Zahlkörper, Jahresber. deut. Math Verein, 1894: 413.

After setting $a=1, 2, 3, \ldots, p-2$ in turn, we obtain by elimination a result which yields the theorem that if (1) is satisfied in rational integers x, y, z, none zero and all prime to the odd prime p, then

$$f_{p-n}(t)\left[\frac{d^n \log \gamma(e^v)}{dv^n}\right]_{v=0} \equiv 0 \pmod{p},$$

$n=2, 3, \ldots, p-2$; $-t=x/y$. Here $\gamma(\alpha)$ is an integer in the field $\Omega(\alpha)$ and the principal ideal $(\gamma(\alpha))$ is the pth power of an ideal in $\Omega(\alpha)$ which is prime to (z) and (p).

This result yields the following corollaries:

If there exists in addition to the solution (x, y, z) of (1) (xyz prime to p) another solution (x_1, y_1, z_1) z_1 prime to z and $x_1y_1z_1 \not\equiv 0 \pmod{p}$, then

$$f_{p-n}(t)f_n(t_1) \equiv 0 \pmod{p}$$

$t_1=-x_1/y_1$, $n=2, 3, \ldots, p-2$.

If (1) is satisfied for $xyz \not\equiv 0 \pmod{p}$, then

$$f_{p-n}(t)f_n(1-t) \equiv 0 \pmod{p}$$

$n=2, 3, \ldots, p-2$.

If (1) is satisfied in integers prime to the odd prime p, then

$$\left[\frac{d^{p-a} \log \gamma(e^v)}{dv^{p-a}}\right]_{v=0} \equiv 0 \pmod{p}.$$

for $a=2$ and 3.

VANDIVER[82] employed the relation

$$\prod_{\nu=1}^{k-1} \prod_{r=1}^{\left[\frac{\nu p}{k}\right]} (x+\alpha^{[1:r]}y)^2 = \alpha^{\frac{-2kyq(k)}{x+y}} \omega^{2p} \tag{49}$$

where k is an integer, $1<k<p$, ω is an integer in the field $\Omega(\alpha)$,

$$q(k) = \frac{k^{p-1}-1}{p}$$

and $[1:r]$ is the least positive solution of $Xr \equiv 1 \pmod{p}$. Cf. Vandiver.[69] First it is proved that

$$(x+y)^{p-1} \equiv 1 \pmod{p^3}.$$

By means of this with (49) we obtain

$$(p-1)D_{np}\Sigma[1:r]^{np} \equiv p[D_{np}(\log \theta)]_{v=0} \pmod{p^2}$$

where

$$[D_{np}(\log \theta)]_{v=0} = \left[\frac{d^{np} \log \theta}{dv^{np}}\right]_{v=0}$$

$$D_{np} = [D_{np}(\log(x+e^v y))]_{v=0}.$$

[82] Annals of Math., (2), 26: 217-232 (1925).

The summation extending over all values of r as given in (49), n is any integer, $\theta=\omega^{p-1}$. From this it is shown that

$$D_{p(p-2m)}\Sigma[1:r]^{p(p-2m)}\equiv -p\,\frac{2\text{ ind. }E_m(a)\,(k-k^{p-2m})}{\gamma^{2m}-1}\pmod{p^2},$$

where m is any positive integer not greater than $p-1$ and

$$E_m(a)=e(a)e(a^{\gamma})^{\gamma^{-2m}}e(a^{\gamma^2})^{\gamma^{-4m}}\ldots(e^{\gamma^{\mu-1}})^{\gamma^{-2m(\mu-1)}}$$

γ being any primitive root of p, $\mu=(p-1)/2$. Also ind $E_m(a)$ is the value of M in the relation

$$\left\{\frac{E_m(a)}{\prod_{s=1}^{i}\mathfrak{P}^{(s)}}\right\}=a^M,$$

where

$$E_m(a)^{\frac{N(\mathfrak{P})-1}{p}}\equiv\left\{\frac{E_m(a)}{\mathfrak{P}}\right\}\pmod{\mathfrak{P}}$$

$\mathfrak{P}$ being a prime ideal divisor of the principal ideal $(x+ay)$, that is,

$$x+ay=(\mathfrak{P}^{(1)}\mathfrak{P}^{(2)}\ldots\mathfrak{P}^{(i)})^p,$$

where $\mathfrak{P}^{(1)}$, $\mathfrak{P}^{(2)}$, ..., $\mathfrak{P}^{(i)}$ are prime ideals in $\Omega(a)$, and also

$$\left\{\frac{E_m(a)}{\prod_{s=1}^{i}\mathfrak{P}^{(s)}}\right\}=\prod_{s=1}^{i}\left\{\frac{E_m(a)}{\mathfrak{P}^{(s)}}\right\}.$$

This relation yields, if $\Pi\mathfrak{P}^{(i)}=Q$

(50) $$\text{ind}\left(\frac{1-a^s}{1-a}\right)\equiv\frac{N(Q)-1}{2p}(s-1)+\sum_{m=1}^{\mu-1}\frac{(-1)^{l/2}B_{l/2}D_{p(p-2m)}(s^{2m}-1)}{2mp}\pmod{p},$$

where s is any integer prime to p and the B's are the numbers of Bernoulli, $B_1=1/6$, $B_2=1/30$, etc. In the relation (49) put $k=2$, $a^h=a$, and take p^{th} power characters of each side of the equation with respect to Q, and we obtain, with the use of $x+y=u^h$,

$$\prod_r\left\{\frac{\epsilon}{Q}\right\}=1$$

where

$$\epsilon=\frac{a^{\pm h[1:r]-1}-1}{a-1}$$

the sign of h being selected so that $h[1:r]\not\equiv 1\pmod{p}$.

Using the value of $\text{ind}((1-a^s)/(1-a))$ given in (50), and letting h range over the values 1, 2, ..., $\mu-1$, we obtain $\mu-1$ congruences which yield on elimination certain congruences involving x and y, which in turn give

$$B_a D_{3p} \equiv B_{a-p} D_{5p} \equiv B_{a-2p} D_{7p} \equiv B_{a-3p} D_{9p} \equiv 0 \pmod{p^2}.$$

Finally, after some transformations, there is obtained the theorem that if (1) is satisfied in Case I, then

$$B_s \equiv 0 \pmod{p^2}$$

$s=(lp+1)/2$, $l=p-4$, $p-6$, $p-8$, $p-10$.

The above result also yields the theorem that if (1) is satisfied in Case I, then the first factor of the class number of the field $\Omega(e^{2i\pi/p})$ is divisible by p^8. It is noted that

$$B_s \not\equiv 0 \pmod{p^2}$$

$s=(lp+1)/2$, $l=p-4$, $p-6$, $p-8$, $p-10$, for any $p<167$.

VANDIVER [83] attacked the last theorem by means of the theory of power characters in relative cyclic fields. Considering the relations (1) and (49), let n be a prime $\not\equiv 0$ or 1 (mod p) and suppose that $xy \not\equiv 0 \pmod{n}$ then $x^{n-1}-y^{n-1} \equiv 0 \pmod{n}$, hence there is some integer in the set 0, 1, ..., $n-2$, such that

$$x+\beta^a y \equiv 0 \pmod{\mathfrak{p}}$$

where β is a primitive $(n-1)$th root of unity, and $\mathfrak{p}$ is a particular prime ideal divisor of n in the field $\Omega(\alpha\beta)$. If θ is an integer in $\Omega(\alpha\beta)$, θ prime to (p) and $\mathfrak{p}$, then we define the pth power character of θ as $(\theta/\mathfrak{p})$, which is the power of α appearing in the relation

$$\theta^{\frac{N(\mathfrak{p})-1}{p}} \equiv \left\{\frac{\theta}{\mathfrak{p}}\right\} \pmod{\mathfrak{p}},$$

where $N(\mathfrak{p})$ is the norm of $\mathfrak{p}$.

In (49) set α^m for α and in the resulting equation take the pth power characters of each member with respect to $\mathfrak{p}$. Noting that

$$x+\alpha^c y = x+\beta^a y + y(\alpha^c-\beta^a),$$

and using (49), we have

$$\left\{\frac{x+\alpha^c y}{\mathfrak{p}}\right\} = \left\{\frac{\alpha^c-\beta^a}{\mathfrak{p}}\right\},$$

and therefore

$$\left.\begin{aligned} &\mu(k-1)D_0 m^{p-1}+\Sigma(m[1:r])^{p-2}D_1 \\ &\quad+\ldots+m\Sigma[1:r]D_{p-2}-\frac{mky}{x+y}\,q(k)I(\alpha)\equiv 0 \pmod{p}, \end{aligned}\right\}$$

[83] Proc. Nat. Acad. Sci., 12: 106-109 (1926).

where $\mu=(p-1)/2$, Σ stands for

$$\sum_{\nu=1}^{k-1}\sum_{r=1}^{[\nu p/k]};\left\{\frac{\theta}{\mathfrak{p}}\right\}=a^{I(\theta)},$$

$$D_s=\sum_{d=1}^{p-1}d^sI(a^d-\beta^a).$$

Letting m range over the integers 1, 2, . . ., $p-1$, we obtain by elimination

$$(51)\qquad \left\{\begin{aligned}&D_0\equiv\Sigma[1:r]^{p-s}D_{s-1}\equiv 0 \pmod p),\\ &\qquad s=2,3,\ldots,p-2;\\ &\Sigma[1:r]D_{p-2}-\frac{kyq(k)}{x+y}I(a)\equiv 0 \pmod p)\end{aligned}\right\}$$

We also have, if one of the integers x, y, z, say y, is divisible by p,

$$\prod_h(z+a^{[1:h]}x)^{p-1}=p^{\mu}a^{\mu\Sigma[1:h]}\omega_1{}^p$$

where h ranges over the positive integers $<p$, such that $h+|rh|>p$, $|rh|$ representing the least positive residue of rh, modulo p, and ω_1 is an integer in $\Omega(a)$. Taking p^{th} power characters of both sides of this with respect to $\mathfrak{p}$, and proceeding as in the preceding treatment of (49) we obtain

$$(52)\qquad \left\{\begin{aligned}&D'_s\equiv\Sigma[1:h]^{p-s}D'_{s-1}\equiv 0 \pmod p),\\ &\qquad s=2,3,\ldots,p-2;\\ &\Sigma[1:h]D'_{p-2}+\frac{\Sigma[1:h]I(a)}{2}\equiv 0 \pmod p),\end{aligned}\right\}$$

where

$$D'_s=\sum_{d=1}^{p-1}d^s(a^d-\beta^b)$$

b some integer, $0\leqq b<n-1$. A few transformations of (51) and (52) yield the theorems: (all details of proof not given).

If $x^p+y^p+z^p=0$ is satisfied in integers none zero and each prime to the odd prime p, then

$$q(n)D_0\equiv 0,\quad q(n)B_{\frac{s+1}{2}}D_s\equiv 0 \pmod p)$$

$$s=1,3,\ldots,p-4,$$

where

$$D_s=\sum_{d=1}^{p-1}d^sI(a^d-\beta^a),\ \left\{\frac{\theta}{\mathfrak{p}}\right\}=a^{I(\theta)},$$

$\mathfrak{p}$ is a prime ideal divisor in the field $\Omega(a\beta)$ of a rational odd prime n which is $\not\equiv 0$ or 1 (mod p); $a=e^{2i\pi/p}$; $\beta=e^{2i\pi/(n-1)}$, a is some integer in the set 1, 2, . . ., $n-2$ other than $(n-1)/2$; the B's are the numbers of Bernoulli, $B_1=1/6$, $B_2=1/30$, etc.

If $x^p+y^p+z^p=0$ is satisfied in integers none zero and each prime to the odd prime p, then

$$q(n)\prod_{a=0}^{n-2}((1-v)D_{p-2}+I(a))\equiv 0 \pmod{p},$$

where v has any one of the six values $t,\ \frac{1}{t},\ 1-t,\ \frac{1}{1-t},\ \frac{t-1}{t},\ \frac{t}{t-1},\ x/y=t$ the other symbols being defined as in the above theorem.

If p is an odd prime and $x^p+y^p+z^p=0$ where $y\equiv 0 \pmod{p}$, $xz\not\equiv 0 \pmod{p}$, $x+z\not\equiv 0 \pmod{n}$, then

$$q(n)D_0\equiv 0$$
$$q(n)B_{s+1}D_s\equiv 0 \pmod{p},$$

$s=1, 3, \ldots, p-4$; and in addition one of the two relations

$$q(n)D_{p-2}\equiv 0, \qquad q(n)\left(D_{p-2}+\frac{I(a)}{2}\right)\equiv 0 \pmod{p},$$

is satisfied, the other symbols being defined as above.

If $x^p+y^p+z^p=0$ is satisfied in integers none zero and all prime to the odd prime p, then

$$q(n)\prod_{a=1}^{n-2}((1-v)\operatorname{ind}(\alpha\beta^a-1)-q(n))\equiv 0 \pmod{p},$$

where

$$\left\{\frac{\alpha\beta^a-1}{\mathfrak{q}}\right\}=\alpha^i, \qquad i=\operatorname{ind}(\alpha\beta^a-1),$$

$\mathfrak{q}=(\beta-r,\ n)$; r a primitive root of n; v being defined as in the first theorem of this paper.

If $x^p+y^p+z^p=0$ is satisfied in integers none zero and all prime to the odd prime p, then

$$q(n)\prod_{a,\ b}(\operatorname{ind}(\alpha\beta^a-1)\operatorname{ind}(\alpha\beta^b-1)$$
$$-q(n)(\operatorname{ind}(\alpha\beta^a-1)+\operatorname{ind}(\alpha\beta^b-1)))\equiv 0 \pmod{p},$$

where a and b each range independently over the integers, 1, 2, ..., $n-2$, the other symbols being defined as in the first theorem.

If $xyz\not\equiv 0 \pmod{n}$, $z\not\equiv 0 \pmod{p}$, n a prime $\not\equiv 0 \pmod{p}$, then we have $q(n)\equiv 0 \pmod{p}$, or

$$\left.\begin{aligned}&\sum_{s=2}^{p-2}(-1)^s k^s\left[\frac{d^s\log(x+e^v y)}{dv^s}\right]_{v=0}\left[\frac{d^{p-s}\log\gamma(e^v)}{dv^{p-s}}\right]_{v=0}\\ &\qquad\equiv -\frac{kyh}{x+y}I(a)+hI\left(\frac{a^k-\beta^a}{1-\beta^a}\right) \pmod{p},\end{aligned}\right\}$$

where h is the integer to which the ideal $\mathfrak{Q}$ belongs, $\mathfrak{Q}$ being a prime ideal divisor of n in the field $\Omega(a)$, $\mathfrak{Q}^h=(\gamma(a))$, $\gamma(a)$ being an integer in $\Omega(a)$, k is any integer $\not\equiv 0 \pmod{p}$, a is some integer in the set 1, 2, ..., $n-2$, the other symbols being defined as in the first theorem, as criteria for the solution of (1) in rational integers, none zero.

VANDIVER[84] proved by means of Furtwängler's[50] theorem that if there exists an odd prime q such that $\xi^p+\eta^p+\zeta^p\equiv 0 \pmod{q}$ has no set of integral solutions each not divisible by q and such that $q\not\equiv 1 \pmod{p^2}$ then (1) has no solutions each prime to p. He also proved, using Sophie Germain's[1] result, a theorem due to Wendt.[28] These two theorems prove that if the above congruence has no set of integral solutions each prime to q, where $q=1+mp$ and $m<10p$, then (1) has no solutions in integers each prime to p.

VANDIVER[85] proved that if

$$u^p+v^p+w^p=0$$

is satisfied by any integers prime to the odd prime p, then

$$(53)\qquad \sum_{l=0}^{k-1} h_n^{(k,\,l)}(t)\,h_{(p-n)}^{(k,\,k-l)}(t)\equiv 0 \pmod{p},$$

$$n=1, 2, \ldots, p-1,$$

k being any positive integer, where

$$h_n^{(k,\,l)}(x)=\sum_{s=0}^{p-1}(ks+l)^{n-1}x^s.$$

For $k=2$, this reduces to

$$h_n^{(2,\,1)}(t)\,h_{p-n}^{(2,\,1)}(t)\equiv 0 \pmod{p}.$$

The proof of this result is obtained by means of transformations of the Kummer criteria (23). We start with the relation

$$1^n+2^n+\ldots+(p-1)^n\equiv b_n p \pmod{p^2},$$

$$(n<p-1),$$

where $b_0=1$, $b_1=-1/2$, $b_{2i}=(-1)^{i-1}B_i$, $b_{2i+1}=0$, $i>0$, and $B_1=1/6$, $B_2=1/30$, etc., are the numbers of Bernoulli. From the obvious identity

$$\frac{x-y^k}{(x-1)(y-1)}=\frac{y^k}{y-1}-\frac{x(y^k-1)}{(x-1)(y-1)}$$

there is obtained the identical congruence

$$(x^p-1)G_n^{(k)}(x)-(x^m-1)K_m^{(k)}(x)\equiv H_m^{(k)}(x) \pmod{p}$$

where

$$K_n^{(k)}(x)=-\sum_{n=0}^{p-2}\left(-\frac{m}{k}\right)^n b_n f_{p-n}(x),$$

$$G_m^{(k)}(x)=\frac{x(x^m-1)}{x-1}\sum_{\rho}\frac{F_p(\rho)(1-\rho^k)}{mp(x-\rho^k)},$$

$$H_m^{(k)}(x)=x(x^m-1)\sum_{l=0}^{k-1}\sum_{\rho}\frac{\rho^l h_a^{(k,\,l)}(x)}{x-\rho^k}.$$

[84] Annals of Math., (2), 27: 54-56 (1926).
[85] Annals of Math., (2), 27: 171-176 (1926).

Cf. Mirimanoff,[41] Vandiver,[55] Frobenius,[56] Pollaczek.[61] Multiplying through by (x^p-1), setting $m=1$ and $x=xe^{vk}$, differentiating $(p-1-a)$ times with respect to v, we have for $v=0$ the congruences (53).

VANDIVER [86] gave complete proofs of all the theorems of Vandiver,[83] with the exception of the last.

VANDIVER [87] gave among other theorems the following:

Under the assumptions: (1) The class number of the field $k(\alpha)$, $\alpha=e^{2i\pi/\lambda}$, λ, an odd prime, is divisible by λ but not by λ^2. (2) If $B_\nu \equiv 0 \pmod{\lambda}$, $\nu<(\lambda-1)/2$, and $B_{\nu\lambda} \not\equiv 0 \pmod{\lambda^3}$; the relation $x^\lambda+y^\lambda+z^\lambda=0$ is not satisfied in rational integers, none zero, where B's are the Bernoulli numbers. This theorem is equivalent to the one which Kummer attempted to prove in his 1857 memoir, and the proof is obtained here by modifications and extensions of Kummer's argument, taking into consideration also the results of Vandiver,[74] where theorems I and IV of Kummer's paper were proved. In the present article Kummer's theorem II is proved and it is noted that theorem III is unnecessary for the proof of the above result. It follows that if Kummer's computations (p. 73) are correct that the Last Theorem is established for all prime exponents $\lambda<100$.

A proof is also outlined of the following:

Under the assumptions,

1. None of the Bernoulli numbers

$$B_k, \quad k=(s\lambda+1)/2, \qquad (s=1,\ 3,\ \ldots,\ \lambda-4)$$

is divisible by λ^2;

2. The second factor of the class number of the field $\Omega(\alpha)$ is prime to λ; then

$$x^\lambda+y^\lambda+z^\lambda=0$$

is not satisfied in rational integers, x, y, z, none zero, if λ is an odd prime.

References noted on the subject of this chapter after the report was in press:

LANDAU, Vorlesungen über Zahlentheorie, III, 200-328, Leipzig, (1927).

HENSEL, Jahresber. Deut. Math. Ver., 36: 49-52 (1927).

TAKAGI, J. reine angew. Math., 157: 230-8 (1927).

[86] Trans. Am. Math. Soc., 28: 554-560 (1926); 29: 154-162 (1927).

[87] Proc. Nat. Acad. Sci., 12: 767-772 (1926).

BASIC GEOMETRY

By G. D. BIRKHOFF and R. BEATLEY

A highly recommended high-school text by two eminent scholars.

"is in accord with the present approach to plane geometry. It offers a sound mathematical development . . . and at the same time enables the student to move rapidly into the heart of geometry."—*The Mathematics Teacher.*

"should be required reading for every teacher of Geometry."—*Mathematical Gazette.*

—Third edition. 1959. 294 pp. 5¼x8. [120] **$3.95**

KREIS UND KUGEL

By W. BLASCHKE

Isoperimetric properties of the circle and sphere, the (Brunn-Minkowski) theory of convex bodies, and differential-geometric properties (in the large) of convex bodies. A standard work.

—x + 169 pp. 5½x8½. [59] Cloth **$3.50**
[115] Paper **$1.50**

INTEGRALGEOMETRIE

By W. BLASCHKE and E. KÄHLER

THREE VOLUMES IN ONE.

VORLESUNGEN UEBER INTEGRALGEOMETRIE, Vols. I and II, by *W. Blaschke.*

EINFUEHRUNG IN DIE THEORIE DER SYSTEME VON DIFFERENTIALGLEICHUNGEN, by *E. Kähler.*

—222 pp. 5½x8½. [64] Three Vols. in One **$4.95**

VORLESUNGEN ÜBER FOURIERSCHE INTEGRALE

By S. BOCHNER

"A readable account of those parts of the subject useful for applications to problems of mathematical physics or pure analysis."

—*Bulletin of the A. M. S.*

—1932. 237 pp. 5½x8½. Orig. pub. at $6.40. [42] **$3.50**

ALMOST PERIODIC FUNCTIONS

By H. BOHR

Translated by H. COHN. From the famous series *Ergebnisse der Mathematik und ihrer Grenzgebiete,* a beautiful exposition of the theory of Almost Periodic Functions written by the creator of that theory.

—1951. 120 pp. Lithotyped. [27] **$2.75**

LECTURES ON THE CALCULUS OF VARIATIONS

By O. BOLZA

A standard text by a major contributor to the theory. Suitable for individual study by anyone with a good background in the Calculus and the elements of Real Variables. The present, second edition differs from the first primarily by the inclusion within the text itself of various addenda to the first edition, as well as some notational improvements.

—2nd (corr.) ed. 1961. 280 pp. 5⅜x8. [145] Cloth **$3.25**
[152] Paper **$1.19**

VORLESUNGEN UEBER VARIATIONSRECHNUNG

By O. BOLZA

A standard text and reference work, by one of the major contributors to the theory.

—1963. Corr. repr. of 1st ed. ix+715 pp. 5⅜x8. [160] **$8.00**

THEORIE DER KONVEXEN KÖRPER

By T. BONNESEN and W. FENCHEL

"Remarkable monograph."

—*J. D. Tamarkin, Bulletin of the A. M. S.*

—1934. 171 pp. 5½x8½. Orig. publ. at $7.50 [54] **$3.95**

THE CALCULUS OF FINITE DIFFERENCES

By G. BOOLE

A standard work on the subject of finite differences and difference equations by one of the seminal minds in the field of finite mathematics.

Numerous exercises with answers.

—Fourth edition. 1958. xii + 336 pp. 5x8. [121] Cloth **$3.95**
[148] Paper **$1.39**

A TREATISE ON DIFFERENTIAL EQUATIONS

By G. BOOLE

Including the Supplementary Volume.

—Fifth edition. 1959. xxiv + 735 pp. 5¼x8. [128] **$6.00**

CAJORI, "History of Slide Rule," see Ball

VORLESUNGEN ÜBER REELLE FUNKTIONEN

By C. CARATHÉODORY

This great classic is at once a book for the beginner, a reference work for the advanced scholar and a source of inspiration for the research worker.

—In prep. 2nd ed. 5⅜x8. 728 pp. [38]

CARSLAW, "Non-Euclidean Plane Geometry," see Ball

COLLECTED PAPERS (OEUVRES)

By P. L. CHEBYSHEV

One of Russia's greatest mathematicians, Chebyshev (Tchebycheff) did work of the highest importance in the Theory of Probability, Number Theory, and other subjects. The present work contains his post-doctoral papers (sixty in number) and miscellaneous writings. The language is French, in which most of his work was originally published; those papers originally published in Russian are here presented in French translation.

—1962. Repr. of 1st ed. 1,480 pp. 5⅜x8¼.
[157] Two Vol. set. **$27.50**

TEXTBOOK OF ALGEBRA

By G. CHRYSTAL

In addition to the standard topics, Chrystal's *Algebra* contains many topics not often found in an Algebra book: inequalities, the elements of sub stitution theory, and so forth. Especially extensive is Chrystal's treatment of infinite series, infinite products, and (finite and infinite) continued fractions.

The range of entries in the newly added Subject Index is very wide. To mention a few out of many hundreds: Horner's method, multinomial theorem, binary scale, Demoivre's theorem, mortality table, arithmetico-geometric series, Pellian equation, Bernoulli numbers, irrationality of *e*, Gudermannian, Euler numbers, continuant, Stirling's theorem, Riemann surface.

OVER 2,400 EXERCISES (with solutions).

—7th ed. 1964. 2 vols. xxiv+584 pp.; xxiv+626 pp. 5⅜x8.
[84] Cloth Each vol. **$3.95**
[181] Paper Each vol. **$2.35**

HISTORY OF THE THEORY OF NUMBERS

By L. E. DICKSON

"**A monumental work** . . . Dickson always has in mind the needs of the investigator . . . The author has [often] expressed in a nut-shell the main results of a long and involved paper *in a much clearer way than the writer of the article did himself*. The ability to reduce complicated mathematical arguments to simple and elementary terms is highly developed in Dickson."—*Bulletin of A. M. S.*

—Vol. I (Divisibility and Primality) xii + 486 pp. Vol. II (Diophantine Analysis) xxv + 803 pp. Vol. III (Quadratic and Higher Forms) v + 313 pp. [86] Three vol. set **$19.95**

STUDIES IN THE THEORY OF NUMBERS

By L. E. DICKSON

A systematic exposition, starting from first principles, of the arithmetic of quadratic forms, chiefly (but not entirely) ternary forms, including numerous original investigations and correct proofs of a number of classical results that have been stated or proved erroneously in the literature.

—1930-62 viii+230 pp. 5⅜x8. [151] **$3.95**

AUTOMORPHIC FUNCTIONS

By L. R. FORD

"Comprehensive . . . remarkably clear and explicit."—*Bulletin of the A. M. S.*

—2nd ed. (Cor. repr.) x + 333 pp. 5⅜x8. [85] **$6.00**

THE CALCULUS OF EXTENSION

By H. G. FORDER

—1941-60. xvi + 490 pp. 5⅜x8. [135] **$4.95**

RUSSIAN MATHEMATICAL BIBLIOGRAPHY

By G. E. FORSYTHE

A bibliography of Russian Mathematics Books for the quarter century 1920-55. Added subject index.

—1956. 106 pp. 5x8. [111] **$3.95**

CURVE TRACING

By P. FROST

This much-quoted and charming treatise gives a very readable treatment of a topic that can only be touched upon briefly in courses on Analytic Geometry. Teachers will find it invaluable as supplementary reading for their more interested students and for reference. The Calculus is not used.

Seventeen plates, containing over 200 figures, illustrate the discussion in the text.

—5th (unaltered) ed. 1960. 210 pp. + 17 fold-out plates. 5⅜x8. [140] **$3.95**

THE THEORY OF MATRICES

By F. R. GANTMACHER

This treatise, by one of Russia's leading mathematicians gives, in easily accessible form, a coherent account of matrix theory with a view to applications in mathematics, theoretical physics, statistics, electrical engineering, etc. The individual chapters have been kept as far as possible independent of each other, so that the reader acquainted with the contents of Chapter I can proceed immediately to the chapters that especially interest him. Much of the material has been available until now only in the periodical literature.

Partial Contents. VOL. ONE. I. Matrices and Matrix Operations. II. The Algorithm of Gauss and Applications. III. Linear Operators in an n-Dimensional Vector Space. IV. Characteristic Polynomial and Minimal Polynomial of a Matrix (Generalized Bézout Theorem, Method of Faddeev for Simultaneous Computation of Coefficients of Characteristic Polynomial and Adjoint Matrix, . . .). V. Functions of Matrices (Various Forms of the Definition, Components, Application to Integration of System of Linear Differential Eqns, Stability of Motion, . . .). VI. Equivalent Transformations of Polynomial Matrices; Analytic Theory of Elementary Divisors. VII. The Structure of a Linear Operator in an n-Dimensional Space (Minimal Polynomial, Congruence, Factor Space, Jordan Form, Krylov's Method of Transforming Secular Eqn, . . .). VIII. Matrix Equations (Matrix Polynomial Eqns, Roots and Logarithm of

Matrices, . . .). IX. Linear Operators in a Unitary Space. X. Quadratic and Hermitian Forms.

VOL. TWO. XI. Complex Symmetric, Skew-symmetric, and Orthogonal Matrices. XII. Singular Pencils of Matrices. XIII. Matrices with Non-Negative Elements (Gen'l and Spectral Properties, Reducible M's, Primitive and Imprimitive M's, Stochastic M's, Totally Non-Negative M's, . . .). XIV. Applications of the Theory of Matrices to the Investigation of Systems of Linear Differential Equations. XV. The Problem of Routh-Hurwitz and Related Questions (Routh's Algorithm, Lyapunov's Theorem, Infinite Hankel M's, Supplements to Routh-Hurwitz Theorem, Stability Criterion of Liénard and Chipart, Hurwitz Polynomials, Stieltjes' Theorem, Domain of Stability, Markov Parameters, Problem of Moments, Markov and Chebyshev Theorems, Generalized Routh-Hurwitz Problem, . . .). BIBLIOGRAPHY.

—Vol. I. 1960. x + 374 pp. 6x9. [131] **$6.00**
—Vol. II. 1960. x + 277 pp. 6x9. [133] **$6.00**

LECTURES ON ANALYTICAL MECHANICS

By F. R. GANTMACHER

Translated from the Russian by PROF. B. D. SECKLER, with additions and revisions by Prof. Gantmacher.

Partial Contents: CHAP. I. Differential Equations of Motion of a System of Particles. II. Equations of Motion in a Potential Field. III. Variational Principles and Integral-Invariants. IV. Canonical Transformations and the Hamilton-Jacobi Equation. V. Stable Equilibrium and Stability of Motion of a System (Lagrange's Theorem on stable equilibrium, Tests for unstable E., Theorems of Lyapunov and Chetayev, Asymptotically stable E., Stability of linear systems, Stability on basis of linear approximation, . . .). VI. Small Oscillations. VII. Systems with Cyclic Coordinates. BIBLIOGRAPHY.

—Approx. 300 pp. 6x9. [175] **In prep.**

ARITHMETISCHE UNTERSUCHUNGEN

By C. F. GAUSS

The German translation of his *Disquisitiones Arithmeticae.*

—Repr. of 1st German ed. x + 685 pp. 5⅜x8. [191] Prob. **$9.50**

COMMUTATIVE NORMED RINGS

By I. M. GELFAND, D. A. RAĬKOV, and G. E. SHILOV

Translated from the Russian.

Partial Contents: CHAPS. I AND II. General Theory of Commutative Normed Rings. III. Ring of Absolutely Integrable Functions and their Discrete Analogues. IV. Harmonic Analysis on Commutative Locally Compact Groups. V. Ring of Functions of Bounded Variation on a Line. VI. Regular Rings. VII. Rings with Uniform Convergence. VIII. Normed Rings with an Involution and their Representations. IX. Decomposition of Normed Ring into Direct Sum of Ideals. HISTORICO-BIBLIOGRAPHICAL NOTES. BIBLIOGRAPHY.

—1964. 306 pp. 6x9. [170] **$6.50**

DIFFERENTIALGLEICHUNGEN: LOESUNGSMETHODEN UND LOESUNGEN

By E. KAMKE

Everything possible that can be of use when one has a given differential equation to solve, or when one wishes to investigate that solution thoroughly.

PART A: General Methods of Solution and the Properties of the Solutions.

PART B: Boundary and Characteristic Value Problems.

PART C: Dictionary of some 1600 Equations in Lexicographical Order, with solution, techniques for solving, and references.

"A reference work of outstanding importance which should be in every mathematical library."

—*Mathematical Gazette.*

—Third ed. 692 pp. 6x9. Orig. Publ. at $15.00. [44] **$9.50**

KEMPE, "How to Draw a Straight Line," see Hobson

ASYMPTOTISCHE GESETZE DER WAHRSCHEINLICHKEITSRECHNUNG

By A. A. KHINTCHINE

—1933. 82 pp. (Ergeb. der Math.) 5½x8½. Orig. pub. at $3.85. [36] Paper **$2.00**

VORLESUNGEN UEBER NICHT-EUKLIDISCHE GEOMETRIE

By F. KLEIN

CHAPTER HEADINGS: I. Concept of Projective Geometry. II. Structures of the Second Degree. III. Collineations that Carry Structure of Second Degree into Itself. IV. Introduction of the Euclidean Metric into Projective Geometry. V. Projective Coordinates Independent of Euclidean Geometry. VI. Projective Determination of Measure. VII. Relation between Elliptic, Euclidean, and Hyperbolic Geometries. VIII. The Two Non-Euclidean Geometries. IX. The Problem of the Structure of Space. X AND XI. Relation between Non-Euclidean Geometry and other Branches of Mathematics.

—1928. xii + 326 pp. 5x8. [129] **$4.95**

ENTWICKLUNG DER MATHEMATIK IM 19. JAHRHUNDERT

By F. KLEIN

TWO VOLUMES IN ONE.

Vol. I treats of the various branches of advanced mathematics of the prolific 19th century; Klein himself was in the forefront of the mathematical activity of latter part of the 19th and early part of the 20th centuries.

Vol. II deals with the mathematics of relativity theory.

—616 pp. 5¼x8¼. Orig. $14.40. [74] 2 Vols. in one **$7.50**

FAMOUS PROBLEMS, and other monographs

By KLEIN, SHEPPARD, MacMAHON, and MORDELL

FOUR VOLUMES IN ONE.

FAMOUS PROBLEMS OF ELEMENTARY GEOMETRY, by *Klein.* A fascinating little book. A simple, easily understandable, account of the famous problems of Geometry—The Duplication of the Cube, Trisection of the Angle, Squaring of the Circle—and the proofs that these cannot be solved by ruler and compass—presentable, say, before an undergraduate math club (no calculus required). Also, the modern problems about transcendental numbers, the existence of such numbers, and proofs of the transcendence of *e.*

FROM DETERMINANT TO TENSOR, by *Sheppard.* A novel and charming introduction. Written with the utmost simplicity. PT I. Origin of Determinants. II. Properties of Determinants. III. Solution of Simultaneous Equations. IV. Properties. V. Tensor Notation. PT II. VI. Sets. VII. Cogredience, etc. VIII. Examples from Statistics. IX. Tensors in Theory of Relativity.

INTRODUCTION TO COMBINATORY ANALYSIS, by *MacMahon.* A concise introduction to this field. Written as introduction to the author's two-volume work.

THREE LECTURES ON FERMAT'S LAST THEOREM, by *Mordell.* This famous problem is so easy that a high-school student might not unreasonably hope to solve it; it is so difficult that tens of thousands of amateur and professional mathematicians, Euler and Gauss among them, have failed to find a complete solution. Mordell's very small book begins with an impartial investigation of whether Fermat himself had a solution (as he said he did) and explains what has been accomplished. This is one of the masterpieces of mathematical exposition.

—2nd ed. 1962. 350 pp. 5⅜x8. Four Vols. in one.
[108] Cloth **$3.95**
[166] Paper **$1.95**

VORLESUNGEN ÜBER HÖHERE GEOMETRIE

By FELIX KLEIN

In this third edition there has been added to the first two sections of *Klein's* classical work a third section written by Professors *Blaschke, Radon, Artin* and *Schreier* on recent developments.

—Third ed. 413 pp. 5½x8. Orig. publ. at $10.80. [65] **$4.95**

THEORIE DER ENDLICHEN UND UNENDLICHEN GRAPHEN

By D. KONIG

"Elegant applications to Matrix Theory . . . Abstract Set Theory . . . Linear Forms . . . Electricity . . . Basis Problems . . . Logic, Theory of Games, Group Theory."—*L. Kalmar, Acta Szeged.*

—1936. 269 pp. 5¼x8¼. Orig. publ. at $7.20. [72] **$4.95**

DIOPHANTISCHE APPROXIMATIONEN

By J. F. KOKSMA

—(Ergeb. der Math.) 1936. 165 pp. 5½x8½. Orig. publ. at $7.25. [66] **$3.50**

VORLESUNGEN ÜBER ZAHLENTHEORIE

By E. LANDAU

The various sections of this important work (Additive, Analytic, Geometric, and Algebraic Number Theory) can be read independently of one another.

—Vol. I, Pt. 2. *(Additive Number Theory) xii + 180 pp. Vol. II. (Analytical Number Theory and Geometrical Number Theory) viii + 308 pp. Vol. III. (Algebraic Number Theory and Fermat's Last Theorem) viii + 341 pp. 5¼x8¼. *(Vol. I, Pt. 1 is issued as **Elementare Zahlentheorie** (in German) or as **Elementary Number Theory** (in English). Orig. publ. at $26.40. [32] Three Vols. in one. **$14.00**

FOUNDATIONS OF ANALYSIS

By E. LANDAU

"Certainly no clearer treatment of the foundations of the number system can be offered. . . . One can only be thankful to the author for this fundamental piece of exposition, which is alive with his vitality and genius."—*J. F. Ritt, Amer. Math. Monthly.*

—2nd ed. 1960. 6x9. [79] **$3.95**

HANDBUCH DER LEHRE VON DER VERTEILUNG DER PRIMZAHLEN

By E. LANDAU

TWO VOLUMES IN ONE.

To Landau's monumental work on prime-number theory there has been added, in this edition, two of Landau's papers and an up-to-date guide to the work: an Appendix by Prof. Paul T. Bateman.

2nd ed. 1953. 1,028 pp. 5⅜x8. 2 Vols. in 1. [96] **$14.00**

LANDAU, "Neuere Funktiontheorie," see Weyl

EINFÜHRUNG IN DIE ELEMENTARE UND ANALYTISCHE THEORIE DER ALGEBRAISCHE ZAHLEN UND DER IDEALE

By E. LANDAU

—2nd ed. vii + 147 pp. 5½x8. [62] **$2.95**

CELESTIAL MECHANICS

By P. S. LAPLACE

One of the landmarks in the history of human thought. Four volumes translated from the original French by NATHANIEL BOWDITCH, with an extensive commentary by the Translator.

A detailed Table of Contents is available on request.

Note: A set of the original edition of Bowditch's translation (when available) costs between $600.00 and $700.00 in the second-hand book market.

—Vol. I: xxiv+746+136 pp. Vol. II: xviii+990 pp. Vol. III: xxx+910 pp.+approx. 100 pp. of tables. Vol. IV: xxxvi+1,018 pp. 6½x9¼. [194]

THE THEORY OF SUBSTITUTIONS

By E. NETTO

Partial Contents: CHAP. I. Symmetric and Alternating Functions. II. Multiple- valued Functions and Groups of Substitutions. III. The Different Values of a Multiple-valued Function and their Algebraic Relation to One Another. IV. Transitivity and Primitivity; Simple and Compound Groups; Isomorphism. V. Algebraic Relations between Functions Belonging to the Same Group . . . VII. Certain Special Classes of Groups. VIII. Analytical Representation of Substitutions. The Linear Group. IX. Equations of Second, Third, Fourth Degrees. Groups of an Equation. X. Cyclotomic Equations. XI. Abelian Equations . . . XIII. Algebraic Solution of Equations. XIV. Group of an Algebraic Equation. XV. Algebraically Solvable equations. INDEX.

—2nd ed. (Corr. repr. of 1st ed.) xi+304 pp. 5⅜x8. [165] **$3.95**

VORLESUNGEN ÜBER DIFFERENZENRECHNUNG

By N. H. NÖRLUND

—ix+551 pp. 5⅜x8. Orig. publ. at $11.50 [100] **$6.50**

FUNCTIONS OF REAL VARIABLES FUNCTIONS OF A COMPLEX VARIABLE

By W. F. OSGOOD

TWO VOLUMES IN ONE.

"*Well-organized courses, systematic, lucid, fundamental,* with many brief sets of appropriate exercises, and occasional suggestions for more extensive reading. The technical terms have been kept to a minimum, and have been clearly explained. The aim has been to develop the student's power and to furnish him with a substantial body of classic theorems, whose proofs illustrate the methods and whose results provide equipment for further progress."—*Bulletin of A. M. S*

—676 pp. 5x8. 2 vols. in 1. [124] **$6.00**

LEHRBUCH DER FUNKTIONENTHEORIE, *II*

By W. F. OSGOOD

Osgood's *Funktionentheorie* originally appeared in three volumes: VOLUME I, *General Theory* (5th ed., 1928, 818 pages). VOLUME II_1, *Theory of Functions of Several Complex Variables* (2nd ed., 1929, 307 pages). VOLUME II_2, *Abelian Integrals and Periodic Functions* (1932, 378 pages).

The present work is a reprint, in one volume, of the second and third of the three volumes, paged consecutively, and with a common index.

—2nd ed. xiv+686 pp. 5⅜x8. [182] Prob. **$8.50**

IRRATIONALZAHLEN

By O. PERRON

—2nd ed. 1939. 207 pp. 5⅜x8. [47] Cloth **$3.75**
[113] Paper **$1.50**

EINFÜHRUNG IN DIE KOMBINATORISCHE TOPOLOGIE

By K. REIDEMEISTER

Group Theory occupies the first half of the book; applications to Topology, the second. This well-known book is of interest both to algebraists and topologists.

—221 pp. 5½x8¼. [76] **$3.50**

KNOTENTHEORIE

By K. REIDEMEISTER

—(Ergeb. der Math.) 1932. 78 pp. 5½x8½. [40] **$2.25**

FOURIER SERIES

By W. ROGOSINSKI

Translated by H. COHN. Designed for beginners with no more background than a year of calculus, this text covers, nevertheless, an amazing amount of ground. It is suitable for self-study courses as well as classroom use.

"The field covered is extensive and the treatment is thoroughly modern in outlook . . . An admirable guide to the theory."—*Mathematical Gazette.*

—2nd ed. 1959. vi+176 pp. 4½x6½ [67] **$2.50**

CONIC SECTIONS

By G. SALMON

"The classic book on the subject, covering the whole ground and full of touches of genius."

—*Mathematical Association.*

—6th ed. xv+400 pp. 5⅜ x 8. [99] Cloth **$3.95**

[98] Paper **$1.95**

HIGHER PLANE CURVES

By G. SALMON

CHAPTER HEADINGS: I. Coordinates. II. General Properties of Algebraic Curves. III. Envelopes. IV. Metrical Properties. V. Cubics. VI. Quartics. VII. Transcendental Curves. VIII. Transformation of Curves. IX. General Theory of Curves.

—3rd ed. xix + 395 pp. 5⅜x8. [138] **$4.95**

ANALYTIC GEOMETRY OF THREE DIMENSIONS

By G. SALMON

A rich and detailed treatment by the author of *Conic Sections, Higher Plane Curves,* etc.

—Seventh edition. (V. 1). 496 pp. 5x8. [122] **$4.95**